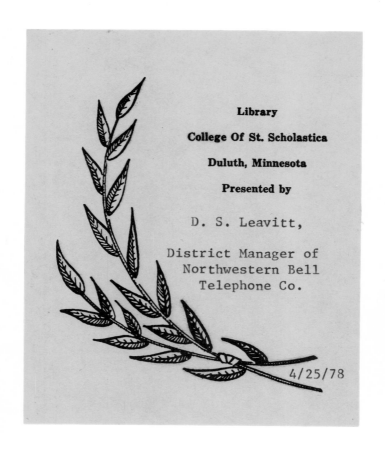

The Diary of a Dream . . .

GOODBYE, CENTRAL; HELLO, WORLD

*A Centennial History
of Northwestern Bell*

by

James Crockett Rippey

Research: Cynthia L. Hadsell
Book Design: Karl L. Kling

Published for
The Telephone Pioneers
of America

Hawkeye Chapter No. 17
Iowa

C. P. Wainman Chapter No. 18
Minnesota and North Dakota

Casper E. Yost Chapter No. 19
Nebraska and South Dakota

PRINTED IN THE UNITED STATES OF AMERICA

Copyright © 1975 by Northwestern Bell
Library of Congress catalog card number: 75-13986

PRIESMAN GRAPHICS, OMAHA, NEBR.
COMPOSITORS

WAGNERS PRINTERS, INC., DAVENPORT, IOWA
PRINTERS AND BINDERS

PREFACE

This history had its genesis nearly 35 years ago. At the 1941 General Assembly of the Telephone Pioneers of America, local chapters were urged to organize historical committees and begin preparation of company histories.

In the late 1940s and early 1950s, O. C. Michelmann of Northwestern Bell spent several years collecting and organizing historical material, including that gathered by Pioneers in Northwestern Bell territory. Michelmann eventually wrote hundreds of pages of historical articles which were invaluable in the preparation of this volume.

The memoirs and historical essays of Charles E. Hall were a prime source of early-day information, as were the lively items Flemon Drake included in the exchange histories found in Casper Yost's "bible." Yost's correspondence (15,000 letters) yielded many gems, even though most of the letters remain unread and uncatalogued.

Back issues of *NWB Magazine, NWB News* and NWB Annual Reports also provided excellent material. And the Lincoln Telephone and Telegraph Company's published history was particularly helpful.

The author wishes to thank all his fellow workers for their assistance: those who wrote special articles for this history, those who verified countless references and all those who read endless galleys of proof.

Particular thanks are due Don Herring and John Felt for hours of patient editorial counsel; to Karl Kling for book design and production; to Cindy Hadsell for her research and valuable editorial suggestions and many hours of cheerful overtime work, and to Barbara Rippey for her editorial suggestions, her enduring faith and patience.

Finally, the author would like to express appreciation to the officers of the Company for allowing him freedom to chronicle past mistakes and the human failings of the people who built this Company.

All of us who have worked with the huge quantities of source material are painfully conscious that several other interesting books could be written using material left out of this one.

Space and time limitations are hard taskmasters.

J. C. R.

June 1975
Omaha, Nebr.

CONTENTS

*To all of the thousands
of people whose hard work
and heroism built this Company.
Particularly to those whose
names are not recorded
in this history.*

INTRODUCTION

This is a history not so much about a company as it is about the men and women who built that company.

There are among us, I suppose, some who may prefer to think that great organizations are built from carefully formulated plans. It is a comforting thought, but I think that it is not so. I can't give you an exact recipe for Northwestern Bell. I suspect that it was built from varying parts of curiosity and chance and vision. As much by linemen and operators as by Company presidents. This book portrays that.

I think, too, that there is a common bond among telephone people. In a simpler time, we used to call it "spirit of service." Some might call it duty. Perhaps it is indescribable, but it does command, from every telephone employee I have ever met, a commitment to provide the customer with the best possible telephone service, anytime, anywhere. It is most visible in times of trial, but it is there during the routine, day-to-day tasks, too.

That commitment is portrayed in this history, in page after page, and in story after story about the people who built . . . and are building . . . this Company.

THOMAS S. NURNBERGER

June 1975

Chapter I

The Emperor as a press agent

The beginnings of telephony

THIS IS THE STORY of the telephone in the Upper Midwest. It begins in an unlikely place with an unlikely cast of characters.

The place was Philadelphia, Pa., and the time was June 25, 1876. Only a handful of people had ever heard of the telephone, and they were mostly in the Boston area where it had been invented three months earlier. The transcontinental railroad was just seven years old and the West was still untamed. In fact, the Indians won one of their greatest victories on the very day the telephone was in the spotlight at Philadelphia. Americans remember the battle as Custer's Last Stand on the Little Big Horn in Montana.

From a Northwestern Bell point of view, there were six principals in the telephone drama at Philadelphia. First, of course, was Alexander Graham Bell. After years of trying, he had finally managed to transmit understandable speech over an electric wire.

The others were a farmer from North Dakota, a telegrapher from Omaha, two businessmen — one from Duluth, Minn., another from Dubuque, Iowa — and finally, Dom Pedro, the emperor of Brazil.

Emperor Dom Pedro   **Alexander Graham Bell**

The event that brought them all together was the Philadelphia Centennial Exposition, celebrating the 100th anniversary of the Declaration of Independence. At the time, Dom Pedro's was the only name that was newsworthy. But the Exposition itself was news.

Midwestern newspapers reported it extensively; many had their own correspondents there. These reporters rhapsodized over such things as a display of Indian rubber, an ostrich egg hatcher, Swiss and American watches and the machinery exhibits — "all kinds of machinery in active action. Above all . . . the great Corliss engine." There was no mention of Prof. Bell or the telephone.

Bell himself almost missed the Exposition. For years, he had been obsessed with the telephone idea. He had neglected his work with the deaf, his health had broken and he had suffered innumerable frustrations as he and Thomas Watson had tried to make the telephone work. During this period, one of his principal financial backers had demanded that Bell forget the telephone idea and concentrate on perfecting the harmonic telegraph, which he had originally set out to develop.

Despite the setbacks and opposition, Bell had persevered. His crude instruments finally transmitted the first historic words on March 10, 1876. A patent was granted. And the telephone was successfully demonstrated in public on May 10. The *Boston Transcript* reported it accurately, without fanfare.

But if the newspaper took it matter-of-factly, Gardiner Hubbard did not. He was the financial backer who had opposed wasting time on the telephone notion. Now that those phones actually worked, his head was full of grandiose plans.

Unfortunately, Bell's enthusiasm lagged just as Hubbard's soared. Bell had proved his point: speech *could* be transmitted electrically over a wire. Now he felt that he must get back to his long-neglected work with the deaf. (In later years, Bell said he preferred to be remembered as a teacher of the deaf rather than as the inventor of the telephone.)

Curiously, Dom Pedro was partly to blame. He, too, was very interested in helping the deaf. While in Boston earlier that year, he had met with Prof. Bell. The fact that the Emperor had seemed impressed with his work only added to Bell's sense of dedication. If his techniques were to be used even in faraway Brazil, he had no business spending any more time on the telephone.

The Philadelphia Centennial Exposition, where Bell's telephone was first displayed, 1876

So when Hubbard urged him to exhibit the telephone at Philadelphia, Bell refused. He didn't relent until Hubbard's pretty daughter, Mabel, pleaded the cause. Mabel herself was deaf, had received some instruction from Bell and was engaged to be his wife.

Even after Bell had gone to Philadelphia and gotten the exhibit ready, his moment of triumph was almost spoiled by hot weather. And that's where Dom Pedro came through as press agent extraordinary.

Since the Exposition was closed to the public on Sundays, that was an ideal time for the judges to examine the electrical exhibits. As it happened, Dom Pedro's party and the judges toured the exhibits together.

June 25, 1876, was a miserably hot day and the judges were exhausted by the time they had seen the other exhibits. Bell's was next but it was up a flight of stairs clear at the other end of the building. Some of the judges were inclined to put off seeing it.

Bell had joined the judges' group by this time. And as he liked to tell the story in later years (perhaps taking a bit of poetic license), it was at this point that Dom Pedro came over, greeted him warmly, linked arms, and led the way to the Bell exhibit.

The first two men to try out Bell's apparatus were Sir William Thomson, an outstanding electrical scientist from England, and the Emperor Dom Pedro. Both were so startled at hearing Bell's voice come out of the receiver that each, in turn, hurried excitedly to the distant point from which Bell was speaking. Their reaction prompted the other judges to crowd in for their turns at listening.

Soon afterwards, the Bell exhibit was moved to a more prominent place in the Exposition. And Sir William, later to become Lord Kelvin, immediately began telling his scientific colleagues about the telephone, declaring it the most wonderful thing he had seen in America.

But much remained to be done, despite the heady success at Philadelphia. Throughout the rest of 1876, Bell and Watson refined the equipment, methodically altering each part until they found what would work best. By the end of the year, they were ready to file for a new patent covering the improvements and setting out in more detail the telephone theory which Bell had developed. Issued on Jan. 30th, this patent was the second of Bell's two basic

"Mr. Watson, come here. I want you!" On March 10, 1876, Alexander Graham Bell transmitted the first speech over the telephone using this transmitter (left) and receiver (below). He was calling his assistant, Thomas Watson.

When Bell exhibited his invention at the Philadelphia Exposition, he built another model of the telephone. The display caught the attention of Dom Pedro, who heard his first demonstration of the phone over this transmitter (above) and receiver (right).

patents. In subsequent years, these two enabled him to win a series of patent infringement suits.

By February of 1877, the telephone's fame had spread so widely that Bell was receiving numerous requests for his instruments, some from distant places. But the struggling, loosely organized firm wasn't ready for paying customers until May. A man named James Emery, Jr., paid the first telephone bill on May 30. A wholesale fish dealer at Charlestown, Mass., Emery paid $20 to lease two telephones for a year. He paid the money to Charles Williams, Jr., owner of the shop where Bell's assistant, Thomas Watson, was employed and where the first telephones were made. Williams carried the money around in his pocket for eight days, not knowing what to do with it.

Actually, a banker named Roswell C. Downer was the Bell System's first customer. He rented a pair of telephones May 1 to connect his home in Somerville, Mass., with his office at 28 State St. in Boston, three miles away. But Emery paid his bill before Downer did.

By June of 1877, there were at least 234 phones in use in the world. Many of them had been loaned or rented with no provision for service. With the Downer and Emery contracts, however, the concept of selling service was established.

Gardiner G. Hubbard is credited with making the decision to sell service rather than things. Selling the phones outright would have brought money in faster. And with money scarce, it was a difficult decision. Hubbard had invested in Bell's experiments and was devoting a tremendous amount of time promoting the venture. But his partner, Thomas Sanders, came up with the biggest share of money. He had $110,000 invested in the telephone before he realized a cent in return.

The two were an odd pair to be double-harnessed. Each respected the other's efforts, but that didn't keep them from bickering.

While Hubbard was junketing around the country demonstrating the telephone and signing up promoters, Sanders was back home minding the store and worrying a lot. He borrowed all he could and bombarded Hubbard with letters pleading for help in raising money. Watson and others at the Charles Williams shop couldn't make phones fast enough to keep up with the demand. And

Gardiner G. Hubbard   Thomas Sanders

Sanders couldn't get money fast enough to pay the bills.

But Hubbard remained certain that the telephone business would ultimately reap great rewards for its backers and cheerily urged Sanders to close out his leather business and devote all his time and money to the new venture.

Sanders was just as blunt in his letters. In one, he told Hubbard: "You have a certain blissful disregard of money, an enviable trait to possess, but scarcely a desirable one in a business partner . . ."

All their struggles might have been avoided if Western Union had been willing to buy the telephone patents. Early in 1877, Bell was anxious to repay Sanders and Hubbard. He was particularly anxious to become solvent so he could get Hubbard's permission to marry Mabel. It was at this point that Hubbard offered to sell the patents to Western Union for $100,000. He was turned down.

Hubbard had recently been appointed by President Ulysses S. Grant as chairman of a special commission to investigate railway mail transportation. In that post, he became an outspoken enthusiast for the proposed postal telegraph system which would compete with Western Union.

This made his name a dirty word at Western Union headquarters. As the story goes (and some question it), that was why Western Union refused. Regardless of the details, the offer was made and refused. If both look silly now, that's hindsight.

Most of the telephone service provided in 1877 consisted of pairs of phones connecting two places. But limited exchange service did become available to a few private organizations on the East Coast during the year.

None of these exchanges tried to serve the general public. But each did have a crude switching device that enabled the various customers to talk to each other. One was set up to interconnect phones a brass company put at its office in Ansonia, Conn., and at its nearby mills. Another used the wires a burglar alarm company already had in Boston. A third used the wires of a social telegraph system in Bridgeport, Conn.

And a fourth was promoted by a druggist in Hartford, Conn. He talked several doctors and livery stable operators into subscribing. Within six months, this private phone system had proved its worth and had attracted much favorable attention. On Jan. 15, 1878, following a middle-of-the-night train wreck, it was used to awaken 21 doctors who were put aboard a special rescue train.

Just a few brief notes are needed to wrap up the loose ends for 1877 on the East Coast:

Bell and Mabel Hubbard got married (July 11) and the Bell Telephone Company was organized with Hubbard as trustee. The original seven stockholders and their number of shares were: Sanders, 1497; Mabel G. Bell, 1497; Hubbard, 1397; Watson, 499; Gertrude McC. Hubbard, 100; Bell, 10, and Charles E. Hubbard, 10. Robert W. Devonshire became the Bell System's first employee, hired as a bookkeeper Aug. 10. Bell and his bride sailed for England, not to return for more than a year.

Meanwhile in the Midwest, quite a bit of telephone activity took place during 1877 in the territory that is now Northwestern Bell. As mentioned earlier, at least four men from that territory saw Professor Bell's telephones at Philadelphia and became enthusiastic about the possibilities. The infant telephone industry was going to need such enthusiasm in the years just ahead.

The four men were J. L. Grandin, the farmer from north of Fargo, N.D.; Louis H. Korty, the Omaha telegrapher; and Walter Van Brunt of Duluth, Minn., and Edward T. Keim of Dubuque, Iowa, the two businessmen.

During the Exposition, Korty had a chance to visit with Dom Pedro and absorb some of his enthusiasm. Keim even helped the Bell people with demonstrations. But for the next couple of years, his activities aren't recorded.

Edward T. Keim

Grandin and Korty, however, each had pairs of telephones operating in what is now Northwestern Bell territory before the next year (1877) had ended. So did several others. And Van Brunt had a phone line operating in Duluth in 1877 or 1878.

Thanks to the scientific publicity, Iowa's first telephones were in operation sometime early in 1877. Theodore Birchard, a Marshalltown, Iowa boy studying technology in New Jersey, built a pair of telephones from drawings published in a scientific journal. He sent them home and they were put into operation between his father's drug store and the family residence four blocks away.

Later that year, a 14-year-old Marshalltown boy named George E. McFarland built a pair of homemade telephones and used them to connect his house with that of a friend. He had trouble at first, but after getting a look at the telephones young Birchard had made, McFarland was able to get his working, too. As this history unfolds, McFarland's name will come up again many times.

By 1880 Korty (the Omaha telegrapher) had become the Bell telephone licensing agent for a large territory. He is reported as putting on several demonstrations in 1877, one at a Presbyterian church fair in Omaha and another linking the home of Brig. Gen. George Crook in Omaha with post headquarters at Ft. Omaha, four miles away. No dates are recorded, but it is known that by Nov. 18, 1877, Korty had phones operating between the Union Pacific telegraph office in Omaha and the company's yards at Spoon Lake in Council Bluffs.

To get this line into operation, Korty enlisted the aid of his boss, J. J. Dickey, superintendent of telegraph for the Union Pacific. Because of his business abilities and his connections in Omaha, Dickey has often received credit for the first phones in Omaha. The evidence, however, indicates that it was Korty who enlisted Dickey, and it was Korty who guided the formation of many exchanges in Iowa and Nebraska.

Meanwhile in Duluth, Van Brunt's business activities included writing insurance for a grain elevator. Every evening at dinnertime, he walked 10 blocks to the elevator to get the daily receipts, back to the office to write up the insurance, back again to the elevator with the policy.

Somewhere in the course of all this walking, he decided that a pair of telephones like those he had seen in Philadelphia would save a lot of time and shoe leather. He ordered a pair and installed one in his office (C. H. Graves & Co.), the other at the elevator.

But perhaps the very first telephone installation in what is now Northwestern Bell territory was a line a druggist in Little Falls, Minn., is reported to have set up between his home and his clerk's house in 1876.* At least, that is the date recorded in a set of telephone exchange records used by Arthur A. Lowman when he was president of Northwestern Bell (1935-42).

If that 1876 date for Little Falls is wrong, then young Birchard's phone in Marshalltown was probably first. And the second installation may well have been an experimental line R. H. Hankinson set up in Minneapolis between his office and his residence. This line was operating by June of 1877.

Hankinson was general manager of the Northwestern Telegraph Co. at the time and had a private telegraph line that ran from his office to his bedroom closet at home. And he may have been one of the first to use the telephone in a practical joke. When he got a set of telephones, Hankinson, without telling Mrs. Hankinson, hooked up one *to the telegraph* line in his closet and attached the other in his office. Every now and then, he would say a few words into his office phone.

Eventually, of course, Mrs. H. happened to be in the bedroom at the right time and heard this eerie voice in the closet. Dumbfounded, she scurried to Mr. H.'s office to tell him about it.

She must have taken it like a good sport when he explained because she was soon helping demonstrate this wondrous new invention. An accomplished vocalist, she would sing into the instrument at home whenever her hus-

---

* The local historical society says a Charles H. Brown bought this "Rhodes Drugstore" in 1892. Brown traveled for a Michigan drug firm in the '70s and '80s and could well have brought the first phones out from the East.

The pioneer of pioneers

Soon after the Philadelphia Centennial Exposition opened in 1876, telephones showed up in Rochester, N. Y. There to help the invention get off the ground was Arlington Storrs, the man who was to become the dean of the telephone industry and an important figure in Northwestern Bell's development.

Storrs' telephone career began when he was only 15. One day, as he was watching a crew put in phone lines, a worker asked him if he wanted a job. "Sure," Storrs replied. That was that.

During the first few years, Storrs did telephone construction work in cities such as Syracuse, Albany and New York. After landing in the hospital with injuries from a battle during a telephone strike, he moved west to Illinois, then Iowa.

By the time Storrs reached Iowa, he was one of the country's best-trained telephone men. And he soon proved it, by bringing phones into dozens of communities in Iowa. He'd go into a town, solicit subscribers, lay out the plant, order materials, hire crews, install wires and switchboards, train operators and managers, then leave for another town.

In 1897 Storrs became assistant to the vice president and general manager of the Nebraska Telephone Company and moved to Omaha. When the company became part of Northwestern Bell, Storrs stayed on and eventually became superintendent of supplies. Standardization of equipment was one of his major interests, and his work did much to bring about this practice in the industry.

In the years to come, Storrs would be remembered for still another thing. At the time of his retirement in 1928, he had the earliest service date of all telephone employees in the United States. The man from Rochester was a telephone pioneer in more ways than one.

band had an audience assembled in his office.

An item from Charles E. Hall's memoirs indicates the degree of skepticism some people had. Hall, who retired as secretary of Northwestern Bell in 1930, recalled he first heard of the telephone in 1876 when he was 15 and visiting in Michigan. An adult whom Hall admired read to him a *Detroit Free Press* article describing Bell's exhibit at Philadelphia, then added:

"You need not believe that story; it is doubtless some newspaper writer's yarn like the sea serpent stories one comes across now and then. If he would have Prof. Bell talking through a tube, it might be possible to do so, but to talk through a solid wire is sheer nonsense; it can't be done."

Despite the skepticism or indifference of most people, still other telephones went into service in various parts of Northwestern Bell territory as 1877 unfolded. The Grandin family operated a number of farms near the present town of Grandin, N.D. Still excited by what he had seen at Philadelphia, J. L. Grandin obtained a pair of phones sometime during 1877 and used them to connect two of the family's farms. This proved so useful that other pairs were obtained shortly afterwards to connect the other farms.

In November 1877, a Bell promoter named P. D. Richards had a demonstration phone line operating in Cedar Rapids between the Pope-Billau Drug Store and H. C. Waite's music store. Richards had hoped to interest local people in financing a Bell company, but left town in December, thinking he had failed.

Later in 1877 or early in '78, Western Union phones connected the office and mill of the Moore Lumber Company in Dubuque, Iowa. And perhaps as early as 1877, there were phones connecting A. J. Barkley's office in Boone, Iowa, with the county courthouse two miles away. All of this was before there was any exchange service in the area. In fact, there wasn't any commercial telephone exchange service available to the public anywhere in the U.S. But the time was ripe.

Chapter II

The dark before the dawn

The first exchanges, competition and a man named Vail

THE YEAR 1878 started off well for the infant Bell Telephone Company. In January, the first two public telephone exchanges opened in New Haven and Meriden, Conn.

San Francisco's exchange opened Feb. 17; Albany, N.Y., got its exchange on March 18, and the ball was obviously rolling. But there was considerable dispute as to whose ball it was.

The Western Union Company had begun elbowing into the telephone business, using transmitters designed by Thomas Edison and receivers by Elisha Gray. Western Union claimed that Bell's patent was faulty. To make matters worse, the Edison transmitter out-performed Bell's. Then there was the money pinch. The Bell Company was struggling, and Western Union had vast resources.

That's probably why the first documented exchange service in Northwestern Bell territory was under the Western Union banner. It opened at Keokuk, Iowa, Sept. 1, 1878. However, NWB's first might have been the Bell exchange at Deadwood, S.D. There's a good case for believing it opened in 1878, though the month isn't recorded.

At that, having even one exchange in a state was an accomplishment. Pennsylvania, for example, had no exchange service until mid-November 1878, and then only in

Philadelphia. The first telephone exchange in Washington, D.C., opened Dec. 1 with the White House listed as No. 1, the Capitol as No. 2 and the Associated Press as No. 3. President Rutherford B. Hayes had to go to a booth outside his office to use his phone.*

Firemen in Burlington, Iowa, had exchange telephone service before the President did. It was, however, a private exchange connecting five fire stations with 18 outlying locations. It was ready for testing early in September.

George B. Engle, Jr., promoted that system, and Burlington was soon acclaimed as "the first city in the world to use the telephone exclusively for fire alarm purposes."

Engle was from Indianapolis. He had been visiting a brother in Cedar Rapids, Iowa, when the Bell promoter, Richards, was there late in 1877. The telephone intrigued Engle and soon he had formed a telephone business with Col. D. H. Ogden. A telegrapher and retired soldier, Ogden was Cedar Rapids agent for the Burlington, Cedar Rapids and Northern Railway.

David H. Ogden

The exact chronology is hazy, but Engle's and Ogden's early efforts came to the attention of Gardiner Hubbard in Boston. He met with the men in Chicago and, for $40,000, offered them a tremendous opportunity: the right to lease telephones in Illinois, Wisconsin, Iowa and Minnesota. They made a three-month attempt to raise the money, but failed. So instead, they were appointed general agents for the National Bell Company in eastern Iowa. This must have been in the spring of 1879.

Meanwhile, Ogden fashioned a crude switching mechanism to interconnect several private lines in Cedar Rapids. This was used intermittently in 1878 or 1879, at least a year before there was commercial exchange service there.

In making this switchboard, Ogden drew on experi-

---

* Herbert Hoover was the first president to have a phone on his desk. His was installed March 27, 1929.

ments he and another young telegrapher had made more than a dozen years earlier in Michigan. They had worked out a dial switch (later patented by others) for intercity telegraph switching. Before they could follow through, the other young man, E. T. Gilliland, moved away. Gilliland eventually became famous as a maker of switchboards.

Two other experimental phone systems were in operation in Minnesota, probably in 1878. Richard Hankinson, the Minneapolis man who spooked his wife with the phone in the closet, had one. Apparently he furnished exchange service from the City Hall in 1878. Ten subscribers were listed, including Pillsbury Mills and the Nicollet Hotel. Curiously, the same records tell of the "opening" of the Minneapolis exchange with 53 subscribers the following year. Perhaps the first exchange was only experimental. Or its service may not have been offered to the public.

The other phone system operating about this time was in Duluth. When Walter Van Brunt installed his line to the elevator, other businessmen clamored for a connection. He soon had an eight-point switch.

Apparently he started out doing this as a favor. But soon it was too much trouble. Van Brunt had to do all the maintenance himself, and the elevator line was always busy when he wanted it. So he took the switch out and

Bell talks with reporters in Boston, 1877.

told his friends: "Walk, damn you, walk."

At the close of 1878, the score in Northwestern Bell territory was: one private Bell exchange operating in Burlington; one public (but patent-violating) exchange in Keokuk; probably a Bell public exchange in Deadwood; some sort of limited exchange service in Minneapolis, and experimental, non-commercial systems in Cedar Rapids and Duluth.

The Midwest's greatest contribution to the struggling telephone industry during this period was a man of unique talents — a transplanted Easterner named Theodore Newton Vail.

Eventually, two different generations of telephone people would acclaim him as the man most responsible for the Bell System's survival and growth into a universal, nationwide telephone system. Considering that, it is strange that there were so few clues in his early life to indicate the tremendous organizational ability and public-spirited leadership he demonstrated later.

His father, Davis Vail, certainly would not have imagined it. When Theodore was a teenager, Davis glumly predicted he'd have to support the boy all his life. "Doe," as the family called him, was an erratic scholar. He did badly in penmanship, spelling and English composition, but was good at math. He solved mechanical problems easily and was quite interested in scientific subjects. Some of his teachers took special interest in him, but others found him exasperating. One strapped Doe so vigorously he played hooky for a week, hiding at the family's iron works at Speedwell, near Morristown, N.J.

There was a certain magic associated with the Speedwell Iron Works. It had been in the family ever since Stephen Vail, Doe's great-uncle, bought a half-interest years earlier. History had been made there. The engines for the *Savannah,* the first steamship to cross the Atlantic, were built at Speedwell in 1818. Parts for America's first steam locomotives were built there, too.

And it was at Speedwell that Samuel F. B. Morse first publicly demonstrated his electro-magnetic telegraph in 1838. Stephen Vail and his son, Alfred, had backed Morse. Alfred Vail is credited with many of the developments that made telegraphy practical. This family association must surely have influenced Doe Vail.

The Telephone.

THE proprietors of the Telephone, the invention of Alexander Graham Bell, for which patents have been issued by the United States and Great Britain, are now prepared to furnish Telephones for the transmission of articulate speech through instruments not more than twenty miles apart. Conversation can be easily carried on after slight practice without the occasional repetition of a word or sentence. On first listening to the Telephone, though the sound is perfectly audible, the articulation seems to be indistinct; but after a few trials the ear becomes accustomed to the peculiar sound and finds little difficulty in understanding the words.

The Telephone should be set in a quiet place, where there is no noise which would interrupt ordinary conversation.

The advantages of the Telephone over the Telegraph for local business are

1st. That no skilled operator is required, but direct communication may be had by speech without the intervention of a third person.

2d. That the communication is much more rapid, the average number of words transmitted a minute by Morse Sounder being from fifteen to twenty, by Telephone from one to two hundred.

3d. That no expense is required either for its operation, maintenance, or repair. It needs no battery, and has no complicated machinery. It is unsurpassed for economy and simplicity.

The Terms for leasing two Telephones for social purposes connecting a dwelling-house with any other building will be $ 20 a year, for business purposes $ 40 a year, payable semiannually in advance, with the cost of expressage from Boston, New York, Cincinnati, Chicago, St. Louis, or San Francisco. The instruments will be kept in good working order by the lessors, free of expense, except from injuries resulting from great carelessness.

Several Telephones can be placed on the same line at an additional rental of $ 10 for each instrument; but the use of more than two on the same line where privacy is required is not advised. Any person within ordinary hearing distance can hear the voice calling through the Telephone. If a louder call is required one can be furnished for $ 5.

Telegraph lines will be constructed by the proprietors if desired. The price will vary from $ 100 to $ 150 a mile; any good mechanic can construct a line; No. 9 wire costs $8\frac{1}{2}$ cents a pound, 320 pounds to the mile; 34 insulators at 25 cents each; the price of poles and setting varies in every locality; stringing wire $ 5 per mile; sundries $ 10 per mile.

Parties leasing the Telephones incur no expense beyond the annual rental and the repair of the line wire. On the following pages are extracts from the Press and other sources relating to the Telephone.

GARDINER G. HUBBARD.

CAMBRIDGE, MASS., May, 1877.

For further information and orders address

THOS. A. WATSON, 109 COURT ST., BOSTON.

First telephone advertisement, Cambridge, Mass., 1877

But the boy's promise was slow in flowering. When he graduated from high school, Doe took a job as a clerk in a drug store. In his spare time, he built telegraphs and learned Morse code. Two years later, at the age of 19, he began studying medicine with his uncle. This lasted a few months. Then there was a sharp clash within the family. Doe left home and by September of 1864, was working in a telegraph office in New York City.

His diary entries in the next two years reveal a feeling he should do something responsible with his life, but he didn't know what. His chief ambition at the time was to own a sable coat and a ruby ring.

In the spring of 1866, his father, then 55, decided to start a new life on the Iowa prairie. The rift in the family had healed and Doe joined the venture. When they arrived in Waterloo, Doe gained immediate prestige. The local hotel manager was considered one of the best billiards players in town, and Doe beat him.

Soon, Doe was invited to play baseball on a local team. Eventually he became catcher for a snappily uniformed group called the Empire Club, the best in town. They often challenged neighboring towns to "championship games." Once they beat Cedar Falls 84 to 30, scoring 33 runs in a single inning. Later, the Empires played a three-game series with the pride of Marshalltown, a team captained by a young man named A. C. Anson.

The Empires won the first game, then lost the next two. Nevertheless, the players unanimously awarded a belt and the title "Champion Player of Iowa" to Doe Vail.*

During the Waterloo years, Doe helped the family build a home nine miles from town. He also drove the three-horse team that broke 80 acres of virgin sod. In the fall of 1867, he did harvest work near Cedar Rapids to earn extra money, and his diary shows that he continued to worry about his ability to make a living. Later in the fall, he took a job teaching school three miles from his home. By spring, he had itchy feet again.

He soon lined up an appointment as night telegraph operator at Pine Bluff, Wyo., a bustling supply station for the Union Pacific's big westward push. When Vail stepped off the train at Pine Bluff, he was greeted by the sight of a dead man lying on the platform. Then the day telegrapher advised him he'd better get rid of his white shirt, collar and stiff hat if he wanted to survive.

Survive he did, though it was close at times. Once when he was out riding, cavalrymen happened along just in time to cover his galloping escape from Indians. By spring of the next year he was day operator, but decided that he wanted to be a railway mail clerk. The clerks, he

---

* The Marshalltown captain, however, did all right for himself, too. He went on to national fame as the celebrated "Cap," later "Pop" Anson who, in the 1880s, sparked Chicago to five National League championships.

Theodore N. Vail   Casper E. Yost

felt, had a better life — at least they lived in Omaha. Using family connections, he got an appointment.

With Omaha as a more civilized home base, the young man felt he could finally propose marriage to his cousin, Emma Louise Righter, whom he hadn't seen for three years. They were married in the East and by fall of 1869, were settled in an Omaha boarding house.

At the time, most mail sorting was still done in the postal stations. Only rough sorting of what was gathered in route was attempted on the trains. Letters took weeks, even months, to reach their destination. Soon, Vail was sorting and bundling mail, not only for the stations along the UP line, but also for outlying towns reached by connecting stagecoach. He bought maps, marked routes and memorized town names — routines all unheard of then. When reports of what he was doing reached headquarters, Vail was transferred to a run between Iowa City and Chicago to give his ideas a better trial.

The Vails made their home in Iowa City for several months, and their son Davis was born there. With the trial successful, Vail transferred back to Omaha as chief clerk of the Union Pacific division. He seemed quite content to consider Omaha his permanent home. He and his wife liked the hearty Western friendliness there and soon built a modest home. Vail began reading law with a friend, hoping someday to become prosecuting attorney.

This life lasted four years, and the Vail home became a popular meeting place. One of the frequent visitors was the postmaster, Casper E. Yost. "Yosty," as they called him, was a jolly companion, and always willing to lend money to his friends. The mail clerks often needed a loan to tide them over till payday, and Vail was no exception. He was struggling to pay off an addition to the house, and he'd even bought a piano on installments.

In Washington, meanwhile, postal authorities were pleased with the methods of expediting mail that were developed in the West. They wanted them spread throughout the entire sluggish, politically oriented mail service. Vail was picked for the job. In February of 1873, he was asked to report to Washington as soon as possible.

The summons was a bombshell, not only in the Omaha Post Office, but also in the Vail household. For one thing, there wasn't enough cash on hand to pay for the trip. At this point, Casper Yost made the first of his many important contributions to the success of the telephone industry. He loaned Vail money for the trip.

It was in Washington that Vail became close friends with that wild-dreaming telephone promoter, Gardiner G. Hubbard. As noted, Hubbard was chairman of a committee investigating railway mail service. This threw him in contact with Vail, who had become general superintendent of the Railway Mail Service in 1876. Vail was in charge of a cross-country inspection tour which Hubbard's committee made. On the tour, Hubbard enthusiastically demonstrated Bell's telephones at every opportunity.

At the end of the trip, Vail was a telephone promoter, too. But a year or so was to pass before he would leave the postal service for the first of his two telephone careers.

In the months before Vail was hired, the tiny Bell firm had its back to the wall. The competition from Western Union hurt in two ways. First was the long-range threat. The telegraph giant had hired three famous inventors — Edison, Elisha Gray and A. E. Dolbear — and it brazenly announced it had the only original telephone and was ready to supply it to all comers.

Then there was the unexpected, more immediate threat. Western Union's endorsement of the telephone put a stamp of approval on the whole idea. The Bell Company was swamped with orders it could not fill.

In February of 1878, Sanders was convinced Western Union was going to ruin them all. In a despairing letter to Hubbard, he wrote:

"How on earth can we make our position better by fighting when we have nothing to fight with? . . . The WU has frightened everyone connected with us, directly or indirectly . . . My notes have been thrust onto the market at a high rate of discount from the feeling that I am largely interested in a shaky concern . . . Absolute bankruptcy of the whole concern must result if we do not procure money from some source . . . Charles Williams calls daily for thousands and in addition to that we have to pay lawyers . . . I must stop the manufacture of telephones if some arrangement is not made to pay for them."

Sometime earlier, Sanders had proposed selling stock. Hubbard had brushed it aside as unnecessary. He couldn't see what they'd do with all that money. But Sanders' continued pleas finally convinced him. As a result, Sanders corralled friends and relatives and organized the New England Telephone Company with paid-in capital of $50,000. This bailed Sanders out of his immediate predicament and bought time for finding a competent business manager.

In return, the new company received an assignment of the Bell patent rights for licensing in New England.*

Ever since the transcontinental inspection tour with Hubbard, Vail had been intensely interested in the Bell

---

* This firm had no connection with the present New England Telephone and Telegraph Company, organized five years later.

Minneapolis' first telephone exchange, housed in City Hall

venture. He borrowed money to invest in it and urged his friends to do likewise. Hubbard often suggested that Vail quit the postal service and join the company.

Early in 1878, however, the talks grew serious. The competitive situation with Western Union just whetted Vail's appetite. And he was tired of being at the mercy of Congressional whims.

Hubbard brought Sanders and Watson down from Boston to meet Vail. Later, probably in May, they reached an agreement: Vail was to become general manager of the telephone company. He gave up a postal salary of more than $4,500 to accept an offer of $2,500 a year, plus a bonus of $1,000 if his work was satisfactory.

During June, a new Bell Telephone Company was organized to license and promote telephone service in areas not already covered by the New England Company. (It succeeded a Trusteeship set up in 1877.)

Officers were Hubbard, president; Sanders, treasurer; Bell, electrician; Watson, general superintendent; and Vail, general manager. Vail was the only salaried officer and reported directly to the executive committee. A public announcement stated that the company had been organized "with a large cash capital."

The "large cash capital" consisted of $25,000 to be borrowed against $100,000 worth of authorized but unissued stock. Another $25,000 was to come from sale of 500 shares of stock at $50 per share. As might be expected, Sanders ended up advancing the $25,000 loan. And his friend and relative, George L. Bradley, took on the job of disposing of the 500 shares.

At last they had a little capital and a real company.* Right away, Vail sent copies of the Bell patents to all the Bell agents, urging them to stick to their guns.

"We have the only original telephone patents. We have organized and introduced the business and we do not propose to have it taken from us by any corporation."

In September, the Bell Company filed a patent infringement suit against the head of the Western Union telephone subsidiary. The Bell officers were convinced they had a good case, but it promised to drag on.

---

* Sanders had complained earlier that the Trusteeship wasn't an organized corporation; it never held meetings.

ness. National Bell agreed to buy the Western Union telephone properties and to stay out of the telegraph business.*

In the territory now served by Northwestern Bell, Western Union had established at least five exchanges, all in Iowa. Keokuk opened in 1878 and the others started in 1879: Davenport on Sept. 15, Ottumwa on Sept. 24, Des Moines on Oct. 28, and Dubuque, no date recorded.

---

*Western Union had tried to force an agreement that would have left it in control of long distance circuits. At the time, they weren't worth much. But Vail was looking far ahead. He held out until Western Union finally agreed to his terms.

First Bell telephone exchange in Marshalltown, Iowa, about 1881. George McFarland, then superintendent, is shown second from left.

This Dubuque exchange was established in competition with a Bell exchange that had gone into operation on June 15, 1879. Dubuque was the first town in Iowa to have Bell-licensed public exchange service. It was also the first town in what is now NWB territory to have two competing exchanges.

Besides Dubuque, five other towns in what is now NWB territory had verified, Bell-licensed public exchange service in 1879. These were Minneapolis on Feb. 15, St. Paul on March 3, Omaha on June 1, Burlington, Iowa, on July 12 and Council Bluffs, Iowa, on Nov. 15.

Lead, S.D., and Duluth, Minn., end up in the uncertain catgory. In Duluth, after Van Brunt cut off his non-paying friends, he started a commercial exchange with 15 subscribers in 1879 or 1880. At first he operated on his own. Then on Feb. 12, 1881, the Duluth Telephone Company was incorporated with Van Brunt as treasurer and manager.*

The next two years saw many exchanges started. In 1880 Iowa exchanges were built at Cedar Rapids (March 1), Maquoketa (March 10), Sioux City (autumn), Clinton, Glenwood and possibly at DeWitt; in Minnesota at Winona (February) and Stillwater; in Nebraska at Lincoln (April 26), Beatrice (June) and Grand Island (October).†

North Dakota made the list in 1881 when the Fargo exchange was opened in April. Iowa added Iowa City (April), Waterloo (August), Cedar Falls, Indianola, Manchester, Marshalltown, McGregor, Mt. Vernon, Muscatine, Orange City, Oskaloosa, Red Oak, Storm Lake, Webster City, Winterset, and possibly New Hampton, Sheldon and Spencer.

In Minnesota, Moorhead got exchange service out of Fargo in April. Apparently Rochester had exchange service early in the year but it was discontinued by summer. Nebraska added Nebraska City (July), Hastings (August)

---

*Oddly, Charles E. Hall's records list December 1881, as the date the exchange opened.

†AT&T's records list the Deadwood, S.D., exchange as opening in October 1880. But Northwestern Bell records make it seem more likely that it opened in 1878.

and possibly Crete, Columbus and Kearney in 1881. And in South Dakota, the Yankton exchange opened in March. Rapid City probably had local exchange service. At the very least, it did have a long distance station connected to the Deadwood board. And so did Hill City.* Marion, Iowa, had a similar toll station out of Cedar Rapids.

It's almost certain the lists are incomplete. Historian Charles Hall states that Northwestern Bell's predecessor companies were operating 79 exchanges in Iowa in 1884. Yet today's records list only 60. There are undoubtedly omissions in the other states, too.

Even so, the stage is set to tell the story of the companies that eventually became Northwestern Bell. More than anything else, it is a story of remarkable people.

The man who brought the first telephone to Minneapolis was R. H. Hankinson, general manager of the Northwestern Telegraph Company. When he began leasing phones in 1878, he operated as the Northwestern Telephone Company. Upon incorporation Dec. 10, 1878, Northwestern Telephone Exchange Company was adopted as the name and the property of the older company was taken over.† That makes the Northwestern Telephone Exchange Company the oldest of Northwestern Bell's predecessor companies.‡

When the Northwestern Telephone Exchange Company was organized, it had authorized capital stock of $10,000. Hankinson was its president. Other officers were John Watson, general manager; F. B. Jilson, treasurer; and L. M. Towne, secretary. Zachariah T. Morrison, a foreman for Northwestern Telegraph, became wire chief and installed many of the early lines.

Hankinson and John Watson made several trips to Boston to get technical assistance. Noisy circuits were a particular problem. In fact, Morrison and one of the ear-

---

*Sioux Falls didn't get exchange service until 1882 and the Dakota Central Company's first exchange at Aberdeen, S.D., wasn't established until 1886.

†Operating under a sub-lease of the Bell license granted to C. H. Haskins of Milwaukee, a telegraph associate of Hankinson.

‡The histories of the Nebraska, Iowa, Dakota Central and Tri-State companies will be traced in subsequent chapters.

liest customers got into an angry exchange over it.

The customer, a Mr. Fletcher of Loring and Fletcher, frequently complained of the noise. Morrison told him it couldn't be eliminated because the line ran due west to Fletcher's mill and therefore crossed the earth's magnetic currents. The only way to solve the problem was to move the mill, Morrison said.

Fletcher countered by telling Morrison to go to hell. He wasn't about to move his mill to accommodate the telephone company. And, furthermore, he said, unless the telephone company constructed its line of something besides hay wire, they could just take it down. (Finally, the noise was stopped, and the two men became friends.)

Walter Van Brunt   R. H. Hankinson

Morrison was also one of the switchboard operators when the exchange first opened. However, women operators were hired very early in Minneapolis. In some of the larger eastern cities, all the operators were young men. But in the early 1880s, most exchanges found that women made better operators. A telephone official in Cleveland said, "the service [of women] is very much superior to that of boys and men. They are steadier, do not drink beer and are always on hand."

Nevertheless, men were still used as night operators for a long time — it wasn't proper for a lady to work at night. Even as night operators, some males were a problem. Customers frequently complained about the "saucy and crabbed manner of the night operator."

In Duluth, Van Brunt hired a boy to sleep in the exchange. The boy was supposed to wake up and handle the few night calls that came in. Soon, subscribers com-

St. Paul telephone operators, 1901

plained they could never get the operator after 11 p.m. Van Brunt tells the story this way:

"I had to jack up the boy. Then I connected up a 12-inch gong with the board and expected no more trouble."

But one night shortly afterwards, the gong rang so long it woke Van Brunt. He went to see what was wrong. Said Van Brunt: "The boy, being afraid that he wouldn't awaken, had taken two chairs and put them in front of the switchboard. He was sound asleep with his head within three feet of the gong. What could you do?"

The first women operators had their idiosyncrasies, too. The early switchboards in Minneapolis didn't have modern lightning arresters and, during a severe storm, electricity would sometimes flash along the board. When this happened, the women would leave the board (understandably) and climb up on a table at the rear of the room. When asked why they got up on the table, they would only answer "because."

Another example of how things were done then: Watson, the general manager, suggested to Morrison that valuable operator time could be saved if various customers with common interests could be grouped on the same party line. So Morrison put a doctor, a drug store, an undertaker and a livery stable together. They could ring each other without going through the switchboard.

But despite such whimsical sidelights, the company was making progress. After the first year's operation, Hankinson reported that he had "strung up in one year 301 miles of wire and put in nearly 700 instruments. Of this wire, 241 miles was strung in Minneapolis and St. Paul and the balance at Stillwater and Winona and on various private lines . . . it remains but to predict that before two years shall have elapsed, every town within a radius of 50 miles of Minneapolis and St. Paul will be in telephone connection with these cities."

This is a remarkable record, particularly since the Minneapolis exchange started out with the early-style Bell phones, ones that didn't have the improved transmitter that Francis Blake invented. The earlier Bell phones used a single instrument as both transmitter and receiver. The very earliest were enclosed in boxes and the user had to bend down and put his ear to the opening to hear. These were soon replaced by hand-held devices that looked like the receivers used on the later-day upright phones.

Neither model used batteries. The pressure of sound

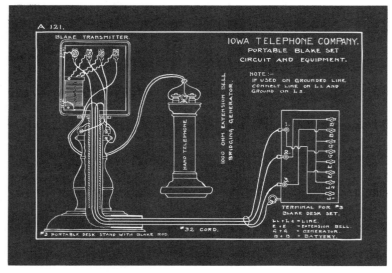

Blueprint of Blake transmitter

waves on the mechanism produced a varying current that reproduced the sound through an identical instrument at the other end of the line. But the current produced was so weak that it didn't work well over distances of more than a few miles. (Edison's light bulb, invented in 1879, required a current 500 million times stronger.) And since the same instrument was both receiver and transmitter, there was another problem. People often got confused and tried to talk with their ears or to listen with their mouths.

Addition of the Blake transmitter solved both problems. It could only be used to transmit. To hear, you had to have a receiver, too. The receiver was essentially the same device that the older phones used as both transmitter and receiver. The Blake transmitter (also called a microphone at the time) had to have battery current flowing into it. Voice pressure, acting on this transmitter, converted the steady battery current into one that varied. The receiver at the other end would then convert this varying current back into voice sounds. With this stronger current, telephones could operate over much greater distances or in noisy locations. However, subscribers had to have their own batteries in order to talk.

Obviously, the addition of the transmitter meant additional costs, and these had to be passed on to the subscriber. Some must have resisted because, on May 3, 1881, the directors of the Northwestern Telephone Exchange Company adopted this resolution:

"On motion of Hankinson on the question of permitting older subscribers to retain telephones without microphones, it was left to the option of local managers, but no new subscriber was hereafter to be allowed to use the hand telephone alone."

(This turned out to be a wise decision. Failure to have a similar policy at Yankton, S.D., led to considerable bitterness and prompted the local businessmen to establish a competing telephone exchange there about 1898.)

In 1881 Hankinson resigned from his telegraph job and moved his family to Richland County in the southeast corner of North Dakota. In his earlier years as a construction superintendent, Hankinson had built the first telegraph line in North Dakota (Fargo to Winnipeg, 1871), the first Fargo-Bismarck line and many others in the state. When he moved back to North Dakota in 1881, he

How to become a telephone expert

Officials at the American Bell Telephone Company were well aware of the need to inform the public about their product, so in 1880, the company put out a catalog called "A Description of the Telephone and of the Apparatus Used in Connection Therewith." In read-

ability, the booklet left something to be desired. But it contained enough information to make an expert out of most anyone.

One of the subjects covered in the catalog dealt with lightning arresters, oblong plates directly under the bells of a phone. During a thunderstorm, a person was supposed to insert a small metallic plug from each bell into a hole between the two plates. This gave the line a direct connection with the ground. "No danger from lightning need be apprehended at a telephone station," the booklet said, "as the wire really acts as a lightning rod and is as efficient for this purpose as most lightning rods in use. We have yet to learn of an accident from this cause."

The booklet also gave directions for "working a line," as operating a telephone was called: "In speaking through the telephone, the lips must be placed as closely to it as can be done without impeding their motion, and in listening, it must be pressed firmly against the ear."

Explaining the purpose of a "secrecy switch," the booklet noted: "When any two of the stations on a party line are conversing, a person at the third station can put his telephone into circuit by removing it from the hook, and overhear all that is said. It is sometimes desirable that this sort of eavesdropping should be rendered impossible."

lived in Richland County until 1911. The town of Hankinson was platted by and is named for him.

He did retain his interest in the Northwestern Telephone Exchange Company until 1883, however. In March of that year, the original incorporators sold their interest to a Lowell, Mass., syndicate that took title in the name of the Erie Telephone and Telegraph Company.

Electrical Review for March 29, 1883, reported that the Lowell syndicate appointed "General Manager Downs of Lowell, Mass., and Ex-Superintendent Temple of Salem, Mass., to take over the new field." The Northwestern Company was then operated as a subsidiary of Erie.

At that time, Zachariah Morrison left the telephone business to install the first fire alarm system in Minneapolis. He was superintendent of the alarm system until he retired in 1927. What happened to Watson, the old general manager, isn't recorded. Nor do the names of the new executives, Downs and Temple, appear in the various surviving accounts of activities in Northwestern territory.

P. J. Reynolds, another Northwestern Telegraph employee who had joined the phone company along with Hankinson and Morrison, stayed on. Eventually he became general superintendent of construction for both the Northwestern Telephone Exchange Company and the Southwestern Telephone and Telegraph Company. Both were Erie subsidiaries, along with the Cleveland Telephone Company. (Bell System officials declined to recognize the Erie Company and asked that all correspondence be conducted on the letterheads of the respective companies.)

About the time the Lowell syndicate took over, the Northwestern Telephone Exchange Company began building an exchange in St. Cloud, Minn. It was located in the rear of the Thomas Jones blacksmith shop. By fall, a long distance line was operating, too. A story in the *St. Cloud Daily Times,* Oct. 17, 1883, reports that a concert was transmitted from St. Cloud to an audience in St. Paul.

About the same time, a *St. Cloud Journal Press* story reported that in addition to offering telephone service, the telephone company was doing a brisk business in commercial gold, silver and nickel plating — something to keep the central office batteries profitably employed, perhaps.

But this wasn't enough to keep the exchange afloat. On Aug. 7, 1884, the *Journal Press* put it bluntly:

"Unless the telephone company can improve their service between this city and St. Paul, they might as well take their wires down. It is and from the first has been almost impossible to get an intelligible message between the two cities. The thing is so continually and wretchedly out of order as to be practically useless. When the exchange was established here, subscribers were promised that connection with St. Paul and other cities would be maintained, a condition which has not been fulfilled."

On Dec. 12, 1884, all phones were removed and the exchange was closed.

Long distance troubles weren't just a problem in Minnesota. But the experts in Boston were struggling to find answers. Theodore Vail had been an early believer in the potential of long distance telephony. It was his idea to have the American Company finance Thomas B. Doolittle's efforts to perfect hard-drawn copper wire.* When AT&T was formed early in 1885, Doolittle was one of the incorporators and Vail was the first president.

Vail continued to serve as general manager of the parent company, American Bell, until the summer of 1885 when he resigned that position for several reasons. He felt the directors were paying excessive dividends at the expense of service quality, he needed to ease the strain on his health by cutting his work load, and he wanted to devote more time to AT&T and the long distance network. By September of 1887, AT&T was an acknowledged success, with brisk traffic on the long distance lines connecting Boston, New York City, Philadelphia and many

---

*Doolittle had been associated with telephony almost from the beginning. He established one of the first telephone exchanges in 1877, using the wires of a social telegraph system he operated as a hobby. He soon recognized that, because of the weak current put out by telephone transmitters, the iron wire used in telegraph systems wasn't a good enough conductor. Copper was much better, but the copper wire then available wasn't strong enough to support its own weight between poles. Doolittle experimented and found that by drawing copper rod through a series of progressively smaller dies, without heat, he got a much stronger wire. This was the process Vail helped him perfect. Without it, long distance telephony would have been virtually impossible. Doolittle was also one of the three men who founded the Telephone Pioneer association in 1911.

George McFarland (left) and W. E. Coffey, manager, are standing on the platform for this pre-safety standards photograph in Burlington, Iowa, 1887.

smaller cities. But Vail had continued working too hard and still was not well. He resigned from AT&T, and did not return to the telephone business for 20 years.

Meanwhile, back in the Upper Midwest, the Northwestern Company established an exchange in Sioux Falls using local capital. That was probably 1882. The following year, the local people sold to the Erie Company (by then the parent company of Northwestern, also) and a period of rapid growth began.

To meet the demand, the company put in a pole line on Phillips Avenue. On Oct. 6, 1883, the City Council passed an ordinance forbidding the company to erect poles on either Phillips or Main and ordering it to take out those already placed. When the company ignored the ordinance, the mayor had the poles cut down.

After some legal jousting, the company got an injunction from a South Dakota Supreme Court justice prohibiting the city from interfering with the company's pole setting. Nevertheless, the City Council ordered the city marshal to enforce the ordinance.

When the company started digging pole holes at 10th and Phillips a week or so later, the marshal arrested the three workmen — John Reynolds, Frank Dockery and Peter McCarrier. A local judge, ignoring the injunction, fined them each $3 and costs. Within a month, another Supreme Court justice signed an order requiring the councilmen to show cause why they shouldn't be cited for contempt.

A hearing on that question followed, but the only subsequent action was the filing of a brief indicating the case was settled. One of the attorneys involved wrote 16 years later that "less than $25 disposed of the whole matter, and the poles were never erected on Phillips and Main."

A history of Sioux Falls written around the turn of the century observed that "it was only a short time before the property was transferred to the Northwestern Telephone Exchange Company, and under its management the system in Sioux Falls has been greatly improved."

The original Bell license for Wisconsin, Minnesota and the northern half of the Dakota territory was held by C. H. Haskins of Milwaukee, another official of Northwestern Telegraph. It was Haskins who furnished that first pair of phones to Hankinson. Later, Haskins assigned his Bell license rights for Minnesota and Dakota to Hankinson, who reassigned them to the Northwestern Telephone Exchange Company.

Northwestern, in turn, sold sub-licenses to various local companies because it didn't have the capital to build every place there was demand. The exchanges at Bismarck, Fargo, Grand Forks and Jamestown, N.D., were established this way. The right to operate in Pembina, N.D., was transferred to Bell of Canada late in 1881. The Duluth exchange also was operated under a sub-license.

Two of the North Dakota exchanges met the same fate suffered earlier by St. Cloud — they had to be closed. The Bismarck exchange was built by C. E. V. Draper and operated by him for a few years. Various owners followed until the Northwestern Company took title sometime before October of 1886. The exchange was finally closed July 1, 1889, when it was down to 21 subscribers.

The exchange at Grand Forks was established by D. M. Holmes and was acquired by Northwestern in 1883. It closed in 1887 when the subscribers dropped to 30.

A man named John B. Inman is credited with building the Fargo-Moorhead exchange. It was bought by Northwestern in 1883. The Jamestown exchange opened in 1883. It wasn't acquired by Northwestern until 1898.

In Minnesota, at least three other exchanges foundered in those early years (and before competition was a problem). The exchange at Fergus Falls was opened in 1882, sold to Northwestern in 1883 and discontinued in 1892. The first exchange in Crookston was established in 1884 and was discontinued a few years later. The Erie Company established an exchange at Owatonna in 1884 and had to discontinue it in 1885. Still, in 1885, a Mr. Porter is reported to have opened a new exchange there,

St. Cloud, Minn. telephone operators, 1900

operating it until Northwestern bought it in 1902. (The record doesn't show whether or not Porter had a Bell sub-license.)

In 1886 Charles P. Wainman was appointed general superintendent of Northwestern. He had been manager of the American District Telegraph office in Cleveland when the telephone was invented. Working in the Charles Bush laboratory there, Wainman built the first switchboard used in that city. It was installed in the tallest building on Superior Street in 1878 and served 25 phones.

Wainman then became an electrician for the phone company, and in 1882, was promoted to general superintendent. The Cleveland Company became an Erie subsidiary in 1883 and Wainman moved to Minneapolis.

Before long, Wainman's name begins to appear in connection with activity around the territory. In 1887 a long distance line was run from Fargo west to Casselton, N.D. A booth was placed in C. R. Meredith's store on Fourth Avenue. Meredith recalled negotiating with Wainman.

He remembered that the station soon had more business than the line could handle. Other lines were then built, including one north to Mayville and another to Valley City and on west to Jamestown. In 1891, at Wainman's urging, Meredith opened an exchange in Casselton.

Shortly afterward, probably in the winter of 1892-93, there was a bad sleet storm. Meredith's long distance line to Fargo was the only one that survived. Even the railroad telegraph lines to Fargo were out. For 48 hours, Meredith relayed all train orders to Fargo from the superintendent at Jamestown. He received them by wire and sent them on by telephone. Both he and the Northwestern Company donated this emergency service.

Wainman is also recorded as rebuilding the St. Cloud exchange so it could be reopened in 1889.

During the early years, Duluth was operating under a Bell sub-license. Soon this paid off handsomely. Van Brunt, who had built the exchange, had a terrible problem and the Bell people helped him solve it.

However, the problem takes a little explaining. In the 1880s, most telephones were magneto sets that furnished a strong ringing current when cranked vigorously. (Customers still had to have their own batteries for talking

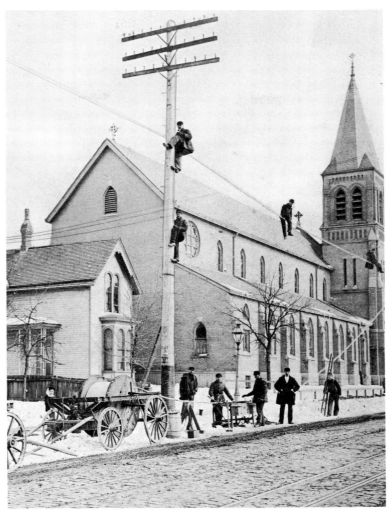

St. Paul construction crew

power.) With this magneto, a customer could ring up anyone on his own party line simply by cranking out the
proper combination of long and short rings.

But placing a call through the central office was more
complicated. Bells were obviously not the answer. The

operator needed some quick way to identify which customer wanted to place a call. The device that resulted was
called the annunciator, or drop. On the switchboard, every
subscriber's line was covered by a small metal shutter.
These were operated by electromagnets. When a customer
cranked his magneto, the current tripped the electromag-
net and caused his line shutter to drop.

The operator would plug into the line and ask what
number the customer wanted. Then, after making the connection, she would tell the customer to ring. He would
crank his magneto again, and that would ring the bell at
the called number. When the call was completed, the
operator pulled the cords and pushed the drop back up.

The problem that was giving Van Brunt fits was
caused by Duluth's new electric streetcars. The first of
these was installed in 1883, making Duluth one of the first
cities in the nation to have them. Unfortunately, a streetcar line went by the telephone office. Whenever a car
passed, all the drops* on the switchboard would fall. It
was enough to give the operators apoplexy.

Van Brunt sent a distress call to Bell System headquarters and the experts there diagnosed the problem as
induction interference. The powerful electric currents surg-
ing through the streetcar lines were "inducing" sympathetic currents in nearby telephone lines. And these
sympathetic currents were strong enough to trip the drops.

In those days, nearly all telephone circuits used the
ground — the earth — for a return. (Electric power lines
still do.)† With both the telephone and streetcar lines
using the ground for a return, the chances for induction
interference were greatly increased.

The Bell System engineers suggested to Van Brunt
that he isolate his telephone lines from the ground by
using a common return wire. Voice current would then
travel from one person's transmitter to another's receiver
via an individual wire. But, after passing through the re-

---

*Unfortunately, the word "drop" is also used to designate the line from
a cable into a customer's premises.

†That's why it's dangerous to handle electrical equipment while standing on wet floors. The current may "return" through your body to the
ground and on to its source. (Three-wire grounded plugs and wall outlets are designed to minimize this hazard.)

ceiver and being heard, the current would then return to its source via a common return wire. All phones in a neighborhood would use the same return.

This solved Van Brunt's immediate problem, and these common returns (McCluer returns, as they were called) were used in various parts of the territory now served by Northwestern Bell. But they were only a partial solution to the overall problem of induction interference.

Even today, induction interference continues to be a headache for telephone engineers and plant people. Whenever you hear another conversation while you are talking ("crosstalk"), it's probably being picked up on your line via induction. Today's telephone specialists know how to cure it, if they can find the source. But that can sometimes be a tough job even today.

It was worse in the 1880s when they didn't know how to cure it. Minneapolis was plagued with induction noises from telegraph lines from the start. And when electric streetcars appeared about 1889, induction noise problems threatened to ruin the telephone business in the Twin Cities, according to J. W. Christie.

Christie had started as a night operator in Minneapolis in 1884. Subsequently, he was cashier and then local manager in the late '80s and during the '90s. Later he was general superintendent of the Northwestern Telephone Exchange Company. When he retired in 1924, he was secretary of Northwestern Bell.

Minneapolis test desk, 1898

In an *NWB* magazine story at the time of his retirement, Christie recalled that when the electric streetcars came to Minneapolis, "telephone wires immediately became so noisy that conversation was almost impossible over them." He said that after an urgent plea for help, six of the Bell System's best engineers were assigned to the problem. One of the men was J. J. Carty, who later became AT&T's vice president in charge of research and development and in that post laid the cornerstone for today's Bell Telephone Laboratories.

It isn't clear whether these engineers made a special trip to study the Minneapolis problem. It is known that Carty and others were working on the induction problem prior to 1889. And in 1889, at a meeting of the National Telephone Exchange Association in Minneapolis, Carty read a report they had prepared. It was an important policy statement titled "The New Era in Telephony."

What Carty called for, in simplest terms, was the rebuilding of the entire Bell System plant. All the old grounded lines were to be replaced with pairs of wires (metallic circuits). And all the switchboards, engineered to use a common ground, were to be rewired to eliminate it. Every line must be electrically isolated from every other.

Moreover, this stupendous rebuilding task would have to be carried out without interrupting telephone service anywhere. In the interim, techniques would have to be found that would make it possible to interconnect the new circuits with the old grounded systems.

The old era of rugged individualism and homemade equipment had served its function. An industry had been born. Now its growing pains were so severe it must develop as a fully integrated system. As Carty put it:

"The new service requires proper engineering and a force educated and trained to carry out the plans."

Eliminating the induction noise problem was going to take a tremendous amount of money and effort. Yet within the next 10 years, virtually all the Bell System had been converted to metallic circuits.

Chapter IV

Nebraska—
a time for growth

Korty, Dickey
and a general manager
with a flair for colorful phrases

WHILE HANKINSON, VAN BRUNT and the others were organizing the north country into the Northwestern Telephone Exchange system, similiar developments were taking place in other states.

In Nebraska, Louis H. Korty and John J. Dickey were encouraged by the success of their early telephone demonstrations. Soon they were leasing pairs of phones. Probably in 1878, they began planning for a telephone exchange in Omaha. But at that point, the Western Union competition intruded on their partnership.

Dickey was superintendent of telegraph for the Union Pacific Railroad and Korty was his assistant. In addition, Dickey was a Western Union representative and that made him an agent for the Western Union telephone subsidiary. For a few months, the two men were in the awkward position of promoting competing telephone systems.

Nevertheless, they remained friends and financial partners. An associate gives a glimpse of how they handled their rival loyalties:

"This competition waged so fiercely that (Korty and Dickey) spent whole afternoons consulting together as to how they would work some luckless business house for one kind of telephone or the other — no difference which — only so they got a signature to an order."*

Korty and Dickey must have anticipated Western Union's settlement with Bell. They organized the Omaha Electric Company early in 1879 and, through it, operated Omaha's first telephone exchange which opened June 1, 1879, under the Bell banner. C. W. Mead was president, Dickey was vice president, and Korty, secretary. H. E. Jennison is listed as an incorporator, and John Morse was general manager.

Theodore N. Vail sent three letters to Korty in the months preceding the opening of the Omaha exchange. On April 15, he wrote: "I enclose your appointment as agent as made by Mr. Madden. It is affording me more than usual pleasure in doing this, for I had some fear that Omaha would not avail herself of the advantages of our system for some time to come, and, remembering all the associations, I had more than the usual desire to see Omaha provided."

A second letter, written the same day, said: "I will have sent to you as soon as possible a couple full sets of our instruments in order that you may exhibit them, and show their work. I wrote Mr. Dickey today in regard to the switchboard and apparatus to be used in connection with the exchange. I think it would be well to let our Mr. [Thomas A.] Watson supervise the construction of the apparatus for your central office system, as he can bring to bear upon it an experience of over two years."

On May 12, Vail wrote: "I'm glad to hear the Omaha Electric Company has organized. I am sure with the list of stockholders you give, opposition will be impossible."

Late in 1879, Korty and Dickey joined Gen. Grenville M. Dodge, J. W. Rodefer and others in organizing a company to build an exchange in Council Bluffs, Iowa. When it opened in November, Rodefer was the manager. Free service between Council Bluffs and Omaha was offered as an inducement to subscribers and proved popular.

---

*This anecdote is one of many observations found in a ledger that Casper E. Yost used while president of the Nebraska Telephone Company. Most of the entries, including the one just quoted, were made by Flemon Drake, general manager of Nebraska Telephone during the 1880s. The ledger, sometimes called "Yost's Bible," is a rich source of Nebraska telephone history and is quoted frequently in these pages.

Louis H. Korty

John Jay Dickey

At Lincoln, two local men — H. D. Hathaway and J. R. Clarke — joined Korty and Dickey in incorporating the Lincoln Telephone Exchange Company, which opened April 26, 1880. A similar pattern was followed in many parts of the state. The Grand Island exchange opened late in 1880, Columbus and Kearney in 1881, and the exchanges at Fremont and Plattsmouth in 1882, all with Korty and Dickey as stockholders.

Late in 1881, Fremont's exchange was being built. On Dec. 22, the *Fremont Tribune* reported:

"A large number of poles have been set on Main and 6th Streets and the instruments are being put in the exchange office which is located in W. J. Biggar's telegraph office . . . They are expected to be in operation in about 10 days . . . Fremont is booming in every particular. Fine new buildings going up on every hand and our telephone system puts us 'away up.' We predict the time will come when water works and gas will be an absolute necessity."*

Beatrice, Hastings and Nebraska City all had franchises directly from American Bell, rather than using the Korty-Dickey license. Historian Charles Hall says the Beatrice exchange was opened in June of 1880, operated by the Beatrice Telephone Company. The Hastings exchange probably opened in 1881.

Korty and Dickey had a small interest in the Nebraska City Telephone Exchange which opened in

---

*On Feb. 9, 1882, the *Tribune* reported there were 43 subscribers, including the newspaper: "The *Tribune* has joined the telephone list and those creditors who want money will please collect by telephone. We always had some reluctance about meeting them personally."

1881. John T. Burke built the exchange and managed it until 1890.

In addition to their full-time telegraph jobs and all their Nebraska telephone companies, Korty and Dickey had telephone investments in Iowa, too. They were also among the six men who incorporated the Rocky Mountain Bell Telephone Company on April 2, 1883, in Salt Lake City. Dickey was president until 1889.

Financing all these adventures was definitely a strain on Korty's bank account, and probably a strain for Dickey, too. However, Dickey seems to have been more affluent.*

The Kortys mortgaged their home to invest in the telephone company and eventually sold it. In later years, Mrs. Korty wrote these recollections:

"There were struggles . . . many of them. I thought we would sink everything we had or ever would have into these telephones, but Mr. Korty had an unshaken faith in the project and never gave up hope. We had a little home, our first, and it was sold for $1,800 and every cent went toward financing the business."

Perhaps faith came readily to Korty because of the many twists of fate he'd experienced. During the Civil War he had been a telegrapher and cipher code expert. Once at Memphis, Tenn., he and another young telegrapher named Thomas Edison had narrowly escaped capture by Confederate Gen. Pickett. Later, Korty contracted yellow fever and was one of the few Union soldiers to recover from it. He recalled seeing soldiers deliver an empty coffin to his hospital door.

As a railroad telegrapher, Korty had known the young railway mail clerk, Theodore Vail. And when the nation was joined by rail at Promontory Point, Utah, Korty had played a key role in the communications. Strategically situated at Omaha, he made the connection to Washington that transmitted the telegraph signals set off by the historic sledgehammer blows.

---

*Son of an Illinois Supreme Court justice, Dickey left home to teach school when 16. He was head bookkeeper for the Illinois and Mississippi Telegraph Company five years and then chief clerk for Western Union in Chicago. He had been superintendent of telegraph for the Union Pacific 10 years when the Omaha exchange opened.

Finally there was the chance visit to the telephone exhibit at Philadelphia and the conversation with the enthusiastic Dom Pedro. With a life like that behind him, Louis Korty could afford to be optimistic.

In 1882 Korty and Dickey formed the Nebraska Telephone Company, which eventually absorbed the other Nebraska companies they'd founded. The new company's experiences at Fairmont were typical of the ups and downs of the business in those days.

Agitation for the Fairmont exchange was led by a Mr. Gaylord, an abstractor and real estate dealer. He and others in Fairmont wanted both an exchange and a connection to Geneva, the county seat located eight miles south. Korty and Dickey said they would invest in an exchange serving both towns if the Fairmont people would subscribe $800 and the Geneva people, $600.

However, the Geneva people weren't very interested, and Korty and Dickey were ready to give it up when Gaylord asked for 48 hours. In that time, he raised the entire $1,400 in Fairmont. The office opened with 40 subscribers in Fairmont early in 1883.

Home of Omaha's first telephone office, 1879

Nebraska Telephone Company crew, Omaha

Business ultimately fell off, and the Fairmont exchange was closed in 1888. It was not reopened (by Bell, at least) until 1902. Geneva finally got service in 1899.

With the founding of the Nebraska Telephone Company in 1882, consolidation began. The Nebraska Company was granted a permanent franchise from American Bell on the condition that it buy all the Bell properties in the state within a certain time. Articles of incorporation for the company were signed July 1, 1882, by S.H.H. Clark, president of the Union Pacific Railroad, along with Dickey, Korty, Thomas L. Kimball and J. W. Gannett. Capital stock was $250,000. Clark was elected president; Dickey, vice president; and Korty, secretary-treasurer. On May 24, 1883, Flemon Drake became general manager.

Buying up the Bell properties was no problem in the exchanges where Korty and Dickey held a controlling interest. By spring of 1883, all had been absorbed, along with the locally owned Beatrice Company. But Hastings, in which Korty and Dickey held no interest, and Nebraska City, in which they had only a minority interest, held out for prices the Nebraska Company thought exorbitant.

Both of these companies were operating on five-year franchises from the American Company. With three years to go, they could afford to delay. As a result, the Nebraska

Company couldn't fulfill its commitment. A new contract was negotiated, giving the American Company a larger stock interest in the Nebraska Company. This was in return for dropping the requirement that all Bell companies in the state be absorbed promptly.

During this period, the Hastings and Nebraska City people encouraged each other to hold out. The Hastings situation was a particular thorn in the Nebraska Company's side. Rates there were embarrassingly low ($2.50 per month for residence phones vs. $3 in similar cities). In addition, the Hastings people often opposed the Nebraska Company in matters before the legislature.

In 1884 the Nebraska Company made another attempt to purchase Hastings. Drake inspected the property and reported it was poorly constructed and needed maintenance. He said the Hastings people wanted $8,000 cash for plant that had cost about $2,600 to build . . . "and half worn out, at that."

The Nebraska Company again declined to buy, figuring the American Company would force the issue by not renewing the Hastings franchise in 1886. But the American Company did renew it on a month-to-month basis. Meanwhile, the people of Hastings grew more antagonistic toward the Nebraska Company.

Finally, on advice of the American Company, the Nebraska Company agreed to buy the Hastings property for $12,000 on condition the American Company subscribe to $6,000 worth of Nebraska stock at par. The property changed hands Oct. 1, 1886. But the animosity toward the Nebraska Company wasn't dissipated until 1888, when the entire Hastings outside plant was rebuilt at a cost of about $6,000. Drake also credited the "good judgment and tact" of Manager John Musselman for smoothing over the hostile feelings.

The Nebraska City purchase was much easier. The local interests there agreed to sell for $3,000 cash when their five-year franchise expired in 1886. Drake notes that service had always been good, thanks to the efforts of John T. Burke, who constructed the exchange and managed it. Burke stayed on until 1890.

Shortly after the Nebraska Company was organized, the officers decided to build long distance lines to connect Omaha, Fremont, Blair, Plattsmouth and Lincoln.

Subscriptions were sold in all the connecting cities. The subscriptions could be redeemed in long distance service when the line was established. The Omaha to Arlington to Fremont link was completed in October 1882. It consisted of 41 miles of No. 10 gauge galvanized iron wire (a single-wire grounded circuit). It was the first commercial long distance line in Nebraska.*

The first line to Lincoln was of the same construction as the Fremont line and was completed Dec. 24, 1882. It worked for one day and then began to act up. According to Drake, a roaring noise would come on the line every day. It started in mid-morning, reached its worst in the afternoon, and disappeared entirely in the evening. When the noise wasn't on the line, the circuit worked fine.

A lineman was sent out from Lincoln with orders to make a test every mile. Every fifth pole had a lightning rod that stuck up five inches above the pole and ran down into the ground. The lineman would climb a pole, cut the Lincoln-Omaha wire and fasten his test equipment to the

---

*Earlier, however, there were long distance circuits between Omaha and Council Bluffs. And even before that, there had been experimental hookups. One reported in the *New York Herald* Jan. 26, 1880, told of "an important experiment" made the previous day. Telephones had been hooked up to telegraph lines between Omaha and St. Louis, Mo., a distance of 410 miles. "This is said to be the longest distance over which the telephone has been successfully operated," the *Herald* noted.

One of the first switchboards, built in 1878

Omaha end, using the lightning rod for the return to the ground. On the second day, 12 miles out, the lineman made his test hookup and rang for Drake. When Drake answered, he found himself talking to both the lineman and the Lincoln operator. Yet the line to Lincoln was definitely cut and tied to the insulator on the pole.

Given the fact that the Lincoln-Omaha conversation was technically impossible, there was one other unusual thing about the line. The upper end of the lightning rod wire was bent over and stuck into the top of the pole. After a lot of head-scratching, Drake told the lineman to pull the wire out. Immediately, the circuit to Lincoln disappeared. The noise was gone, too, never to return.*

Early in 1887, a line (12-gauge copper wire) was built from Omaha to Ashland. In June of 1889, it was extended to Lincoln. In the spring of 1892, a third line of galvanized iron was completed between the two cities. This line was then used with the original iron line to make a complete metallic (two-wire) circuit between Lincoln and Omaha. Drake said it worked well.

Gradually, as the 1880s unfolded, long distance lines were built to many towns in Nebraska. And the Nebraska Company built exchanges at Ashland, Seward, Blue Springs, Wilber, Wahoo, Crete and Schuyler in Nebraska, and at Avoca, Iowa, between 1883 and 1885.

Drake's comments on people in Nebraska towns were pithy. Of one, he wrote: "The town was a fake. The people have no enterprise. Their grasp on a silver dollar makes the eagle flutter to escape. They won't even patronize a circus. One may judge from this how we fared."

Of another exchange, he wrote: "We attempted to start an exchange here . . . Opened it the first of January and by October had 28 subscribers . . . But by this time, internecine war broke out. For love, for religion, and for politics, the people became so badly split up into factions and embroiled in neighborhood fights that they would not

*Drake put it this way: "[the lineman] said the end of the wire lightning rod was driven into the top of the pole two or three inches. Even so, how could we get a circuit through [the] balance of the wood — even to a spike — thence through the dry wood of the bracket, through the glass insulator to the Lincoln end of the wire. And what had this wire driven into the top of the pole to do with the noise? Give it up . . . I can't explain."

His clothes kept working, even as he slept

In 1894 D. W. Coffey was foreman of a traveling construction crew in Iowa. The work was rugged and the linemen wore their oldest clothes because they knew they'd get quite dirty.

One night, the crew arrived at the little town of Durant, Iowa, where a dance was in progress at the hotel. Coffey's crew was eager to attend, but the men were hardly dressed for it.

As foreman, Coffey had clothes that were fairly decent, but since he didn't know how to dance, he decided to retire for the night. However, being an enterprising foreman, he felt there was no reason for his clothes to go to waste. So he rented them to his men. For 25 cents each, the linemen took turns wearing Coffey's clothing and attending the dance. By the time the dance was over, Coffey had made $2 and considered himself a real promoter. There is no report on what his men thought.

A typically-dressed line crew of the period

talk to each other even by telephone . . . two years of trial ended with the usual result of a small town attempting to do that which it was not yet big enough for."

During the '80s and early '90s, several exchanges were opened, operated for a few years and then closed for lack of patronage. Among them were Fairmont, Friend, Madison, North Bend, Schuyler, Sutton and Wilber.

Even in the larger cities, the Nebraska Company had serious problems. When it took over the Council Bluffs exchange in 1883, service was poor and rates were too low. The first thing the Nebraska Company did was send out a circular announcing that the plant and service would be materially improved, but that rates would be raised and that the free calls between the Bluffs and Omaha would henceforth cost 10 cents each.

"This brought down a storm of indignant protest," Drake wrote. "Meetings of subscribers were held. The Board of Trade and the Council passed resolutions and subscribers dropped from 123 on June 31 to 81 in October. But in the meantime, the company had fulfilled its promise of improved service and had moved into better quarters . . . the people began to realize what efforts the company was making and old subscribers began to return and new ones to come in."

H. Vance Lane, who had been manager at Kearney, was transferred to Council Bluffs in 1885. By 1887 there were five lines to Omaha and these were rebuilt as metallic circuits in 1891. Introduction of electric streetcars in the winter of 1888-89 forced the rebuilding of the lines along Broadway to eliminate induction interference.

At Lincoln, relations with customers were generally pleasant, and growth throughout the 1880s was steady. Starting with 257 subscribers in 1883, the total reached 643 by the end of 1891.

The exchange was moved into a new building in 1887, and a new cord-and-plug board was substituted for the old Gilliland model. More than $15,000 was spent on the new switchboard and on outside plant reconstruction in the years 1887-90. Drake reported that at the start of 1891, the plant was in tip-top shape. He felt that with the expenditure of $1,000 to $2,000 a year in maintenance, it should take care of Lincoln's needs until there were more than 1,000 subscribers.

Electric streetcars such as the one above caused havoc and headaches in a number of telephone offices.

Drake was a bad prophet. In that very year, 1891, the Nebraska Company was forced to spend $18,267 on improvements in Lincoln. Electric streetcars were the culprits again. Virtually every phone line in town had to be rebuilt with McCluer returns.

In Omaha, the Nebraska Company's first crisis was a strike. Shortly after the exchange was purchased by the new company, some adjustments were made in work schedules and wages, along with a shift in management responsibilities. In protest, employees shut the exchange down for three hours one night. However, Drake reported, all employees but one came in the next day.

E. B. Smith, who had been chief operator in Omaha, was appointed manager in March of 1883. He began his telephone career as Chicago's first night operator. Later he was manager at Atlantic, Iowa, and then night chief operator in Omaha. He was later to become general superintendent of the Nebraska Company and general manager of the Iowa Telephone Company.

On May 9, 1883, lightning hit the Omaha exchange tower and set it afire. The exchange was closed for repairs until May 21. There had been 386 Omaha subscribers when the Nebraska Company took over in 1883. The count was 596 when 1884 ended.

All this growth forced the company to discard the old Gilliland switchboards in the middle of 1885. Its new homemade board had 1,000 subscriber jacks in a center section and 500 drops at each end. The drops were wired so that when a customer called, his shutter dropped and he was automatically connected with an "answering operator." She repeated the calling number and the number desired. A "plugging operator" at the center section heard the order and plugged the call through. A "listening-off operator" pulled the cords down when the parties hung up.

By the end of 1886 there were 863 subscribers. Starting in November of 1886, the company had to refuse new subscribers. Obviously, something had to be done again. The old quarters were on the west side of 15th between Farnam and Douglas, upstairs over a printing office. The quarters were too crowded and noisy.

Soon, the exchange was moved into a new building on the southeast corner of 15th and Harney. As Drake put it, "a first-class Western Electric multiple switchboard" was installed. The system of using answering, plugging and listening-off operators was replaced by "a very simple system" in which each operator did all those tasks.

With spare capacity available, the Omaha exchange grew rapidly. Steady yearly gains pushed the number of subscribers to 1,684 by the end of 1891.

As a part of improvements made in 1887, the company installed aerial cable in which dozens of wires were bundled together somewhat like rope. This cut down the congestion of overhead wires converging on the central office. Aerial cable was installed by the company in parts of Lincoln the same year.*

---

*The type of cable used in Omaha isn't recorded, but Drake gives a detailed account of how indoor cable was weatherproofed for outdoor use in Lincoln. They started with Western Electric office cable which had a cotton braid outer covering. This was dipped in hot asphalt, wrapped with rubber tape while still hot and then was painted. A second winding of tape followed, and then another coat of paint. Drake notes proudly that 100-conductor lead-covered cable would have cost 90 cents a foot, plus shipping charges from Chicago. The homemade cable cost 38 cents a foot on the pole and served satisfactorily for several years.

The move into cable was none too soon. As the mass of overhead wires had grown, so had criticism of it. In 1887 the Omaha City Council passed a resolution requiring the removal of overhead telephone and telegraph wires from Douglas, Farnam and Harney Streets in favor of underground cables. The company responded by appointing a committee to investigate underground conduit systems in the East and report on their possible use in Nebraska Telephone territory.

The committee made a detailed report, and much of it was quoted in a long letter sent to the mayor and the council in March of 1889. The report told of the considerable difficulties encountered with various types of cable and conduit systems in such cities as New York, Chicago and Philadelphia. It noted that the high cost of cable burying had forced up rates in other cities. Finally, it pointed out that the growing possibilities for long distance transmission could require conversion to two-wire (metallic circuit) service soon. With that in prospect, it would be unwise to bury old-style cable that might have to be replaced in a few years.

The report was remarkably prophetic. More than six years later, the president of the Nebraska Company was writing letters to the American Company urgently begging for help in dealing with underground cable deterioration of the very type warned against in the report.*

In lieu of buried cable, the company offered to use more aerial cable. Subsequently, the city gave the company a couple of years' grace. Late in 1890, the city council did pass an ordinance granting the company permission to bury cable in the streets, and setting forth regulations on such operations. By mid-1891, conduits were being installed.

Threading cable through underground conduits was a real problem. One creative solution was to tie a fish line to a rat, put the rat in the conduit and turn a ferret loose behind him. Ferrets are weasel-like animals with a yen for rats, and rats know it. With a ferret behind him, a rat

---

*However, one prediction looks foolish now: The committee thought there'd be a negative reaction toward the "popular fad in the matter of underground wires."

would streak to the other end of the conduit, pulling the fish line behind. With the fish line, a heavier wire, and eventually the cable, could be pulled through. Once a frantic rat emerged from a 500-foot conduit run and kept right on going up the inside of a telephone man's pant leg.

In the early part of the 1880s, a few South Omaha customers were served out of Omaha for about $12 per month. On Oct. 31, 1888, an exchange was opened in South Omaha, with 13 subscribers. Within three years, it had grown to 56. Flemon Drake, who wasn't often enthusiastic, was moved to write that "the growth of the city and of business is very flattering."

Outstate, several new exchanges had been added, including Norfolk in October of 1888. There were 73 subscribers at the start. Earlier in the year, Drake had written the editor of the *Norfolk Daily News* apologizing for delay in building the exchange. He explained that two heavy sleet storms in March had required the use of all construction crews to restore damaged plant.

With the dawning of the Gay Nineties, the Nebraska Telephone Company moved into a new era — the Yost Era. Flemon Drake resigned as general manager on Aug. 29, 1889, and Yost was elected vice president and general manager the same date. Drake stayed on as general superintendent. In 1891 Yost was elected president of the Nebraska Company. In 1898 he accepted the presidency of the ailing Iowa Telephone Company as well. Late in 1907, he added the presidency of the Northwestern Telephone Exchange to his other titles.

For 30 years, Casper E. Yost was to wield a tremendous influence on telephone development in the Upper Midwest. The creation of one consolidated company — Northwestern Bell — was his goal for over a decade.

Subject re information as to service, rates &c.

W H FORBES President — W- P DRIVER Treasurer — THEO N VAIL General Manager

THE AMERICAN BELL TELEPHONE CO.

Nº 95 MILK STREET

P O DRAWER 2

Personal

W. A. Leary, Esq.
    Iowa Union Tel. & Tel. Co.
        Davenport, Iowa.

Boston Dec. 28th, 1883.

In reply to yours

Nº

Dear Sir : -

Now that the Telephone business has passed its experimental stage, I would like to get your opinion upon points given below. This opinion to be based upon our existing relations, and upon your own and your associates observation and experience in your particular field : -

Is the Telephone service as it is now being furnished, satisfactory to the public.

Are the prices satisfactory to the public, considering the facilities and service that is given.

Would it be advantageous to furnish the same service now being furnished at any lower rate provided it could be done.

Is it possible in view of the contingencies of storm under ground legislation &c., to make any lower rate to the public for same classes of service.

Is it desirable, and what would be the most practicable way, to provide a service at a rate which would be within the reach of families. etc,.

Is it practicable to give different classes of service within the same Exchange.

What has been the tendency of the relationship between the public and the local Co's., for the past year ie., are the relations between the public and the Co's. improving.

Where there has been any conflict between the local Exchange and the public, what has been the cause of the difficulties, and what has been the result.

A full and detailed reply from you by the 8th, of January, would be of great service to me. Trusting that I am not asking too much,

I am,
        Very respectfully, &c. *Theo N Vail*

Providing the best possible service at the lowest possible cost has long been a Bell System goal. And it was just as true in 1883 when the telephone was less than 10 years old. This aim was the subject of a Dec. 28, 1883, letter from Theodore N. Vail, then general manager of the American Bell Company (predecessor of AT&T). He was writing to W. A. Leary, general manager of the Iowa Union Telephone and Telegraph Company at Davenport, Iowa, which later became part of Northwestern Bell. The letter, from one telephone executive to another, was marked "Personal" and not for public reading. But had the public seen it, they would have been pleased to know the concern that Vail felt.

Chapter V

Iowa—
telephone poor

Feisty linemen,
maverick managers and
a long flirtation with insolvency

"GETTING THERE FIRSTEST with the mostest" may be good strategy in a war but it was bad news for early-day telephone companies in Iowa.

Iowa had the first exchanges in the territory that was later to become Northwestern Bell. For several years, more exchanges were built in Iowa than in Minnesota, Nebraska and the Dakotas combined. Unfortunately, Iowa's exchanges were not very profitable. Many were too small. Investors didn't realize that growing companies constantly need new capital. Also, Iowa's telephone development was fragmented among too many companies.

There were so many, in fact, it is difficult to keep them straight while tracing the family tree. One of the three major companies which ultimately merged to form Northwestern Bell, the Iowa Telephone Company, was formed in 1896 by the merger of Iowa Union Telephone and the Iowa properties of Central Union Telephone.

Central Union's history is relatively uncomplicated. But Iowa Union was a product of an earlier merger of the Iowa Union Telephone and Telegraph Company and the Iowa and Minnesota Telephone Company. Both of those had taken over several smaller companies.

The story starts with George B. Engle, Jr., the Indianapolis man who was visiting in Cedar Rapids when the Bell promoter made his pitch there (see page 14).

Early in 1879, Engle and his partner, D. H. Ogden, organized as the Geo. B. Engle & Co. and were granted a Bell license for most of Iowa. (Korty and Dickey of Omaha already had part of Iowa staked out.) During 1879, Ogden and Engle built the public exchange which opened at Burlington in July. And Ogden started the Cedar Rapids exchange, which opened early in 1880.

During 1879, Ogden also teamed with Edward T. Keim of Dubuque. Keim was the man who had helped demonstrate Prof. Bell's telephones at Philadelphia in 1876. When Keim became serious about building an exchange in Dubuque, he wrote to the Bell Company and was told to contact the Engle Company for leasing rights. Soon Keim and Ogden were partners.

They opened a Bell exchange in Dubuque June 15, 1879. Later in the year, Western Union opened a competing exchange there. Western Union was also operating exchanges in four other Iowa towns then.

W. A. Leary

None of the Bell exchanges had yet been consolidated, but Engle and Odgen were beginning to see the advantages of one large central company handling several local exchanges. On Oct. 28, 1880, they formed a corporation known as Hawkeye Telephone. This was the *great-great* granddaddy of Iowa Telephone.*

Headquarters were at Cedar Rapids. The company was authorized to construct exchanges in seven towns, and by December, Ogden was building the first at Iowa City. It opened in January of 1881. The other six exchanges were built during 1881 or early 1882.

On March 19, 1882, the Hawkeye Company was reorganized as Iowa Telephone and Telegraph (a *great* grandfather of Iowa Telephone).

Meanwhile, when Western Union agreed to get out of the telephone business, it sold its exchanges to various Bell companies. The five Western Union exchanges in Iowa were bought by Western Telephone of Chicago. This firm also bought Keim's exchange in Dubuque and Ogden's in Cedar Rapids. Western Telephone was taken over by Central Union Telephone of Illinois in 1883.†

With the reorganization of Hawkeye into Iowa T&T in 1882, Engle and Ogden sold their interests. The new company was authorized to build in at least 23 more towns. And two important names appear for the first time.

These are W. A. Leary and his brother-in-law, A. F. Cutter. Leary had been a military telegrapher with Gen. Sherman in the Civil War and later chief operator in the Western Union telegraph office in Chicago. (There he became friends with another telegrapher named L. H. Korty, the man who introduced phones in Omaha.) Cutter was a dry goods merchant and introduced Leary to some of the leading businessmen in Davenport.‡ Leary persuaded

---

*Besides Engle and Ogden, backers included J. J. Snouffer, M. L. Lawson and Charles Clark, all of Cedar Rapids.

†Central Union doesn't come back into the consolidation picture until 1896 when it is absorbed by Iowa Telephone.

‡Hall lists Leary's and Cutter's backers: F. H. Griggs, James Thompson, J. T. Lane, Joe R. Lane, W. H. Decker, G. W. Cable, E. A. Benson, E. S. Carl, A. Burdick, E. E. Cook and others of Davenport, plus D. H. Louderback, W. S. Chapman and others of Chicago.

them that the men who could unite the various telephone properties in Iowa would be doing a good turn for the public, the industry and themselves. He was right on all but the last count.

Leary, as general manager, and Cutter, as secretary, administered Iowa T&T. In December 1882, they moved the headquarters from Cedar Rapids to Davenport. And in February 1883, the company was again reorganized, changing its name to Iowa Union Telephone and Telegraph (grandfather of Iowa Telephone).

At the same time Leary was promoting Iowa Union T&T, he was acquiring exchanges in his own name. It appears he built Shenandoah (opened 1883) and bought five others, including the Balch and Root properties near Clinton. In July of 1883, a company called Southwestern Iowa Telephone and Telegraph* was organized. It purchased seven exchanges, including Clarinda, one of Leary's. Leary sold his other exchanges to Iowa Union T&T late in 1883. Southwestern did likewise in June of 1884.

With these acquisitions, Iowa Union T&T owned 44 exchanges. The largest was Burlington with about 250 subscribers. The territory stretched from Glenwood, Iowa, to Sterling, Ill., and from Fort Dodge to Centerville.

Long distance lines were all iron wire, grounded circuits. The general office in Davenport could call only 12 of the 44 exchanges and that did not include Burlington, which was only 100 miles away.

Lines were gradually extended for longer distances, but the early phones weren't equal to the task. Operators along the way had to repeat messages. The test of a good operator was to be able to repeat a message well and get a reply while other operators were trying to do the same thing. Operators in exchanges like Centerville and Osceola were considered lucky — there weren't any long distance connections out of those offices.

Because the exchanges were so isolated, local managers had to be resourceful. They were in charge of plant, commercial, traffic and engineering and got only infre-

---

*This company's role isn't clear. It may have been simply a corporate tool used by Leary and the Davenport interests. Hall ignores it. At any rate, Southwestern disappears after less than a year.

Charles E. Hall   George E. McFarland

quent assistance from the under-manned general office staff.

This was roughly the situation throughout Iowa when young Charles E. Hall came to work for Iowa Union T&T on April 1, 1884. Hall inquired about a job only to please a friend. When Leary realized Hall wasn't very interested, he began a hard sell on the future of the telephone business. Charmed by Leary's magnetism, Hall reported for work the next day, beginning a 46-year telephone career.

With Iowa Union T&T organized, Leary began to build an organization with "ability, zeal and character," according to Hall. As far as possible, Leary established standard practices and uniform accounts. He formed a definite company policy and was one of the country's first telephone executives to see the importance of good public relations.

"Mr. Leary was a splendid executive of charming personality," Hall continues, "very energetic, fair in his dealings, respected by his employees, and with a vision of the future not possessed to the same degree by his backers. He was too advanced. He insisted that new money must be continually poured into the business while his associates felt that they had invested all they cared to. They wished him to run what he had and, out of earnings, take care of expansion.

"He might have done a little, even then, if they had not demanded all the net earnings be paid in dividends . . . His backers found that there were less profits in the telephone business than they had expected and less than they could derive elsewhere."

On Jan. 31, 1887, Iowa Union T&T and Iowa and Minnesota Telephone merged into Iowa Union Telephone. This led to some efficiencies, but didn't solve the basic problem. Leary resigned in July, but stayed on until late in the year to complete construction projects he had begun.*

Merger of the Iowa and Minnesota Company into Iowa Union Telephone closed out a six-year corporate history that had begun in Dubuque. When Keim sold his Dubuque exchange to Western Telephone, he, too, was thinking consolidation. With other Dubuque men, he formed the Iowa and Minnesota Telephone Company Feb. 9, 1881.† It was chartered to operate in 20 cities.

In addition, the company soon built exchanges in six other towns. And it bought three: Sioux City and Marshalltown which had been organized by Korty and Dickey of Omaha with local investors; and Ida Grove which had been established by Northwestern Telephone Exchange.

When Korty began construction at Marshalltown in May of 1880, a 17-year-old boy named George E. McFarland wangled a job. (Three years earlier, McFarland had been the second of two Marshalltown lads who had homemade phones operating.) For a couple of years McFarland worked as chore boy, groundman, lineman, night operator and trouble man.

Then some of the Marshalltown investors asked Keim to buy their interests. He already felt overextended, but he did investigate the possibility of purchasing a controlling interest, while retaining some of the local owners for good community relations. When he had options on nearly enough stock, Keim talked with a Mr. Ketcham, whose 10 shares would give him control.

"I don't know you, Mr. Keim, or your associates," Ketcham told him. "Maybe you can give us as good or better service than we have, though I doubt the latter prospect . . . I will require a guarantee from you that our

---

*Leary moved to Chicago and went into mattress manufacturing, then moved to Norfolk, Va., and manufactured lumber dryers. He died in 1893 at age 45.

†Investing with Keim were J. M. Griffith, W. H. Peabody, J. T. Howard, A. Kamman, J. K. Graves and others of Dubuque.

Managers were expected
to know everything,
often they didn't.

In most of the early telephone exchanges, the manager and a switchboard operator were the entire work force. One such manager was Charles E. Hall.

In 1884 Hall was a green construction lineman in Iowa when the foreman of his crew, without a word of explanation, told him to catch a train to Atlantic, Iowa. Upon his arrival in Atlantic, Hall found a letter from William A. Leary, general manager of the Iowa Telephone and Telegraph Company, informing him that he was now manager of the exchange. His pay was $30 a month.

The same letter outlined his responsibilities. These duties (and Hall's bewildered thoughts) were:

1. Make out all reports. *("I had never seen any of those reports.")*

2. Make out and collect all bills due the Company. *("I had never seen the books nor how the charges accrued.")*

3. Pay all bills incurred by the Company. *("I hadn't a cent to pay anything with.")*

4. Operate the switchboard at night. *("I had never operated a switchboard.")*

5. Keep all lines in repair, exchange and toll. *("I could scarcely climb a pole and had never connected a broken wire at the top of a pole.")*

6. Keep all instruments in repair. *("I had never seen the inside of a Blake transmitter.")*

7. Solicit for new subscribers and install new telephones. *("I had never assembled a telephone nor installed one.")*

good service will continue or I will not sell my stock. This guarantee is that after you secure control, you retain George McFarland in your service as long as he cares to remain. For as long as he has anything to do or say about service, it will be good . . . "

Naturally Keim wanted to see this wonder boy. "I went to the Marshalltown exchange and found it spic-and-span everywhere, in better condition than any of my own," he said. About then McFarland came in, and after one look, Keim thought to himself: "That's the kind of man I need for an assistant." However, he did check out McFarland's parents. "I wanted to see his environment and speculate on his heredity."

Satisfied on this account, Keim then asked the parents if they would consent for their son, not yet 21, to work in Dubuque. They agreed, and within a year McFarland was superintendent of the Iowa and Minnesota Company. In later years, Keim wrote: "I was sure that he would go far. All my predictions about him, all my hopes for his success, have come true."

In 1884 one of Keim's principal backers died and the widow wanted to sell. Also, Mrs. Keim was ill. So Keim decided to sell control of the Iowa and Minnesota Company to the owners of Iowa Union T&T. They operated it as a subsidiary for the next three years. Cutter, already secretary of Iowa Union T&T, was appointed secretary of Iowa and Minnesota also. McFarland, as general superintendent, handled I&M operations.

In 1885 headquarters of I&M were moved to Davenport, and McFarland was installed at a double desk with Hall. Thus began an association that would see the two men working as a team for nearly 30 years. Even in 1885, both already had wide experience. Their stories give an intimate picture of what the early days were like.

Hall had started in 1884 dismantling old magneto bells. Since 15 companies had been consolidated, there was a wide variety of instruments, "every type of magneto then in use or had ever been . . . a wonderful opportunity to learn about the switch and signaling part of telephone equipment." In the shop, magnetos were rebuilt, magnets recharged and the wood cases refinished.

After a month of this, Hall, then only 22, was sent 300 miles west to Farragut. There, by himself, he was to unload a railroad car of telephone poles and then report to a line construction crew.

The construction foreman was George Webster. "Strong as Sandow,"* Hall describes him, "and as gentle to me as a kind brother; a fighter at the drop of the hat, yet polite to me; illiterate and proud; neat and clean, usually . . . a hard drinker and an inveterate gambler, he never asked me to take a drink nor handle a card. He was uncontrollable in the hands of most men; hard and difficult to his associates; fearless in any situation. He was polite, loyal and willing to do his utmost, and make his men do their best, for just three men . . . W. A. Leary, for me, and nearly, if not quite as well, for George E. McFarland."†

The line Webster was building when Hall reported was from Shenandoah to Sidney, with loops into Farragut and Riverton. Hall's job was to dig all the pole holes that had to be located under water. (On this project, Webster erected a pole by himself after five men had slipped down a bank trying to put it into the hole.) Hall earned Webster's approval by doing as much work as anyone, finding good places to eat and keeping the accounts.

The next time Hall saw Webster was at Marengo a year later. Hall was there to boss a line construction crew. When the men showed up, Webster was among them, obviously fallen from grace. Hall immediately announced Webster would be in charge of construction. Hall would be cashier-clerk and relay instructions through Webster.

No other line ever got built so well or so fast, Hall said. Leary was so pleased he made Hall a special agent with a desk in Davenport, gave him nickle-plated spurs (pole-climbing irons) and a case of inspector's tools.

A little later, Leary asked Hall to take his crew to Van Horne and help another line crew that was progressing poorly. It rained the night Hall and his men arrived. In

---

*Eugene Sandow, professional strongman featured at the Chicago World's Fair in 1893, was the "Charles Atlas" of his day.

†Time and again, Hall insisted McFarland was a better telephone man. This is one of the few instances in which Hall admitted there was something he could do better than McFarland.

the morning Hall thought maybe they should let things dry out and start at noon. Webster wanted to get going.

As they slogged out, the superintendent of the other crew called to Webster: "George, you ought to tell Charlie

Hall and H. W. Comstock, Atlantic, Iowa, 1884

that you cannot set poles well on a day like this and every-thing muddy." Webster replied: "Charlie is not running this crew, I am, and we are going to set poles if we have to drive them into the mud with a sledge hammer." This made the superintendent so mad he took his crew home (which is probably what Webster wanted).

On another occasion, Leary was irritated with Hall and ordered him to Webster's crew at Tipton. Hall thought he'd been busted to lineman. But Webster was having trouble, and Hall had really been sent to straighten things out, according to a letter Leary sent to Webster.

Hall spent half a day digging pole holes before he and Webster figured out what was going on. Then Webster poured out his story: "The men sent me ain't no help, Charlie, and you know it. Didn't I have to fire the whole bunch once and let you dig 100 holes yourself? The old man Leary, he sends me a long lank flannel mouth, who knows everything and nothin', and to top it all, there's the old man's kid brother, raising hell all the time and writ-ing the old man stories about me every night, tellin' him 'bout me drownin' folks out and ruinin' their homes."

What had happened was that Webster had installed a phone for people who were away for the summer. He'd bored through a lead water pipe in a wall without know-ing it. Then the person opening the house turned the water on in the morning. When the family arrived that evening, everything was flooded. Webster already hated installa-tion work. After this experience, the thought of doing any more put him in shock.

To solve the problem, Hall said he'd be straw boss of a small crew. They'd finish the work in Tipton while Web-ster and the others built the line on to West Branch. "That will rid you of flannel mouth and kid brother as well as the installing," Hall explained.

Delighted, Webster promised he'd finish the West Branch line in record time. But this solution almost cost Hall his life. As he and his crew were setting a pole, flan-nel mouth and kid brother got into an argument. Flannel mouth let the butt of the pole slip and it knocked Hall out as it fell. At first they thought his neck was broken. From then on, the crew tended to business.

Unfortunately, the Webster story ends inconclusively. His "lapses from rectitude" became more frequent after

The job done, he slid to sleep.

Only a handful of employees have reached 50 years' service with Northwestern Bell. The first was Jonathan W. Nichols of Keokuk, Iowa. (Nichols, however, had begun his career with Western Union and got credit for that service which started April 1, 1876. He joined Bell Telephone Sept. 1, 1878.) Nichols spent all 50 years in Keokuk, working as foreman, trouble-shooter, installer and storeman.

Nichols believed in the "spirit of service." One example of this belief came during one of Iowa's worst sleet storms. Wires, cable and poles were down all over Keokuk, and for over three days, Nichols worked without rest or sleep. He was everywhere — testing at the main frame, clearing debris from the streets, erecting temporary telephone lines, patrolling roads and alleys to keep them safe.

On the morning of the fourth day, Nichols attempted to repair a telephone line running to the city's water pumping station. The connection was important, so Nichols, worn out from work and lack of sleep, tackled the icy telephone pole alone. At 8 a.m., Nichols' crew noticed he was missing. Two hours later, the men found him asleep at the foot of the telephone pole. Nichols had completed his work and slid down the pole. Only then did he give in to exhaustion. Later, Nichols received much praise for his dedication. But he replied, "What have I done? I just did my job, that's all."

Leary resigned and eventually he drifted away, Hall said.

Another construction man Hall admired was D. W. Coffey, a lineman from Burlington who became "one of the best foremen in Southern Iowa." In later years, Coffey himself wrote a few of his recollections.

Coffey started with a crew that was rebuilding the plant in Burlington. Both McFarland and Hall were on hand. One day they needed an extra man up on a pole. As Coffey tells it: "McFarland said, 'Put the kid up there,' so I climbed up on Supt. Hall's shoulders and he carried me up the pole and set me out on the crossarm. There I stayed until he came and got me. It was a 30-foot pole, but it seemed to me like it was 300.

"Next we started on the Jefferson Street wire stringing," Coffey wrote. "We started work early in the morning, cut the old lead down, got the rusty wire off the street before the traffic rush, then Mr. Hall said, 'You've done a corking good job and the breakfast is on me.'

"After a hearty breakfast . . . raindrops commenced to fall . . . McFarland could not have his boys get wet in the rain, so he located a store nearby and purchased a raincoat for each of us . . .

"Now, on such a wet, dreary day it's easy to catch a cold, and realizing that there were a considerable number of thirst parlors on this street anxious for business . . . we stepped over occasionally and had a shot. Mac and Charlie were the only ones of the crew who felt no need for refreshments. We had something like 400 subscribers' phones out of commission at noon and very few men able to climb a pole, which condition thoroughly upset Mac and Charlie . . . In those days firing linemen was poor policy for they were hard to replace."

A severe sleet storm hit central Iowa Jan. 3, 1886, when Hall was manager of the Oskaloosa District. A hard wind broke the wires and then heavy snow buried them. The most important line out of Oskaloosa went to Des Moines. Hall telegraphed Leary to send men and material to Knoxville, 25 miles west. Hall went there by train. For help, he had a boy who could barely climb a pole, a groundman and a livery team. In a few hours they had the line back to Oskaloosa working and started off towards Des Moines.

"The poles were encased in ice an inch thick," Hall said, "and we had to chop a zigzag course up them, cutting away a spot about six inches long every foot. The boy fell down the first two poles and refused to climb any more. I had to climb all the others the next five days.

"To make my troubles worse," he continues, "I had a large boil on the back of my neck and the chug-chug of my spurs into the poles seemed to plunge a lancet into my neck every step. I fell down a half dozen poles myself. It wouldn't have been quite so bad if the temperature had been around zero instead of below . . . There was no heat

Early switchboard operator, Webster City, Iowa

in my room and to keep warm, I crawled into bed every night just as I was dressed for out-of-doors, overcoat, over-shoes, fur cap and all . . .

"Day after day I longed for the men and material I had sent for, but they never came. When we got the circuit working to Des Moines, I was nearly a physical wreck. It was the hardest week I ever experienced.

"Later Mr. Leary explained to me that the wreckage was very bad east of Grinnell, and that he needed all the men and material there. And further, he thought I would get through whether he helped me or not, but he wasn't so sure elsewhere."

McFarland had a reputation for being a tireless worker, too. Once, when the Burlington switchboard was being moved, he worked continuously for more than 60 hours — on the outside lines during the day and on the switchboard at night. Hall reports that Mac worked as hard and took as many risks as his men during the day and then, while they were asleep, he'd stay up half the night making out reports or diagramming the next day's work.

Once, at Burlington, when he and his crew had been working hard since 7 a.m., McFarland started a new task. At that point, a lineman said: "Great Scott, Mac, don't you ever get tired or hungry? It's 7 p.m. now." "Is it possible?" McFarland replied. "I did not realize it was so late. I beg your pardon, boys. We'll quit now, of course."

Another example of McFarland's determination to finish a job came when Hall was planning to go vote. McFarland asked him not to, reasoning that if a superintendent went, so would the men. He said that if Hall went, he'd have to go, too. And since Mac was a Democrat, his vote would cancel Hall's Republican vote. Hall stayed.

The next day, Hall was surprised to see a Republican friend show up. "I thought you went to vote," Hall said. The friend explained that he wasn't going because he'd paired his vote with McFarland. Hall never quite forgave McFarland for that one.

One of the most colorful of the early day managers was C. H. Barrows at Waverly. Once he ordered magneto bells, and Cutter asked Hall to rebuild some for him. As soon as Barrows got them, he wrote back: "Cutter, send me some new bells. Them you sent me ain't any good."

Cutter wrote back that he was "satisfied those bells are all right. Hall made them. Look elsewhere for your trouble." To that, Barrows replied: "Cutter, I don't care who made the bells. They wouldn't ring up the leg of an old settin' hen. I want new bells." So McFarland had to go out. He found the bells were okay. Barrows had seen that they were rebuilt and had made up his mind they weren't any good without even trying them.

Barrows always wrote on order blanks instead of stationery. And he combined letters with orders, which irritated Cutter considerably. One such letter went like this:

"Cutter, you kicked because I put the money in a different bank this time. What difference does it make? Bowman owns all the banks in this town. You just put it in one and take it out of the other. Send me 12 Graverty Zinks [sic]. And because Sweet ain't paid his bill is no sign he won't, he will pay when he gets ready. I ought to have 3 coils of 14 [#14 gauge wire]. Of course I won't cash your checks before I deposit at least 150 dollars. When are we going to get them poles that George McFarland was going to send so fast? C. H. Barrows."

Writing of Barrows 40 years later, Hall said: "In spite of his great eccentricity and apparent insubordination, he had hosts of friends, and was honest to a penny. He would not do for this age, but in his time the results in his exchange compared very favorably with those elsewhere."

Barrows wasn't the only person who had trouble with letters. In the 1880s, instead of using carbon paper, copies were sometimes made by using a damp cloth and pressure to transfer the ink from the letter onto tissue paper. Any process involving ink and water is naturally tricky.

Early in 1887, Hall wrote a letter to Leary and smeared it making a copy. The next day, Hall got two letters from Leary, both unreadable for the same reason. Then Hall got blasted by Leary for sending an illegible letter.

"You had better buy a fresh bottle of ink," Leary wrote, "some new pens, and then in your spare time instead of doing things of little importance, practice up on your penmanship and then maybe we can decipher the stuff you send to us — occasionally."

Hall was already at the breaking point. He was manager at Burlington, but was spending more than half his time traveling for Leary. The letter was the last straw. He telegraphed Leary he'd be in his office the next morning. When he showed up, Leary was irritable and wanted to know what Hall was doing in Davenport.

Hall flopped Leary's two blurred letters and the scorcher on his desk and said: "Your letter of two days ago and these, sir. I don't know what you might have wanted me to do in these sheets and I was afraid to spend any time practicing penmanship for fear I might be neglecting something herein expressed, but indiscernible by mortal eyes, so I thought best to come right here before I incurred any expense for pens, ink or paper."

Leary looked at the letter and called for his own book of copies. The copies were even worse than the originals Hall had received. By then, Hall had cooled down and he apologized for speaking sharply. "Perhaps," Hall said, "I should try another business since I can't please you."

"Hall, forgive me," was Leary's response. "That was a rotten letter I wrote you and the letters my office sent you were worse than any I have ever received from you. My

Line crew in Missouri Valley, Iowa, 1910

position here, with my stockholders and directors, is not the most charming in the world and during my wife's illness, I have had lots to worry over. I can't understand how I ever wrote a letter like that to you. Don't leave me."

Hall was tremendously moved, but still determined to have a better understanding. He said that no man could take proper care of Burlington and travel most of the time. "The people don't like to be told the manager is out of town every time they ask for him." The upshot was that Leary got a replacement manager for Burlington and moved Hall to Davenport, promoting him to superintendent of the company.

But that was April 1, 1887. And things were so bad that, in July, Leary resigned effective Oct. 1. Leary's brother-in-law, Cutter, was still secretary. The directors didn't feel they could afford to replace Leary so Cutter ended up running the company. His task, for nine grim years, was to keep the property up, make it earn what it could, and to expand only out of earnings.

McFarland and Hall continued to divide responsibilities. Mac had the northern territory and Hall, the south.

Cutter's tribulations arose out of conditions beyond his control and "no one can be criticized for them now," Hall wrote in 1930. What Cutter and the others were trying to do was a staggering task — an attempt to create a comprehensive telephone system with insufficient capital, using an undeveloped art in an area of 60,000 square miles with no dense population centers.

"It was heroic," Hall wrote. "We might call it 'Quixotic' today, yet that was what Mr. Cutter and his friends were up against, and once in, there was no way out."

Cost control was almost fanatical. Managers were cautioned to watch pennies when purchasing lamp wicks or feed for the horses or meals for the drivers. They were urged to collect every cent possible and, of course, the standing rule was that they weren't to cash their salary checks until they'd collected enough to make them good.

Wherever workmen could walk, they walked. Telephone repairmen in some cities had pushcarts, which they hated. (Coffey noted that some of the carts met unfortunate ends when "inadvertently" left on railroad tracks.) Hall recalled that he and McFarland often walked from one town to another "because we had the time and a livery rig would have cost 2 or 3 dollars."

Even so, the company was close to insolvency time and again. "It was Mr. Cutter and his friends on the Directorate, who pulled it through," Hall said. "They kissed their telephone investments good-by and later reorganized the company again, this time with better results.

"From 1894 to 1896, Iowa Union Telephone could do little but mark time . . . there came a day when it owed one firm $75,000 and had no money with which to pay . . . In this extremity, Mr. Griggs, a director, and Mr. Cutter went to Boston . . . and there found that the American Company would help, provided the Bell companies in Iowa would merge . . . There was nothing else to do . . . though the stockholders in the Iowa Union lost heavily." Cutter was squeezed out, unjustly so, in Hall's view.

On July 1, 1896, Iowa Union Telephone and Central Union Telephone's Iowa properties were merged and the new firm was called Iowa Telephone. A general manager was brought in from Illinois, but Iowa Telephone continued to have trouble. Within two years, Casper Yost had been asked to take over as president. (He remained president of Nebraska Telephone, also.)

Cutter resigned shortly after the Iowa Company was formed. He went into construction, built over 400 homes in Davenport, plus various buildings. Hall always felt that if Cutter had stayed until Yost had control, Cutter's telephone career would have had a happier ending.

Chapter VI

The Dakotas: first blood and good friends

The Black Hills, Dakota Central and North Dakota Independent stories

IF CASPER YOST HAD KNOWN what was coming, he might have thought twice about becoming a telephone company president. Just a few years after he picked up the reins, the telephone industry was plunged into an extended period of upheaval. Before the Gay Nineties ended, swarms of small independent companies, like angry hornets, were stinging the Bell System in a thousand places.

By the time the 20th Century got underway, the independents were beginning to join forces, and quite a few of them began fighting the Bell System with a new weapon — automatic switching (dial) service.

The 25 years from 1893 to 1918 were particularly difficult for Bell managers. Many times, the only course open was to fight the competition. Other situations required conciliation and accommodation.

In the Dakotas, Yost got some practice in both techniques. In the Black Hills, he had his first taste of all-out competitive warfare. And in his relations with the Dakota Central Company and the North Dakota Independent Company, he saw how well things could go when trust and goodwill governed the dealings.

Actually, the Black Hills and the other companies

didn't have much in common. Telephone activities in the Hills were exciting and colorful, quite out of proportion to the amount of business involved. In contrast, the Dakota Central was a big operation. Its history is a study in courage and in willingness to pioneer new technology. And the North Dakota Independent Company resulted from the merger of smaller companies, whose early struggles weren't recorded.

Each of these major Dakota companies will be treated separately in this chapter. Yet together, the stories make an appropriate introduction to the tumultuous years before World War I.

The Black Hills

Nebraska Telephone's first experiences in western South Dakota couldn't have been more discouraging. The Nebraska Company bought the properties of the Black Hills Telephone and Telegraph Company in 1894 and in little more than a year, half the subscribers had quit. Then an opposition company moved in and started a fierce competitive war.

Not much is known of the telephone's early days in the Hills. What few records there are don't agree. But some of them suggest that Deadwood had exchange service in 1878, and that it was extended to Lead by 1879. National Bell records indicate that an R. O. Adams had a license to operate in the Hills in 1879, but whether he did or not isn't clear. At any rate, the Black Hills Telephone Exchange Company had a license* in 1880 and during 1881, J. L. Baird became the owner of that company.

Paul Rewman was manager during the 1880s. A story in the *Deadwood Daily Pioneer* of Nov. 30, 1906, gives him credit for building up the system. The story also refers to Baird's work in the early '80s, noting that some of the pole lines he installed were still in good shape 25 years later. Baird's policy, according to the story, was: "Use the best, as it is always cheapest in the long run."

Baird had extended exchange service to Spearfish,

---

*Licensing dates aren't the last word. Some exchanges were in operation before a Bell license was granted.

Sturgis, Rapid City, Galena and Central City by the time he sold the property to E. D. Dyar in September of 1883. A month later, Dyar incorporated it as the Black Hills Telephone and Telegraph Company.

When Nebraska Telephone bought Black Hills T&T in 1894, the stockholders were Dyar, then living in Winona, Minn.; L. W. Ingham of Dover, Minn.; and American Bell. The sellers accepted one share of Nebraska Telephone

Office of the Black Hills Company in 1892

stock for every 1½ shares of Black Hills stock. That made the price about $35,000, figuring the Nebraska stock at par.

At the time, Black Hills exchanges were Deadwood, with 120 subscribers; Rapid City, 42; Lead, 22; Hot Springs, 18; Spearfish, 10; Sturgis, 10; Custer, 9; Hill City, 4, for a total of 235. The basic residential rate was $5 per month for local service. For $7 per month, the customer got local service plus unlimited calls to any phone in any of the company's exchanges.

The Nebraska Company's new manager, John Musselman, soon found out that the rate schedule was a joke. The $5 customers were making unlimited calls, too, and even non-subscribers were taking advantage of the "free" long distance service.

On Oct. 1, 1895, the Nebraska Company announced that residential rates in Deadwood would be reduced to $3 per month within a mile of the central office, with 50 cents more charged for each additional half-mile. In the other towns, the residential rate was to be $2.50 per month within a mile of the office. And long distance rates were to be charged by the call. For instance: Deadwood to Lead or Sturgis, 25 cents; to Hill City, Custer or Hot Springs, 75 cents.

Customers were outraged. By Nov. 1, so many had discontinued service, the company quit offering local service in all towns except Deadwood and Rapid City. The number of Deadwood subscribers had dropped to 96 (nine of them "deadheads," people getting free service for one reason or another). Rapid City's list had dropped to 26 (two deadheads). The only other phones left in the Hills were three that the U.S. Government kept at Sturgis.

That was the general situation when competition arrived in 1896. A man named George Cornwall, operating as the Harrison Telephone Company, began with a long distance line connecting Sturgis, Whitewood, Deadwood, Lead and Central City. He offered long distance service at 10 cents a call. The Nebraska Company had to follow suit.

With long distance competition a reality and the threat of local competition growing in Deadwood, Yost wrote to Musselman that "if ever your telephones, transmitter, bells, etc., are to be in the best possible condition, now is the time. Go over every instrument carefully and place and keep them in such condition that ours will compare more than favorably with Cornwall's."

Yost also advised Musselman that if subscribers asked about the possibility of lower rates, he should tell them "we cannot reduce rates unless compelled to . . . Our rates are as low as we can afford to make them. But we will, of course, not be driven out of business by a competitor who knows nothing of the expenses of conducting the business . . . If rates are reduced in order to meet unfair competition, we must again raise them to our current rates after our competitor quits business." This insistence on being forthright with customers remained a Yost trademark in succeeding years.

In 1897 Harrison opened an exchange in Deadwood, charging $2.50 per month with free long distance to White-

Sioux Falls local and toll operators in 1900

wood and Sturgis. The Nebraska Company retaliated by dropping its business rate to $2 per month, its residential rate to $1.50, and by offering the same free long distance service. Later in the year, the Harrison Company built an exchange at Sturgis, and the Nebraska Company followed suit.

Yost anguished over that decision. On Aug. 19, he wrote Musselman that if Cornwall only had 18 subscribers at Sturgis and was paying his manager there $40 per month, he was losing money and it would be best to let him be. In the next few weeks, Yost changed his mind three times, finally deciding to compete at Sturgis "to give him (Cornwall) a dose of his own medicine."

Early in 1898, Musselman had a new worry: he told Yost that Cornwall had opened some of Musselman's mail. Yost answered with this advice: "So much time has elapsed since Cornwall opened any of your mail, I think I would do nothing in the matter. But in case he does any more of it, and you have sure proof, I would then report it to the Post Office Inspector and let him prosecute."*

---

*Yost's letter to Musselman is the only record of this incident. Since Yost had been a postmaster himself, it seems unlikely he would have written this letter had it been simply an "opened by mistake" episode.

In April, Yost wrote he was pleased that the opposition in Rapid City was losing ground. He went on to suggest that, before long, "we ought to be able to gather them in out of the wet, simply as a matter of good will toward our neighbor, so as to keep them from losing so much money."

That jovial mood was soon shattered. On April 18, Yost wrote: "It looks as if the Harrison people are losing ground, when they lose their tempers. It was necessary to arrest the man who cut the wires ... To bring suit for damages would not be desirable unless you deem it necessary for future protection. Be sure and secure a conviction in this case and then we will take up the matter of damages."

When the Harrison Company put a Bell phone in its own office later in 1898, Yost assured Musselman that he should treat them the same as any other customer. "Take it as a matter of course that they cannot do business without having one of your telephones." In subsequent letters, he did urge Musselman to keep checking to be sure the phone wasn't hooked up to the Harrison switchboard.

When subscribers asked Musselman to remove opposition phones from their homes, Yost warned him to be careful. Show them how to do it themselves if they wish, he said, but explain "that neither you nor yours dare to touch same for fear of a lawsuit ... Am glad to see you are getting some of his subscribers away ... "

But even though the tide was turning, Yost's optimism was several years premature. Gradually the Nebraska Company extended and improved its service. Small exchanges were opened at Hill City and Keystone in 1899, and in Belle Fourche in 1902. An exchange with 45 subscribers was opened at Spearfish Feb. 21, 1903.

But 1904 was the big year. A new 200-line board was installed in Rapid City and lines were repaired. The old 150-line board was moved to Sturgis, giving that city three times the telephone capacity it previously had.

In Lead, a new 300-line common battery board was installed in March of 1904. The exchange opened with 239 subscribers, including 82 formerly served out of Deadwood. And in Deadwood, the outside plant was completely overhauled. Underground and aerial cable were installed where needed, and a new 400-line common battery switchboard was put in.

Perhaps it was no coincidence that 1904 was the year the Harrison Company was taken over by new owners.* In 1906 the new owners sold to Nebraska Telephone. About the same time, Musselman resigned and George W. Rutherford was appointed manager.

Yost's deal to buy the opposition apparently had been arranged late in 1905, but the property wasn't transferred until the next July. Four months later, the *Deadwood Daily Pioneer-News* carried an article that was remarkably flattering.

With the simple title, "The Nebraska Telephone Company," the article began by suggesting that Black Hills people didn't often stop to think "of the excellent reasons they have for congratulations on the phone service that is being given by the Nebraska Telephone Company. It has always been said that when the 'monopoly,' as this system is called, had no opposition, that the service would be of the poorest variety and that the prices would soar to the top notch.

"At the present time," the article continued, "the company has no opposition and its service is excellent and the prices are not high considering the prices of everything else . . . "

The story then went into some detail about the history of telephone service in the area and finally concluded on a flowery note, typical of the newspapers of that day: "A better and more modern or more effective service than that enjoyed by the patrons of the Nebraska Telephone Company is seldom enjoyed and shows that competition is not always necessary to good service and low rates."

There is one other footnote to the Black Hills competition story that should be included. It's a brief letter Yost wrote Jan. 11, 1906, to J. L. W. Zietlow, president of Dakota Central. Zietlow had written to tell what he knew about the difficulties the old Harrison Company was having. Yost's answer reveals not only what kind of deal had been made, but also the friendly relationship he and Zietlow had:

---

*The name was changed to the Home Telephone Company and Frank B. Cook of Chicago was president.

"Dear Sir: Please accept my thanks for your letter on the subject of the old Harrison Telephone Company of the Black Hills. I have already arranged to purchase that property at $3750, after the mortgage has been foreclosed and good title can be given. As they are about as slippery an outfit as I ever had dealings with, I am not sure that they will stick to their bargain, but, whether they do or not, it is an absolute wreck and we would buy it only for the purpose of getting it out of the way. It is, in fact, of no value to anyone."

J.L.W. Zietlow

Dakota Central

In 1868 a 17-year-old German boy named J. L. W. Zietlow emigrated to the United States and made his way to the Midwest. He took whatever farm work he could get and saved his money. By the time he was 23, he had a job in a sawmill at Winona, Minn., and money in the bank.

Then misfortune struck twice. Zietlow lost his right arm in a sawmill accident, and, because the bank failed, he lost the money he'd saved. But he wasn't defeated. As soon as he was able, Zietlow took a commercial course at Naperville (Ill.) College. In 1880 he established a homestead near Athol, S.D., and also spent part of the year working at a manufacturing concern associated with the state prison at Stillwater, Minn. There he began to experiment with telephones and other electrical devices. By 1886 he had telephone exchanges operating in Aberdeen, S.D., and in nearby Columbia, then the county seat of Brown County.

There were 65 subscribers at Aberdeen and 37 at Columbia. The company was first called the Dakota Emner Telephone Company, but soon was reorganized as the Aberdeen Telephone Company. In 1887 Zietlow built an exchange at Watertown, with 70 subscribers, and ran a connecting line east to Groton. However, in 1889, he ran into trouble. According to a Dakota Central history, "the owners of the Bell patents made an unsuccessful attempt to close his exchanges, thereby delaying his work until

The first Dakota Central switchboard, Aberdeen, 1886

1896." The record isn't clear but apparently the Bell representative threatened a patent infringement suit.

Zietlow was out of the state and wired his people to keep the exchanges open. On his return, he "fought the matter out with the Bell representative, with the result that none of the exchanges were closed at this time."*

---

*The Columbia exchange was closed later in 1889 when the Brown County seat was moved to Aberdeen.

Dakota Central authorities said they knew of only one other independent exchange that continued to operate during the life of the Bell patents.

This account of what happened was written by Dakota Central people around 1918, while J. L. W. Zietlow and Casper Yost were still alive. Who the Bell representative was and exactly what kind of confrontation took place isn't specified. Perhaps, since Yost and Zietlow had become friends and the companies were cooperating, no one wanted to open old wounds.

A more interesting account of early-day Bell-Dakota Central relations was told in the *Aberdeen American News* on June 17, 1956. This story offered two explanations as to how Zietlow managed to operate without a Bell license.

First, while at Stillwater, Zietlow reportedly did telephone experiments with a convict named Emner. According to the story, Zietlow and Emner perfected a type of phone originally proposed by a German inventor named Reis, using a principle substantially different from the one Bell patented.*

With these phones, Zietlow was able to persuade A. C. Mellette, later governor of South Dakota, and other prominent men to invest in the Dakota Emner Telephone Company. The implication is that these men believed they had a phone that was not subject to Bell patent control. There is no evidence to suggest that Zietlow wasn't sincere. On the other hand, these "Emner-Reis" phones are never mentioned again in Dakota Central histories. And while Zietlow's first switchboard was kept and is on display in Aberdeen, apparently none of the Emner-Reis phones were saved.

Another explanation why the Bell representatives didn't press the patent matter is more plausible, and was confirmed in later years by Zietlow's successor, W. G. Bickelhaupt. Apparently, Zietlow's line from Aberdeen to Columbia went through a place called Bath. When Zietlow built a line from Bath to Groton, he put a switch at

---

*Bell transmitted sound with a variable current (an analog system); Reis attempted to do it with rapid impulses of current (a digital system). Modern pulse code modulation actually does what Reis attempted.

Bath and hired a man to operate it. By operating the switch, any two of the towns could be connected with each other.

To save himself trouble, the switchman figured out a way to connect all three lines permanently so that switching was unnecessary. Zietlow was impressed, and spent some time improving the circuitry of the device during 1887. According to a 1956 newspaper account, Zietlow didn't consider the device worth patenting. But, again according to the news account, a similar device was patented two years later by J. J. Carty, a Bell System engineer.

Here's how that 1956 article tells the rest of the story: "With the original Bell patents (soon to expire) in the '90s, the Carty 'bridging' patent was one of the clubs used by Bell or 'the Trust' as it was called, in fighting the independents.

"When Zietlow showed the Trust that he had been using the device before Carty discovered it, one newspaper account of that time says, 'He (Zietlow) was dropped like a hot potato with every assurance from the Trust that he would be let alone.'"

Whatever the explanation, Zietlow did continue to operate his exchanges independently. One news account, written at the time of Zietlow's death, said that because of the Bell pressure, other members of the firm wanted out and Zietlow had to buy their stock and carry on alone. To make things worse, the early 1890s were hard times in the Dakotas. The Columbia exchange closed and Zietlow lost more than half his subscribers at Aberdeen and Watertown.

Then in 1896, he built a long distance line to Warner, Mellette, Northville, Ashton and Redfield. It was an immediate success. When heavy winter storms and spring floods interrupted rail and telegraph communications, Zietlow kept his line operating most of the time. It was the only communication link the communities had. Once, while trying to repair his line, Zietlow nearly drowned in flood waters. Another time he got a replacement wire across a flooded stream by tying it to a kite.

When good weather finally arrived, Zietlow became a purchasing agent to promote further use of his line. People in outlying communities would phone in what they

W. G. Bickelhaupt

wanted — anything from a boy's suit to window glass or a butter tub — and Zietlow would ship it by rail.

In 1897 he extended his lines to Doland, Huron, Milbank, Wilmot and Sisseton, S.D., and to Ortonville, Minn. Early in 1898, Zietlow met W. G. Bickelhaupt and they incorporated Western Dakota Telephone, constructing a line from Aberdeen to Leola and Eureka. They also incorporated the Dakota Central Lines which built and operated long distance circuits between Aberdeen, Ortonville, Redfield and Doland. In 1904 the exchanges and the various long distance companies were consolidated into the Dakota Central Telephone Company with Zietlow as president; C. N. Herried, vice president; Bickelhaupt, secretary-treasurer; and Zietlow's son, J. Ford Zietlow, as a director.

The year before, the long distance lines of the companies had been connected with the Bell lines. At that time, Casper Yost wrote AT&T President Fish that the company "is the best managed independent company I know of." This sort of friendly relationship was typical in the years after 1889. There never was a time when Dakota Central and the Bell companies competed with each other in the same town.

Dakota Central converted Aberdeen to dial in 1905,* Huron in 1910 and six other exchanges in the next few years: Mitchell, Watertown, Madison, Pierre, Tyndall and Mobridge.

During 1917, overloading of the long distance circuits between Aberdeen, Huron and Watertown prompted establishment of what was probably the first long distance dialing system in the Upper Midwest.† At the time, each city had a direct line to each of the other two and all of these lines were routed through Doland, a smaller town

---

*A three-wire, local battery system.

†The Bell System had used a dial to set up connections on inter-office trunks between Worcester, Mass., and neighboring points for a few years starting in 1885. The modern practice of operator dialing of long distance calls started in Philadelphia in 1938 (regional only).

located midway. In addition, each of the cities had a line to the Doland board which the Doland operator could plug cn through.

To avoid the cost of building additional circuits, the Dakota Central Company decided to install automatic equipment which would allow better utilization of the existing lines. The result was a system in which all the lines terminated in automatic switches located at Doland. An operator at any of the three cities could dial direct to a customer in either of the other cities. The equipment would automatically use any line that was open. The operators could also dial the Doland operator to reach manual customers there.

In 1917 two Minnesota exchanges — White Rock and Russell — and 10 long distance lines in Minnesota were sold to Northwestern Telephone Exchange for $20,500. The same year, the new headquarters building in Aberdeen was built and in 1918, the old Aberdeen dial equipment was replaced with all new dial machinery.

When J. L. W. Zietlow died Nov. 14, 1922, the Dakota Central was a $5 million company with 93 exchanges, 30,000 subscribers, nearly 40,000 miles of long distance lines and 450 employees. Bickelhaupt* was elected president, succeeding Zietlow.

On June 1, 1923, the Dakota Central directors created the new position of general manager and elected W. R. Johnson, Northwestern Bell general commercial supervisor, to the post. Ford Zietlow continued as general superintendent and a director. In February of 1925, Johnson returned to Northwestern as Nebraska division commercial manager. And Northwestern's Nebraska division plant superintendent, W. J. Brazell, became Dakota Central general manager.

Throughout the 1920s, Dakota Central continued to expand and purchase other independent properties. Dividends at the annual rate of $8 per share of common stock, par value $100, were paid regularly. A 10 per cent common stock dividend was issued in 1926 and holders of 6 per cent preferred stock certificates received 6½ per cent

---

*Bickelhaupt's son, C. O. Bickelhaupt, was an AT&T vice president in the early 1940s and later secretary of AT&T from 1945 until he retired in 1952.

Stringing copper wire near Custer, S.D., in 1912

certificates in replacement.

Nevertheless, in the summer of 1928, some stock-holders wanted to convert part of their common stock investment into fixed income securities with a higher rate of return. In addition, the money market appeared favorable to retiring the company's 6 per cent first mortgage bonds and replacing them with a 4½ per cent issue.

With these factors in mind, the directors proposed a complicated reorganization plan. A new corporation was to be organized under Delaware laws to buy all the assets of the old company. Directors, officers and employees would all remain the same. Common stock holders would have the option of receiving, for each share of common stock in the old company, either $170 cash or a preferred stock-debenture combination that would yield $10.20 per year as compared to $8 per year on the old common stock.

Another stockholder proposed a different plan, equally complicated, and both were discussed at several meetings. The stockholders couldn't agree on either. Late in the summer, G. W. Robinson, president of the Tri-State Telephone and Telegraph Company, appeared before Dakota Central stockholders and offered them $200 per share for their stock.

Within 10 days, owners of 70 per cent of the Dakota Central stock had sold to Tri-State. By mid-December, it was almost 99 per cent.* Robinson and other Tri-State men were added to the board of directors, giving Tri-State a clear majority. However, Bickelhaupt and Zietlow were kept on the board and General Manager Brazell was made a director. Bickelhaupt remained president and Zietlow, general superintendent.

Grand Forks, N.D., men posed with their horse named Dan.

When Bickelhaupt turned 65 and retired in July of 1930, he was the last of the old-time Dakota Central people to serve on the board. J. G. Crane, a Tri-State director from Kansas City, became the new president, but served only about three years. Shortly after getting regulatory blessing, Northwestern Bell purchased the Dakota Cen-

---

*Telephone stockholders will still dump their stock if they're dissatisfied with earnings. Many of AT&T's shareholders did just that during the 1960s, at prices a lot less attractive than the Dakota Central stockholders received.

tral in September of 1933. Brazell remained a director and W. R. Johnson (the first Dakota Central general manager) returned as a director. The other new directors were W. B. T. Belt, A. A. Lowman, F. E. Randall and W. F. Cozad, all Northwestern Bell executives. Belt was elected president and Brazell continued as general manager.

For the next nine years, Dakota Central was operated as a subsidiary of Northwestern Bell. Northwestern and Dakota Central employees were transferred back and forth. Ford Zietlow stayed on and was a corporate agent for the General Office when he retired in March of 1940.

Like Gen. MacArthur's fabled "Old Soldier," the Dakota Central didn't really die. It's fading away. Even after formal merger into Northwestern Bell in 1942, it has remained alive in the memory of Northwestern Bell employees who got their start there.

The North Dakota Independent Company

In August of 1906, the North Dakota Independent Telephone Company was created through the consolidation of four smaller independent companies with a total of 16 exchanges.* Officers were H. R. Lyons of Mandan, president; James D. Brown of Hope, vice president; M. B. Cassell of Hope, secretary; and L. D. Richardson of Fargo, general manager.

Richardson proposed the merger. At the time, he was general superintendent of the Tri-State Company. He had begun his career as manager for Wisconsin Telephone at Janesville in 1887.

One of the original exchanges in the merger was Casselton, which had been founded by C. R. Meredith (his early-day telephone experiences are noted in Chapter III). Meredith said he got a good price from North Dakota Independent, "after giving the Bell Company the first chance" to buy him out.

Three other of the original exchanges — Garrison,

---

*The original companies and their exchanges were: the Jones, Weiser and Cox Company — Carrington, Fessenden, Leal, Rogers and Valley City; Casselton Telephone — Casselton; Union Telephone — Erie, Finley, Hope, Page and Sharon; Missouri Valley Telephone — Garrison, Hebron, New Salem, Underwood and Wilton.

First switchboard at Hebron, N.D., 1908

New Salem and Underwood — apparently had Clark Automatic equipment (see Chapter VIII) when North Dakota Independent bought them from the Missouri Valley Telephone Company. Richardson recalled in later years that these independents did not give satisfactory service and they were converted to manual (magneto) in 1906.

Valley City was the largest of the original towns. During 1907 and 1908, new exchanges were built at Cleveland, Dawson and Pingree. When North Dakota Independent and Northwestern Telephone Exchange made an interconnection agreement in 1908, their combined long distance lines made a fairly complete statewide telephone system. In 1910 North Dakota Independent bought the Dickinson exchange and in 1911 or the years just prior, also bought the Bismarck exchange. It had 21 exchanges when Northwestern Telephone Exchange bought control in March of 1911.

In the next few years, North Dakota Independent bought 11 more exchanges and built five more. In 1914 Richardson was elected president of the North Dakota Telephone Association and was reelected in 1915. During this period, North Dakota Independent operations were gradually being merged with those of Northwestern Telephone Exchange. By the time Northwestern Bell was organized in 1921, Richardson was the commercial superintendent for the North Dakota Division. Formal merger of North Dakota Independent into Northwestern Bell was completed in 1924. At that time, there were 36 exchanges and 100 employees. Richardson went on to become the first general manager of the North Dakota Area when Northwestern operating responsibilities were decentralized in 1928. He retired in 1930 and was made an honorary life member of the North Dakota Telephone Association.

Business office, Valley City, N.D., 1919

Chapter VII

The Populists vs. the Octopus

Bell weaknesses, competitive shenanigans and Yost as the lonely prophet

WHEN ALEXANDER GRAHAM BELL'S basic telephone patents expired in 1893-94, anyone who wanted to could manufacture telephones or operate a telephone company.

A lot of people wanted to.

In many locations, boosting the locally owned independent telephone company even took on the fervor of a crusade against the "entrenched forces of evil — monopolistic evil." Competition was seen as the great cure-all.

In 1904 while such sentiments were still running strong, *Telephony* magazine said: "The public demanded relief from the Bell octopus and the Independent movement was the outcome — an enterprise the growth of which in its myriad branches, has attained such a vastness as to become the marvel of millions, the wonder of the world of industry. It satisfies a crying need of a monopoly-oppressed nation as nothing else has in modern times, and its mission has only fairly begun."

Some of the criticism the Bell System got in those days was deserved. But the bitterness with which it was expressed was at least partly a reflection of political undercurrents. Populist ideas were then dominating the political landscape in the South and West. At times, it seemed that the Populists headquartered in what is now Northwestern Bell territory.

Vail's biographer refers to Populism as "a kind of mild Bolshevism [that] raged beyond the Mississippi." The unrest that produced it had several sources. Farm income had not kept up with the general prosperity. A protective tariff established in 1890 had been followed by a sharp rise in the cost of many products manu-factured in the East.

William J. Bryan

Many midwestern farms were mortgaged to eastern banks. Money was growing tighter, tied as it was to the value of gold which was scarce and increasing in value. As a result, the discontented farmers had a common cause with the silver mining interests who wanted a freer money supply — one based on silver as well as gold.

All these were factors in the 1890 Democratic Party landslide which gave the Democrats control of the House. That show of strength led to the forming of the People's (or Populist) Party* which held its first national convention in Omaha in July of 1892. The platform drawn up

---

*Aided by a severe financial panic which began in 1893, Populist ideas were even more potent, politically, in 1896. William Jennings Bryan's eloquent expression of them helped him capture the Democratic presidential nomination that year on a "free silver," Populist-oriented platform. From 1891-1895, Bryan had represented Nebraska's 1st District in Congress and 1894-96, he edited the *Omaha World-Herald*. Perhaps his most famous speech was the one that won him the nomination in 1896, generally known as the "Cross of Gold" speech because of these lines: "You shall not press down upon the brow of labor this crown of thorns; you shall not crucify mankind upon a cross of gold." Later in 1896, the People's Party and the National Silver Party also nominated Bryan as their candidate, but he still lost to William McKinley. However, he did carry Iowa, Minnesota, Nebraska and South Dakota, but not North Dakota.

there called for free coinage of silver, currency expansion, a graduated income tax and government ownership of the railroads, the telegraph and telephone companies.

At the local level, however, Populist sentiments were generally aimed more at establishing local business control of the telephone company than at government ownership. Populists also worked for state laws that would restrict the power and activities of large corporations such as AT&T.

To get some perspective on the impact of the independent movement, one need only look at modern statistics. In the United States today, 18 per cent of the telephones are operated by independent companies. But in the five states where Northwestern Bell operates, 27 per cent are independent-operated.

At the height of the competitive period, the figures were reversed, with the Bell companies on the short end. In the states now served by Northwestern Bell, there was a time when the independents had at least two telephones for every one that was operated by Bell.

Devastating as it was for the Bell companies, competition did produce some benefits for the public. A lot of people got telephone service for the first time; service in general was improved, and the extension of long distance lines and the introduction of automatic central offices was speeded.

On the other hand, thousands of local investors lost their shirts; the public, and businessmen in particular, learned that having two telephone companies in town was both expensive and inconvenient. You had to buy service from both companies if you wanted to call everyone who had a phone. And finally, competitors found out that running a telephone company really was difficult.

One of the reasons so many people had set up independent companies was that the business looked deceptively simple from the outside. Besides that, it appeared to the independents that the Bell companies had made several major errors which left them vulnerable. One independent company's history summarizes the situation this way:

"First . . . they [Bell] followed the line of least resistance and larger profits by serving only the larger cities. There were no farm line telephones in the entire country

Nebraska Telephone building at 18th and Douglas Sts. in Omaha, 1902

when the Bell patents expired . . . thousands of small and medium-sized towns were without a telephone exchange; many of them [even] without connection to the emaciated toll line system . . . Another, perhaps greater mistake, was to allow the dial telephone to remain and develop in the independent field."

There's some truth in those criticisms. But they don't fit every case. For instance, the Bell companies in Iowa did *not* limit their activities to the larger, more profitable towns. They established exchange service in many small towns and practically went broke doing it. When competition came, Iowa was the first of the five states to feel it and, ultimately, was the hardest hit.

In contrast, the Nebraska Company had always been wary of establishing exchanges in towns too small to support them. By 1894 it had trimmed its exchange list to only 27 towns, about one-third the number the Iowa Bell companies had. When the competitive period began, the Nebraska Company was prosperous and virtually debt free. And it didn't get hit by direct competition until late in 1898. By that time, Iowa Bell companies had competition in some 30 towns.

As it turned out, Casper Yost himself had a perceptive grasp of Bell weaknesses. And he was persistently candid in passing them on to the Bell System's top management. Starting in March of 1895, when he was president only of the Nebraska Company, Yost wrote to the American Company:

"Unless our subscribers can have lower rates, new companies will do the business . . . you should no longer ask us to pay rental on telephones . . . sell us at a fair price [those] we are now using."*

Early in 1897, Yost wrote the general manager of Colorado Telephone in Denver that Omaha's metallic circuit rate was $7.50 a month for residences within a mile of the office. "The rate is too high and we have but two or three metallic circuit residence telephones . . . I am sure there is more money in fair rates than there is in robbing the people, by charging them the rates for metallic circuit service that you do in Denver and we do in Omaha . . . " However, Yost hadn't always been so enlightened. A couple of years earlier, he had written that, "as a matter of fact, a residence telephone is a luxury and not a necessity."

May 13, 1897, to American Bell: "I do not desire . . . to be a bore; but I do know that at $5 a month there is money in furnishing metallic circuit service in Omaha . . . Time will prove that I am correct . . . and that seems to be the only way I have of convincing you . . . What the Iowa Company must have is money and plenty of it and at once; and even with that, the man who pulls that company out of the mire is sure to find life a burden and grief galore."

Feb. 21, 1898 (after Yost himself had been called to be president of the Iowa Company): "Our plant is good in very few places in Iowa . . . a very large sum should be spent putting the plant in good fighting condition . . . or

---

*In 1902 AT&T quit charging the operating companies a fixed rental per phone. Instead, it substituted a license contract which required each company to pay AT&T 4½ per cent of its gross revenue. Finally, in 1927, AT&T started selling phones to the companies. See Chapter XIII.

the Iowa Company cannot drive out competition . . . if your company [American Bell] does not solve the problem [by supplying money] the Iowa Company will go into the hands of a receiver . . . "

April 8, 1898: "When, oh when, are we to do away with that abomination known as the Blake transmitter? Our opponents are furnishing a better instrument and a much more attractive one . . . " (Hopelessly obsolete in 1898, this was the same Blake transmitter that had helped save the Bell Company from ruin 19 years earlier.)

Nov. 10, 1898: "The mistake which has been made by all the western licensees of your company was in not

THE OLD STORY.

Casper Yost was criticized for not connecting Omaha with independent companies. *Omaha World-Herald, 1906.*

covering their territory with toll lines. The sooner said mistake is corrected the better position the companies will be in."*

In his memoirs, Charles Hall suggests another Bell weakness. While many telephone people had struggled to deserve public good will, inevitably there were places where Bell tactics had irritated customers. Hall felt this was most true in the towns which had been controlled by Bell companies with headquarters in a distant state.

Competition was fiercer in those towns, he said, and feelings against the Bell System were stronger. The reason, he felt, was because Bell management in these towns had been indifferent, sometimes even arrogant, toward customers.

But even granting the Bell faults, the early enthusiasm of Bell opponents was frequently due to certain myths widely believed at the time. Hard experience eventually proved them all to be false.

The worst of these myths was that all Bell rates were so inflated, an independent company could cut them in half and still make a profit. Another was that once a telephone system was built, very little money was required to keep it in operation. Still another: that installation of shiny new equipment — particularly dial systems — inevitably meant better service. And finally, the more telephones, the more profit.

In 1898 the American Company asked Yost why the people of Iowa seemed to prefer independent companies. Yost made these points in his answer:

—Every three months "the papers are filled with statements about large quarterly dividends paid by American Bell. The people think they are being robbed to help pay those dividends and naturally are opposed to those whom they believe to be robbing them."

—Even where Iowa Company service is superior, nearly every local businessman owns stock in the

---

*This was a mistake Yost had helped make. Feb. 6, 1897, he wrote the American Company: "I admit the western part of our state [Nebraska] does look lonesome owing to absence of telephone lines. It is better that way, than it would be to have lines there and then have our stockholders feel lonesome owing to absence of dividends."

independent and is therefore willing to accept poorer service from it.

—With widespread local ownership, it is easier to get subscribers; every man feels that by supporting the independent, he is helping destroy a gigantic monopoly and obtain lower rates at the same time.

From the Bell point of view, the worst villains were the fly-by-night promoters. They were experts at exploiting local pride and promising great rewards. By creating a big demand for telephone equipment, they encouraged manufacturers to produce on speculation. And that led to even more promotional selling. Sometimes the promoters were also the builders. When they completed initial construction, they turned the plant over to a local corporation, collected *their* money, and went their way.

In a few cases, promoters used even more questionable methods. In 1895 an out-of-town man using the name C. J. Willow organized the Wizard Telephone Company in Council Bluffs, Iowa. Before long, a local stockholder became suspicious. He took a picture of Willow to Kansas City and learned the man had organized another company there under the name, "C. Perry."

In fact, Kansas City police were looking for "Perry" because he had disappeared with a large supply of electrical goods. It turned out these were the same supplies "Willow" had put up in return for a large block of Wizard stock. After Council Bluffs police jailed him, Willow resigned as president of Wizard and the company folded.

Most promoters were reputable — and more successful. In the five states Northwestern Bell serves today, there are perhaps 2,300 towns that got their first telephone exchange service from an independent company, compared to possibly 250-300 established by Bell. (See "A History of Competition," Appendix C.)

Independents did not have to be in direct competition with a Bell exchange to cause trouble. When independents established the first exchange in a town, it made Bell expansion into that town difficult and limited the expansion of the Bell long distance network. As Casper Yost argued, when independents operate in a series of towns, they are bound to build long distance lines.

That not only cut into a profitable side of the Bell business, it also limited the growth of one of the Bell Sys-

tem's strongest features. In some towns, the only reason
the Bell exchanges kept enough customers to stay in business was because those customers needed access to the
Bell long distance network.

In the five states where Northwestern Bell operates
now, there were perhaps 150 towns that did have competing telephone systems. Keokuk, Iowa, and Red Wing,
Minn., apparently were the first, in 1894.* The Nebraska
Company got its first competition at Plattsmouth in 1898,
and there never were very many competing exchanges in
the Dakotas.†

During the interconnection fight in Omaha, an independent company was
formed. It competed with Nebraska Telephone from 1907 to 1912. *Omaha
World-Herald, 1906.*

---

*Not counting Dubuque's brief competition from a Western Union ex-
change in 1879.

†At least 18 towns now served by NWB once had competition between
two independents: Carlisle, Elkader, Garnavillo, Guttenberg, Lorimor,
Manly, Vinton, and Webster City, Iowa; Graceville, Henning,
Keewatin, Kellogg, Northfield, and LeSueur, Minn.; and Emerson,
Gretna, Lyons, and Papillion, Nebr.

The struggles between competing companies produced many interesting stories, some quite light-hearted. One is how ingenuity saved the day in Bloomfield, Iowa. Ernie James, who retired in 1954, was a traveling auditor in Iowa during the competitive years. He recalled that the Bell exchange in Bloomfield had 25 "not-too-well-paying customers" but held on because the town was a county seat and the long distance business was good. But many of the townsfolk either had no phone or had independent service, so the Bell people frequently had to pay a messenger to summon the person wanted on long distance. These messenger fees were charged to the person making the call and that often led to an argument.

To avoid this, the Bell manager had an independent phone put in his office and was using it to notify people who had long distance calls. The independent directors heard about it and jerked the phone out. At that point, the Bell manager decided to use the balcony outside his second floor office. By standing on the balcony and shouting into a megaphone, the manager was often able to notify businessmen that they had a long distance call.

Good humor and ingenuity could solve some competitive problems, but, inevitably, there were hassles. And these seem to be what people remember most clearly, even though they were the exception rather than the rule.

In his recollections, E. E. Avery* wrote about being sent to Lanesboro, Minn., to install new central office equipment. An independent exchange was already in operation and local sentiment favored the independents. Avery took along all the screws, bolts and other hardware he might need because he was afraid the local hardware dealer wouldn't sell supplies to Bell employees.

When Avery arrived, construction crews were sometimes digging two or three holes before they could place a pole. As soon as they dug one hole, an irate housewife would jump into it and refuse to get out as long as any Bell people were around. But the second day he was in town, Avery attended a meeting of his fraternal lodge. There he met the secretary of the competing company and they became friends. After that the local people gradually became less hostile.

*Minneapolis district plant results supervisor when he retired in 1950.

First pay phone at the Iowa State Fair, 1901

Once, when the Bell manager in Des Moines announced plans to build a new pole line along Grand Avenue, local residents threatened an injunction to prevent the work. D. W. Coffey was the line crew foreman.

This is how Coffey wrote about the Grand Avenue project: "In the wee small hours of the morning we got busy. Every man knew his part and it was not necessary to speak a word. Before daylight we had a pair of No. 12 copper wires shining down Grand Avenue all connected and in service." Coffey doesn't say anything about it, but the Bell Company probably made some new enemies in the process, too.

Tecumseh, Nebr., was the scene of another strange battle. Local people, dissatisfied with Bell's ancient magneto service, invited the independents in and soon the new company had most of the subscribers. Then Bell put in an entirely new plant, undercut independent rates and lured back all but a handful. That prompted the independents to install phones at no fixed monthly rate. They simply billed one cent per call.

These rates won a lot of customers for the independents, but not much revenue. However, the Bell manager filed a complaint with the new Railway Commission* accusing the independents of unfair pricing. Independent officials were haled into court and fined. The townspeople resented this so much they quit Bell in droves.

Some independents would go to great lengths to woo customers. Yost recorded this example: "On many of the farmers' lines in Nebraska, as soon as the morning papers are received, the central office calls up all the farmers who have telephones and reads to them the market reports and any other items of special interest."

In Austin, Minn., the Bell exchange's fate once hung on the stubborn independence of one man. Other merchants had agreed to support the new independent company, but grocer H. B. McBride held out. "I shall decide for myself what telephone service I will have in this store," he said. "Just now I don't intend to order out the old company's service." When townspeople heard what McBride had done, many of them changed their minds, canceled their orders for independent service and stayed with Bell.

When an independent company invaded Fairbury, Nebr., it soon had 100 subscribers compared to the Bell's 68. In a few years, when the Bell people were in a position to finance new construction, they canvassed the whole area and signed up 175 local and farm subscribers. Unfortunately, they promised that there would be telephone connections to a grocer and a butcher. And no grocer or butcher would subscribe for Bell service. Finally, a Bell employee opened a grocery store. But he couldn't get any of the meat packers to sell to him. They were afraid the other Fairbury merchants would boycott them if they sold to a Bell man.

The president of AT&T wrote Yost wanting to know what he had done to stir up the people of Fairbury so much. Yost explained the situation and said he was sending news clippings "which show the frenzied condition of the people!"

Then, with tongue-in-cheek, he wrote that "our hope now is that a large number of the Fairbury merchants will

---

*The Nebraska Railway Commission was created in 1907 and given power to govern telephone company rates. Many independent company officials weren't acquainted with the Act's provisions at first.

In place of a wife

In August of 1885, Charles Hall, then manager in Newton, Iowa, took a leave of absence to go to Waterloo for several days. When he came back married, his boss, W. A. Leary, was outraged.

"You did not tell me you were going to be married," Leary said. "One of the reasons that I chose you to be near me was that you were single and therefore could make this business your wife, home and family. Now I have lost you and I am sorry."

Leary did consent to assigning Hall to a job that wouldn't require any traveling. But he warned, " 'Till then, you will have to be away from your wife as many weeks as the occasions require," then promptly sent Hall out of town.

Three weeks later, Hall arrived back at Newton. But the same day, his wife received a letter requesting her to return home to care for her sick father. Home she went, and Hall did not see her for nearly two more months.

Leary was still disgusted with Hall for getting married, but he liked him. Shortly after Mrs. Hall went home, Leary sent Hall to Waterloo on business so he could be close to her. Once there, however, Hall had trouble with the local manager and sent for Leary. It was a big mistake. Leary was annoyed at having to come, and demoted Hall to a line crew. Although Hall hadn't had a chance to see his wife, he was ordered to go to Tipton, Iowa, at once and begin his new assignment.

In time, however, Hall did get back in Leary's good graces. And, eventually, he was promoted to superintendent of the Iowa Union Telephone Company. Leary later admitted that he didn't blame Hall for marrying. But Hall never forgot how vexed his boss had become when Hall decided the telephone business couldn't take the place of a wife.

shortly be sent to the lunatic asylum, and that others will then take warning by their example and patronize us. The grocery must continue until the people come to their senses."

If Yost sometimes displayed a gallows humor, perhaps it is because he had to deal with so many discouraging situations.

For instance, Charles Hall tells of a truce he made with the Hawkeye Company,* surely with Yost's blessing. The general manager of Hawkeye had suggested that his company would not build a competing exchange in any Iowa Telephone town if Iowa Telephone would promise not to build in any of theirs. The Iowa Company agreed.

Some months later, there were rumors the independent company was going to compete in Winterset, an Iowa Telephone town. Hall went to check, then accosted the independent manager about it.

"Yes," the man said. "I just had to. The people were bound to have a different service from yours, and I thought you would prefer to have me for a competitor than a stranger . . . we're old friends, Charlie, and our agreement can go on just the same, can't it?" Hall made it clear it could not.

Of course the outrages were not all committed by the independents. But human nature being what it is, most memoirs recall only what "the enemy" did. One rare exception was written in 1949 by Dan J. Hegarty, No. 2 man in the Hegarty telephone dynasty. This is his story:

"My introduction to the business came one evening, at the beginning of the century, when H. Vance Lane, then general manager of the Nebraska Company, drove up in front of our house [in Omaha] with a team and buggy to pick up my father for a very special night job. I was permitted to accompany them. And what a night that turned out to be!

"The independent company at Plattsmouth had a franchise to operate at South Omaha and had built a line between those two towns. The purpose of this trip was to insure that this circuit did not work too well. Accordingly, spans of wire disappeared here and there . . . Shorts appeared where fine wire was tied across the circuit

---

*An independent, not the early-day Bell company.

between two insulators. At other points the circuit was grounded with small gauge wire.

"The work was arduous, and sustained effort was required. Between incidents, the necessary additional capacity for physical effort and maintenance of mental stimulus were supplied by liberal swigs of a quart of Old Crow. We returned at 5 a.m., 'mission accomplished.'

"In the light of today's standards, my introduction into the telephone business was, to say the least, a bit unethical, if not illegal."

Fortunately, incidents of this sort weren't standard practice. In the long competition between the Nebraska Company and the independent company at Lincoln, there were heated verbal exchanges and some legal battles. Yet "despite the intensity of feeling . . . the battle was remarkably free from vandalism and destruction of each other's properties." That quote is from the Lincoln Company's official history.

But even when opposition companies avoided violence, they found ingenious ways to harass and insult each other. One was to conduct a public burning of the opposition company's telephones when it finally sold out. Walter Van Brunt, the salty founder of the Duluth Company, described one such incident. He had installed a small Bell exchange in neighboring Superior, Wis.

"A jeweler in Superior started an independent exchange with a cut rate, expecting to drive us out of business. The Town Board told us if we did not drop our prices and eliminate toll rates between Duluth and Superior, they would cut down our poles . . . [They] hired a crew of men with axes . . . and I had to go to Milwaukee to get an injunction preventing them from doing it. This finally blew over and the jeweler concluded that he would never become a millionaire in the phone business. I bought him out for a nominal sum, dismantled the exchange, took it out in the street, and burned it as a lesson to the next aspirant for phone honors."

This practice was at least condoned by the American Company until a change of management in 1901. Then it was generally recognized that such tactics only built resentment and stiffened the resistance of other independents.

This was a good time for the Bell companies to become more reasonable. Independents were beginning to bump up against the hard realities of telephone economics. In his 1903 report to Iowa Company stockholders, Yost wrote:

"There is scarcely an opposition company in the state that has not become convinced that at the low rates at which they have been selling service, they must eventually fail, and very many of them are anxious to sell out to our company for much less money than has been invested by them."

Naturally, the money markets reflected the difficulties various independents were having. In 1907 F. W. Pickernell, assistant to AT&T President Frederick P. Fish, wrote to Yost saying he was convinced the days of easy independent financing were over. He predicted the Bell companies would soon have much less trouble from competing companies.

It was none too soon. In 1907 the Iowa Telephone Company was operating 44,000 telephones, every one of them at a point where it had competition. In those same towns, the independents were operating 54,000 phones.

The independent companies also had another 80,000 phones at points where they didn't have any Bell competition. Fortunately, 72,000 of these phones were connected to the Bell lines under sub-license contracts. Otherwise, the independents might have cornered even more of the long distance business. As it was, they had quite a bit of the short-haul traffic.

By this time, however, many independents couldn't finance the building of more long distance lines. And since quite a few were connecting with Bell lines, Bell long distance revenues finally were growing at a healthy rate.

It was in this climate that Hall came up with an ingenious scheme to take the initiative against independent companies. He believed that they were most vulnerable where they owned rural lines. Since the independents usually charged $15 per year for rural service, Hall's proposal to the farmers was to build new lines and give them service at $12 per year. On top of that, the farmers would actually own the lines in five years.

Of the $12, $3 was to go to Bell immediately as an annual switching charge. The remaining $9 would go into a special fund. When the fund equaled the cost of the lines,

Early Grand Island switchboard. Grand Island had two competing companies from 1903 to 1912.

subscribers would get title. But in no case were they to have to wait more than five years. And they could get credit for contributing materials, labor or board for the work crews.

When Hall explained his proposal, McFarland said it was a great idea but the company would never agree to it. However, he did give Hall permission to present the plan to General Manager E. B. Smith.

Smith also insisted he couldn't authorize giving the company's property away five years in advance. But he was intrigued, and asked Hall if he really believed the plan would rout the independents. Hall said he did.

Then, according to Hall, Smith said: "All right, you can be the goat. Pick out a town and try it out. If it's a success, I will take the glory. If it fails, you will be fired."

Hall took his idea to Nathaniel T. Guernsey, counsel for Iowa Telephone.* Guernsey worked out a simple, comprehensive agreement that made it easy for Bell people to explain the terms of the proposal to prospective subscribers. The contracts were printed on green paper, and were henceforth referred to as the "Green Blanks."

Devising this scheme was a labor of love for Hall. Angry and hurt ever since the Hawkeye Company had broken its agreement by building a competing exchange at Winterset, Hall chose to make his first raid there. The

---

*Guernsey joined AT&T's legal staff in 1912 and later was vice-president and chief counsel for seven years. He retired in 1930.

farmers liked the proposal and soon the Bell exchange increased its list of subscribers several times over. And the independent company's rural lines were idle.

Moving quickly, Hall signed up the rural people near Ankeny, another of the Mutual Company's towns. The Iowa Company had not previously had an exchange there.

Hall then shifted his attack to Indianola where the Bell exchange was so weak, and the Mutual Company so strong, that Mutual had served notice it would raise rates. Hall told the townspeople that Bell would build a new exchange, let the townspeople operate it and charge whatever rate they wanted. All they had to do was pay the Iowa Company 15 per year on the cost of the plant.

The local people were all ready to sign when Mutual wooed them back by promising not to raise rates for seven years and to put in a new switchboard.

After this narrow escape, the independent people were alarmed. According to Hall, they had been making several assumptions: that Bell would never serve farmers or improve rural lines; that it wouldn't lease an exchange; that it wouldn't build an exchange in competition with an independent; and that Bell had certain practices, methods and policies "that were as fixed and immovable as the granite hills" and you could bet on them.

"It was all right for independents to cut our rates in two," Hall wrote. "It was proper for them to call us anything contemptible they could think of, to incite the public against us and libel us . . . but if the Bell struck back, that was atrocious and outside the rules of good business."

The principal independent stockholders in five companies* were so uneasy they sent a representative to Casper Yost in Omaha to tell him "there was a crazy man, one Hall, who was giving [Iowa Telephone] property away for no apparent consideration." And "if Mr. Yost sanctioned such action no business man could compete and [the independents] would like to sell out."

Yost promised to investigate at once. He said he wasn't in favor of giving property away . . . and he might consider buying the five companies "solely in the interest

---

*The Mutual Company of Des Moines, Hawkeye of Perry, Farmers of Dallas Center, Boone County (Boone) and Southern Iowa (Des Moines).

of the public who were suffering from dual telephone exchanges."

Yost went to Des Moines and talked to Smith and McFarland about what was going on. Then he had a long talk with Hall, asked a great many questions but made no comment as to what he thought about the Green Blank scheme. Hall went on about his work. Before long, McFarland told him he could call off his counterattack — the five companies had sold out to Yost and Iowa Telephone (in 1909).*

Partly because of Bell company efforts such as the Green Blank plan, and even more because of independent company financial difficulties, the tide had turned. Within a few years, the telephones in most of Iowa's largest cities became a part of the Bell System.

However, that could mean several things. In some instances, Bell was only able to buy control rather than complete ownership. In these cases, Bell sometimes sold its plant to the independent so consolidation could take place under the independent name. In other cases, formerly rival plants continued to operate in the same city, but *with* interconnection and without competitive tensions. In order to merge a controlled company into its organization, Bell had to buy all the outstanding stock, gain regulatory approval and, sometimes, wait until the independent franchise expired. In Sioux City, Iowa, for instance, the independent franchise prohibited the company from selling out to eliminate competition.

At Marshalltown, Iowa Telephone bought control of the Marshall Telephone Company in 1908 and consolidated the exchanges the same year under the Marshall name. A. A. Moore, a wealthy lumberman, was president of the company and W. G. Bowe was superintendent. Under their leadership, Marshalltown was "probably the best managed plant in the state," according to Hall. For that reason, Iowa Telephone and, later, Northwestern Bell, left the management of the property to Moore and Bowe until they resigned in 1930. Then the

---

*Other Iowa Company exchanges begun under the Green Blank plan were Earlham, DeSoto, Guthrie Center, Adel, Redfield, VanMeter, Polk City, Panora, Stuart, Linden, Waukee, Elkhart and Lorimor.

company was merged into Northwestern.

Iowa didn't have a monopoly on competitive troubles, but it was unique in several respects. Every one of its 17 largest cities had competing telephone companies at some time. All but Fort Dodge now have Bell service. Vinton and Hamburg, Iowa, each had *three* competing telephone companies for a few years.

Clinton, Iowa, was the only large city that still had competition when Northwestern Bell was formed in 1921. Competition did not end there until 1928. And, inevitably, in the five states NWB serves, the last towns to have competition were in Iowa.

For Northwestern Bell, the competitive era finally closed at Stuart, Iowa, in 1946. The Lincoln Mutual Company ended 46 years of operation there when it left the field to NWB. But competition between two independents continued at three other Iowa towns.

In the mid-1940s, the Daubendieck family took over the Middle States Company at Osceola and competed with the Clark County Company until 1949 or 1950. At Forest City, the Farmers Mutual Switchboard Company quit in 1953, leaving the Central Iowa Company as the survivor. Both Forest City and Osceola are now operated by General Telephone.

Finally, at Harlan, the United Telephone Company and Farmers Mutual of Shelby County agreed, in 1955, that United would serve the town customers and Farmers Mutual, the rural. The consolidation was completed in 1957.

There still were more than 400 telephone companies operating in the five states NWB serves. But for the first time in more than 60 years, every one of them was "the only telephone company in town."

Chapter VIII

Goodbye, Central

"Self-serve," "girl-less" and
other automatics

IN 1919 AT&T ANNOUNCED a long-range program to convert its manual central offices to dial. At that time, independent companies had been installing automatic equipment for more than 25 years. But there was more to the situation than met the eye.

Of course, the critics assumed that, after a long struggle against progress, the Bell System had finally been forced to go along. Even today, some people believe that's what happened. The facts do not bear this out.

There is no question that the step-by-step dial system was developed, tested and perfected — outside the Bell System — by Automatic Electric. But that doesn't mean that Bell customers were stuck with second-rate service. Their manual service was generally as good, and sometimes better, than that provided by independents with dial equipment.

On the other hand, Bell System people were very involved in the development and testing of various automatic features. And a surprising amount of it took place in the territory now served by Northwestern Bell.

Even the distinction normally made between "automatic" and "manual" needs to be reexamined. In the

1890-1920 period, a great many automatic features were introduced into the "manual" system. The first common battery central office was installed by Bell at Lexington, Mass., in 1893. By 1900 the Bell System had a good start toward converting its thousands of magneto offices to common battery operation (manual).

Common battery meant exactly that. One large battery at the central office was shared by all. Customers no longer had to have batteries in their phones for talking, nor did they have to crank magnetos for ringing. Common battery systems with automatic ringing had been available to Bell companies more than 10 years when, in 1905, independent suppliers started offering them in dial systems.

Another automatic feature customers got with common battery service was that the operator answered when the customer picked up the receiver. No other signaling was necessary. When customers were done talking, they hung up and the equipment automatically notified the operator.

In contrast, customers of the first automatic systems had to push a button to get the central office switching machines to re-set when they were done talking. Sometimes people forgot. Even after the machines were designed to re-set automatically, they didn't always do it. Then someone would have to re-set it *manually* before the customer could make or receive other calls.

Difficulties of this sort were in J. J. Carty's mind when he addressed European telephone administrators in Paris in 1910. Carty, AT&T's chief engineer, presented a detailed analysis of "automatic" and "manual" systems in the United States. His theme was that "the so-called Automatic System . . . is not an automatic system, but only partly so . . . automatic machinery at the central office can be made to give service only by the aid of mechanicians [sic] constantly in attendance there . . . the so-called Manual System is partly manual and partly automatic . . . the number of automatic operations which take place in making a connection form a large proportion of the total . . . [it is] indeed, a form of semi-automatic."

Long before 1900, Casper Yost and other Bell company presidents were keenly interested in getting some kind of "automatic" service. They were particularly

1903 ad in *Electrical World and Engineer*

anxious to find a system that would work in towns too small to support operator service around the clock. These Bell officials, usually with AT&T's knowledge and help, tried several automatic systems, including ones developed by Bell scientists.

Nebraska got an early start as a testing ground and remained one for nearly 30 years. It began when Nebraska Telephone (Bell) opened its first "automatic" exchange at Aurora on July 15, 1893.

Next, around 1903, the Nebraska Clark Automatic Company (independent) installed perhaps 10 small automatic exchanges in northeastern Nebraska near Sioux City. The Clark system was invented by a Bell employee. And he remained an employee while his invention was being used by competing independent companies. Stranger still, Casper Yost surreptitiously helped the Clark company from time to time and even had one of these automatic systems installed in the Bell exchange at Ravenna. It went into service March 31, 1904.

In June of 1904, a local independent company established an all-automatic exchange in Lincoln. The day it opened, it had more customers than the well-entrenched Bell exchange. By the end of the year, it had 2,500 phones, a lot of automatics for those days. Yet even against this kind of competition, Bell manual service was more than holding its own when the Lincoln Company bought the Bell exchange there in 1912.

Panel switching equipment was the next notable development tested in Nebraska. Omaha customers were the first in the country to use this new concept in dial equipment which Bell scientists had developed.* The cut-over was Dec. 10, 1921, and with it, the staggering job of converting the Bell System to dial had begun.†

A closer examination of each of these Nebraska "automatic" installations helps to explain the Bell System attitude toward automatic service and why it developed as it did.

During the 1892-93 period when the Aurora exchange was being built, Yost carried on an optimistic correspondence with Bell officers in other parts of the country. One letter replied to the general manager of the Colorado Telephone Company in Denver, who had tele-

---

*How well the development work had been done is indicated by the fact this first panel office was in service 38 years before it was replaced.

†The change would ultimately take a half century to complete in Northwestern Bell territory. The Company converted its last exchange (or central office) to dial in 1971. During those 50 years, customers in town after town were saying goodbye, sometimes reluctantly, to "Central," a normal designation for Operator before the advent of the dial phone. "Operator," the title officially proclaimed on the dial phone, would assume Central's long distance duties and continue to help in emergencies, but Central would be missed. She was universally admired in small towns (she always knew where to locate the doctor and the veterinarian) and by lovers and songwriters who had come to expect miracles of her ("Hello Central, Give Me Heaven").

graphed Yost to ask for cost figures on the Aurora installation. In another, to the president of Rocky Mountain Bell in Salt Lake City, Yost reported on a visit he had in Chicago with Franklin Beach, general manager of the Central Union Company and an authority on the sort of automatic that was being installed at Aurora.*

To C. Jay French, American Bell general manager in Boston, Yost wrote: "As soon as the Aurora automatic exchange is built, we can tell if it is thought best to build more of them. West Point [Nebr.] would be a good place for such an exchange."

During the early 1890s, Nebraska Telephone received requests for telephone service from people in several small towns. The answers Yost wrote to these inquiries explains why Bell officials were so interested in the Aurora installation. A letter to A. C. Putnam in Chadron is representative:

"Our experience has taught us that a telephone exchange does not pay in a city the size of Chadron. Lately there has been discovered a system of automatic telephones which does not require a central office. Should this prove a success . . . I think exchanges could be operated in places smaller than under the present system . . . "

Yost constantly referred to the Aurora installation as "automatic," but it didn't involve any dials or remote control switching machines. It was an example of the Village Automatic system patented in 1884 by E. T. Gilliland while he was with American Bell. The first installation was at Leicester, Mass., in 1885. In effect, all lines were connected to every subscriber's phone. The customer, acting as his own operator, would plug into the appropriate line and ring the party he wanted. Some people called it the "self-serve" automatic system.†

Ten four-party lines went into service at Aurora in

---

*Central Union was installing one of these automatic systems at Crawfordsville, Ind., and Yost sent one of his staff men, E. B. Smith, to inspect it.

†In a 1948 letter, Joe Langdon, a retired plant man, recalled building the Aurora "self-serve" exchange and that it gave "pretty good, inexpensive service."

July of 1893; there were 39 subscribers. One customer was the long distance agent and could plug any of the 10 lines into the long distance circuits.

Yost's enthusiasm was still strong the following November when he mentioned the new automatic system as a possibility for Pawnee City in a letter to a man there. In December, he wrote French that he was trying to persuade Plattsmouth subscribers to go automatic.

Apparently the Northwestern Telephone Exchange Company also established Village Automatic systems — at Little Falls and Red Wing, Minn., in 1894 and at Anoka in 1895 or 1896 — but the available records are sketchy.

In December of 1895, Yost wrote that he had tried to get 14 subscribers in Hot Springs, S.D., to try "the automatic system." They would not, and the exchange was closed.

The Village Automatic episode at Aurora, Nebr., ended in October of 1898, when manual service was established. There were 46 subscribers then, 54 a year later. No explanation is recorded as to why the Aurora system was replaced. Growth alone may be the answer.

At any rate, automatics of a more sophisticated sort were capturing the public imagination. Almon B. Strowger, a Kansas City undertaker, had received the first of his automatic switching patents in March of 1891. By Nov. 3, 1892, the world's first "girl-less" automatic telephone exchange was in operation serving 75 subscribers at La Porte, Ind. This Strowger equipment was the direct ancestor of step-by-step systems manufactured by Automatic Electric and, later, by Western Electric.

Albert Lea, Minn., was the second city to get automatic telephones — probably in 1894.*

Strowger reportedly started working on his automatic system because he suspected telephone operators were in cahoots with his competitors — that calls for him were

---

*When he presented a collection of old telephones to the Minnesota Historical Society in 1937, George W. Johnson said he helped install this dial system the winter of 1892-93. However, Automatic Electric records say 1894. According to Automatic Electric, 1893 was spent selling stock and getting the company on its feet. One private dial system was installed at Fort Sheridan, Ill., during 1893. Johnson, a long-time Tri-State employee, retired in 1937.

Albert Lea's Early Automatics

Customers in Albert Lea, Minn., used push-button phones like this when they started "dialing" their own calls in 1894. Theirs was the second city in the world to get automatic service and these phones were the first model put out by the Strowger Automatic Telephone Exchange, the predecessor to Automatic Electric. Five wires to the central office were required and a maximum of 99 customers could be served. To call the number 53, a customer pushed a #10 button five times, then a digit button three times. After that, the customer did his own ringing, then had to push another button to reset the switching machine when done.

1892 Strowger "push-button" telephone

Phones similar to these were installed at Manchester, Iowa, in 1895, and Rochester, Minn., in 1896. Available records don't indicate the fate of Manchester's automatics. Rochester's were in service only a short time.

Apparently Albert Lea obtained the newer Strowger dial phones sometime after they came out in 1897. In 1903, after a rash of technical trouble, Albert Lea converted to manual. Company officials were surprised that customers weren't upset about having their automatic service converted to manual.

Northwestern Telephone Exchange bought control of the Albert Lea Company in 1905 or before. And Tri-State established a competing exchange in 1905. The competition continued until Tri-State took over in the 1918 division of territory. Northwestern Bell acquired Albert Lea in the purchase of Tri-State in 1933.

1896 Strowger dial
telephone with
finger flanges

being diverted to them. Whatever the motivation, a lot of people were working on automatic telephone devices at the time. Nearly 100 such patents were issued in the two decades before 1900.

Among them were four issued to Emery A. Clark and associates of Sioux City, Iowa. Clark began work on his system in 1888 and got his first patent May 30, 1893. The Clark Automatic Telephone Company was incorporated the same year by Clark, J. C. Lawler, J. H. Quick and others. The company arranged for manufacture of the equipment and installation of it in independent company exchanges. Yet throughout this period, Clark was the Bell manager in Sioux City.*

According to a letter Yost wrote to his friend Alonzo Burt in 1896, the Clark company had automatic exchanges at Rock Rapids and Storm Lake, Iowa. At the time, Burt was general manager of the Missouri and Kansas Telephone Company.

Apparently the Clark firm was relatively inactive for the next five years. Then there was a very active period beginning with a full page ad describing the Clark equipment in the August 1901 issue of the *Electrical World and Engineer.* Shortly afterwards, Yost wrote two letters to A. Van Wagenen of Sioux City. In the first, he suggested that the people at Bloomfield, Nebr., might be prospective customers for the automatic system. "Do not let anyone know that I have written," he added.

In the second letter, Yost said he was sure his Bell colleagues weren't interested in buying Clark Automatic stock. But he went on to encourage the Clark firm to

*Clark became Sioux City district manager in 1909, division commercial superintendent in Des Moines the following year. He was transferred to the General Office Commercial staff in Omaha in 1913 and retired in 1919. He died April 21, 1935.

establish automatic exchanges in smaller towns like Pierce and Plainview in Nebraska.

In October of 1902, two new Clark companies were incorporated — Iowa Clark Automatic and Nebraska Clark Automatic. Officers for both were the same: Alfred S. Clarke, president; Van Wagenen, vice president; and J. L. Putnam, secretary-treasurer. Most of the men were from the Sioux City area but, at least in later years, Alfred Clarke lived in Providence, R.I.

Nebraska Clark opened at least eight exchanges during 1903 or early 1904: at Allen, Dakota City, Homer, Laurel, Pilger, Randolph, Waterbury and Winside. One or two might even have opened as early as 1902. Iowa Clark opened exchanges at Salix and Merrill. It seems almost certain these 10 exchanges had Clark Automatic switching machines.

Throughout this period, Yost and Nebraska Telephone hovered in the wings, lending moral (and sometimes physical) support. For instance, Nebraska Telephone had exchanges at Emerson, Homer, Laurel and Randolph in 1902. They were all closed by 1904, possibly in deference to the Clark exchanges.* Yost obviously felt the Clark Automatic was ideally suited for such towns, and relations between the Nebraska and the Clark companies remained harmonious.

A letter Yost wrote to AT&T President Fish on April 2, 1903, stated that all the Nebraska Clark exchanges were using American Bell telephones. These were installed with the Clark dial equipment which was manufactured at Providence, R.I. Yost noted that the Clark people had to remove the induction coils that came with the dial equipment† and substitute coils that would work with the Bell

---

*It isn't clear when the Clark Company began operations in Emerson but they were there in 1905 or 1906. Also, Nebraska Telephone apparently was offering service in Emerson again in 1907, perhaps through some arrangement with Clark. Nebraska Telephone installed a manual board in 1909, but didn't purchase the exchange until 1912.

†Clark Automatic advertisements show a complete unit with dial and telephone combined. It's quite possible that Nebraska Clark made a special deal to use Bell phones in order to obtain long distance interconnection with Bell and to retain the friendship of Yost. The influence of Clark, still a Bell employee, may have been involved, too, even though he had probably assigned away his patent rights.

Joseph Root—
trailblazer in two industries

J. C. Root

Some of the first pioneers of the telephone business went on to found new companies in other industries. One such man was Joseph C. Root. In the early days, he formed a number of telephone companies in Iowa that eventually were consolidated into Northwestern Bell. And later on, he also founded a fraternal life insurance society that today is known nationwide.

Root brought the first telephones to Clinton, Iowa, in 1878. By 1880 he'd built a line connecting Clinton and Lyons, Iowa, and joined with J. K. P. Balch in forming the Clinton and Lyons Telephone Company. Soon after, the two men built exchanges in DeWitt, Iowa, and in three towns in Illinois.

In 1883 Root's Clinton and Lyons Telephone Company was purchased by the Iowa Union Telephone and Telegraph Company of Davenport, Iowa, which was consolidating Bell-franchised companies. So Root turned to the insurance business. He organized a fraternal life insurance society in Illinois, but gave it up in 1889 and came to Omaha. In 1890 Root founded another fraternal life insurance society called the Woodmen of the World. Today, this society, still headquartered in Omaha, has over 678,000 members with nearly $3 billion worth of life insurance in force. And founder J. C. Root claims a special place as trailblazer in both the history of Northwestern Bell and the Woodmen of the World.

phones. He suggested that AT&T send 200 #13 induction coils to the Providence factory to avoid this extra work in the field.

"They [the Clark people] are our friends and it would be a good policy to do as above requested," Yost wrote. He went on to ask: "What progress is being made with the automatic apparatus which your Company was proposing to furnish to its licensees?"

By October, Yost was getting impatient. He wrote Van Wagenen asking for the lowest price the Clark Company would take to rent or sell automatic equipment for a 40-line exchange. He said he didn't want to pay too much because he thought it would be good advertising for the automatic. Two days later, Yost sent another letter saying he would discuss the matter with President Fish in Chicago that weekend. "He may object," Yost wrote.

Apparently he did. On Nov. 26, 1903, Yost wrote to Fish emphasizing that he (Yost) had no financial interest in the Clark Company. "But I am interested in having an automatic switchboard which can be operated as cheaply as theirs; give good satisfaction, and not cost too much . . . When your engineers say that the Clark Automatic is *no good,* as they have said, then I say that the board pleases the subscribers and that is all we care for. Give us as good a board for small exchanges and we will be satisfied, but give it to us now and not several years from now . . . "

November 1903, was also the month that Yost received good news and moral support from his friend, L. G. Richardson of Indianapolis, president of the Central Union Telephone Company. Richardson was so intrigued by what Yost had told him about the Clark Automatics that he sent an engineer named E. H. Bangs out to check.

Bangs' report, which Richardson sent to Yost, was based on a study of the automatic equipment at 10 Nebraska and three Iowa locations operated by the Clark firm. The report also noted that there were 21 towns with Clark equipment within a 100-mile radius of Sioux City.*

---

*These figures indicate that, as of November 1903, there were two or three Clark-operated exchanges in Nebraska which existing records do not list. The third Clark-operated exchange in Iowa might have been at Holstein. In 1971 Leonard F. Gleason, a retired Sioux City switchboardman, recalled that when visiting Holstein as a teenager around 1904, he had seen automatic telephone equipment. It is known that the early-day Clark exchange at Rock Rapids, Iowa, was sold to a local company in 1897. Other Clark exchanges may have been sold in the intervening years, and, of course, Clark equipment was bought and operated by other independent companies. Audubon, Iowa, had dial service 1897 to 1900 and it may have been Clark equipment. The Missouri Valley Company apparently had Clark Automatic equipment at its Garrison, New Salem and Underwood exchanges in North Dakota. These were reconverted to manual in 1906.

According to the report, the "operating expense, maintenance and depreciation for a 50-line exchange puts the annual cost of the Clark system at approximately 40 per cent less than with a manual exchange."

That was all the encouragement Yost needed. Despite the negative report from the AT&T engineers, he ordered a Clark Automatic board for Ravenna, Nebr. There is no further correspondence with President Fish about it. But in May, in a letter to C. Jay French at AT&T, Yost adds this information:

"March 31, 1904, a new exchange was opened at Ravenna with 18 subscribers. We installed a board which we rented from the Clark Automatic Telephone Company. The service is good . . . "

That was the last kind word Casper Yost ever wrote about the Clark Automatic switching system.

In fact, the only existing clue as to what went wrong is a sketchy explanation that C. Lee Pickett, a retired manager, included in a letter of reminiscences in 1951:

"Ravenna had an automatic *Bell* exchange in 1905, the switch in the rear of a drug store, a few telephones, and a half mile of cable. The druggist told me that the main reason for the lack of success of that exchange was [that] the switch would not return to its home point on the completion of a call. This would often require that someone would have to go to the switch and re-set it. This exchange was dismantled and moved away shortly after that."

It's possible the Clark companies were also having trouble, even before Yost had automatic equipment installed at Ravenna. On Feb. 1, 1904, two months before the Ravenna exchange opened, the Nebraska and Iowa Clark companies mortgaged eight Nebraska and two Iowa exchanges to the William B. Banigan Estate of Providence, R.I., for more than $74,000.

Late in 1905, Yost advised AT&T that Nebraska Telephone had placed a Western Electric manual board at Dakota City "for the Nebraska Clark Automatic Company." In January of 1907, the same was done at Pilger. Both were loaned or leased to Clark by Nebraska Telephone.

In June of 1909, Nebraska Telephone contracted with the Clark companies and the Banigan Estate to buy the 10 exchanges for $55,000 as soon as the mortgages could be foreclosed and clear title given. Meanwhile, Nebraska Telephone leased the exchanges for $275 per month and took over management. Letters from Providence during this period indicate the people there were eager to complete the deal and get the money. The transactions were completed by July 1910. By then, Nebraska Telephone had its own manual boards operating in all the Nebraska towns.

The record doesn't show when the last Clark Automatic board was dismantled. Whenever that was, it marked the end of a bright dream. And Casper Yost must certainly be counted among the disappointed. Perhaps the reason there isn't a letter explaining what went wrong with the Clark Automatics is because Yost found the subject embarrassing.

He did have harsh words to eat. Among the strongest (written late in 1903) was a report on a small manual exchange that Nebraska Telephone had just installed. This must have been about the time he made up his mind to try the Clark Automatic equipment at Ravenna.

To his friend, C. Jay French at AT&T, Yost wrote: "This should have been an automatic exchange, but your company does not furnish your licensees with that class of apparatus; and I am sure you will not do so until too late . . . Your company is making a very serious mistake in not at once doing something in the line of furnishing an automatic board . . . Other companies are doing so and are giving good satisfaction to the subscribers."

Ironically, AT&T had been making a real effort to meet the kind of need Yost felt so keenly. Developmental work on a small dial exchange started in 1900. During 1902, an experimental 50-line exchange was installed in Queens, Long Island. It was replaced by a 100-line system the following year. During 1904 and 1905, more than 40 Western Electric dial systems, both 20-line and 100-line, went into commercial service. But they created more problems than they solved, much as the Clark equipment had.

Therefore, around 1905, the Bell System redirected its research. Bell scientists began developing a complex, highly efficient machine switching system that could provide automatic service for tens of thousands of customers in large multi-office metropolitan exchanges.

The University Place automatic exchange of LT&T, 1908

While that research proceeded, independent companies, at considerable expense, did manage to make dial equipment behave well enough to please customers in medium-sized cities. The Automatic Electric Company (Strowger) equipment that the Lincoln (Nebr.) Telephone Company installed in 1904 certainly was an immediate success — with customers.

The number of automatic phones there more than doubled in less than three years, then doubled again in another four years. Customers obviously liked the automatic service. (Rates about half what Nebraska Telephone was charging must have helped, too.)

Nevertheless, there is an important distinction to be made. Early-day dial systems were most successful in cities large enough to have trained people on hand most of the time — people who could make balky equipment behave. What Yost wanted, and what the Clark Company tried to furnish, was equipment that would function without technicians watching over it (as a modern community dial office, CDO, does).

Apparently the Clark Company's activities were so little known that many people have assumed that Lincoln had the first dial installation in Nebraska. That's not the case but Lincoln was the first to have a dial system that performed satisfactorily.

However, there is another facet of the Lincoln automatic story that should be noted. When Nebraska Telephone's properties in southeastern Nebraska were sold to the Lincoln Telephone and Telegraph Company in 1912, the Lincoln Company had extensive tests made. These compared LT&T's automatic operation with the Bell manual.

The results were "disquieting," LT&T reported candidly in its official history. "The manual system was furnishing much more accurate and faster service than the automatic. Service and repair costs of the dial telephone also exceeded that of its simpler manual counterpart."

After considering this information carefully, the Lincoln Company's directors decided to *remove* their automatic equipment in University Place, a suburb of Lincoln, and connect their subscribers to the old Bell manual board there.

But the directors decided to keep their dial system in Lincoln proper and eliminate the Bell manual service there. Customers were sentimentally attached to the old "pot-belly" dial phone despite its occasional erratic behavior. And automatic equipment was constantly being improved. The clincher, perhaps, was the thought that if LT&T converted back to manual, "the door might be left ajar for the entrance of another Independent company."

As a part of the 1912 purchase, the Lincoln Company took over the Bell manual board in Hastings, putting it in competition with its former ally, the local independent company. The Hastings independent had installed automatic equipment in 1905 and had about 1,100 subscribers compared to Bell's 1,200.

Subsequently, LT&T bought the independent and connected the former automatic customers to the Bell manual in 1914.* There's considerable irony in the fact that just five years after Hastings was converted *from dial back to manual,* AT&T announced its long-term program to convert the Bell System *to dial.* The Bell plan was to use the independent-developed step-by-step equipment in small and medium-sized cities and Bell-developed panel equipment in the larger metropolitan areas.

To accomplish this, the Bell System made a long-term contract to buy a considerable amount of step-by-step equipment from Automatic Electric. AT&T also obtained the rights for Western Electric to manufacture step-by-step for the Bell companies. Thus the equipment that undertaker Strowger had fathered, and that Automatic Electric and its independent customers had pioneered, ultimately found its way into every part of the United States and beyond.

Even so, the Bell System had been on solid ground when it maintained that manual service could more than hold its own against the early-day automatics, both in terms of good service and economical operation. It had been on the right track in pushing the development of common battery, automatic ringing and the many other unseen advances gradually built into the manual system.

The decision to develop special switching equipment

---

*Thirty-six years later, LT&T re-converted Hastings to dial.

for large cities was a sound one. The panel equipment that came out of this effort significantly reduced the cost of large, multi-office switching installations.* As a result, thousands of customers got dial service sooner.

But even though AT&T's conservative approach was well founded, the independents did gain an important psychological advantage — a progressive image — by pioneering dial equipment. In this respect, though his faith in the Clark automatics was misplaced, Casper Yost had a genuine feel for what was happening in the world and for what customers wanted.

---

*What was special about this panel equipment was its "common control," in contrast to the "direct dial control" in step-by-step. In a four-digit step-by-step system, a call to No. 5643 would proceed this way: When the "5" is dialed, the electrical impulses cause a "thousands" switch to move to the fifth position. As the "6" is dialed, the impulses go *through* the thousands switch and turn a "hundreds" switch to its sixth position. The "4" goes through the first two switches and causes a final switch to move *up* to its fourth level. Then, as the "3" is dialed, this final switch moves *around* to the third position. Phone No. 5643 begins to ring. Thus, step-by-step is a decimal system with 10 switching positions at each step.

Panel is a non-decimal system and therefore can have more than 10 positions at a step. It has, in fact, 500 lines to a switching group. As a result, it can reach more customers with fewer steps. But the equipment can't be directly controlled by the decimal digits the customer dials. Panel's common control system handles this problem. When a panel customer dials No. 5643, the common control equipment translates the decimal digits into specially coded impulses and stores them momentarily. The stored impulses then direct the call to the group of 500 lines which includes No. 5643. Next, these stored impulses guide a motor driven selector to stop at the position which will reach phone No. 5643.

The simpler step-by-step equipment was more economical than panel in smaller exchanges. But in big-city exchanges where six or seven digit numbers were necessary, panel could handle interconnections with considerably less machinery and wiring than step-by-step. (Today's crossbar and electronic central offices are more sophisticated and more flexible than either panel or step-by-step.)

Munson phone
used from
1907 to 1912

Munson
dial system
in
Minnesota

Dial telephones like this were in operation in Motley, Grey Eagle, and North St. Paul, Minn., in 1907 and for a few years after. Augustus Munson started his telephone career at Motley before 1905. In 1905 he invented and patented his automatic system which he described as both an adding and a step-by-step system.

Munson became acquainted with a banker at Eagle Bend who helped him get financial backing. With the banker's help, the North St. Paul exchange was promoted and Munson moved there in January of 1907 to establish it.

Meanwhile, he had been working at a railroad job, too, in order to obtain more money for the invention. However, the financial panic of 1907 cost Munson his backing and the only way he was able to meet the demand for more phones was to add manual equipment in North St. Paul. He managed to operate a combined manual and automatic exchange for a few years. But with 60 customers at $1 a month, he wasn't able to make ends meet. In addition, he needed a second trunk to St. Paul and wasn't able to get it from Northwestern Telephone Exchange Company.

In 1912 Munson sold to Northwestern Exchange, which converted North St. Paul to all manual. At its peak, the Munson dial system included a 20-line unit at Motley, a 25-line unit at Grey Eagle and a 100-line unit in North St. Paul, with 45 lines in use.

Chapter IX

The Lincoln Telephone and Telegraph Company

The big one that got away

WHEN NEIL THOMPSON went to bed March 8, 1903, he was the manager of the only telephone company in Lincoln, Nebr. The following day, Thompson was surprised to learn that Mayor H. J. Winnett had signed a franchise for a competing independent company. Things were never the same again for Thompson . . . or for Casper Yost and the Nebraska (Bell) Telephone Company. Eventually, even AT&T felt the repercussions.

The formation of the new Lincoln company had been deftly handled. Articles of incorporation had been signed just two days earlier. Then city council approval of the franchise had been quietly maneuvered. The men who signed the articles of incorporation were Col. Charles J. Bills, Judge Allen W. Field and Frank H. Woods. What they had formed was the Lincoln Telephone Company.*

Col. Bills had just moved his investment business from Fairbury to Lincoln. He and a brother, Frank, were both well known as promoters of independent telephone companies.† They had gone to attorney Frank Woods for

---

*For the first three months, the official name was the Western Union Telephone Company.

†Other independent companies the Bills brothers helped promote were at Sioux City and Davenport, Iowa; Sioux Falls, S.D.; Rock Island, Moline and Peoria, Ill., and Hastings and Omaha, Nebr.

The Lincoln Company installed dial equipment in 1904.

legal help and he had agreed to join them in the company.

Of the seven original stockholders, three were Bills —
Charles, Frank and Fred — and three were Woods —
Frank, Mark and George. Judge Field was the seventh. It
was Frank Woods who got the franchise approved before
Nebraska Telephone even knew the enemy was in town.

"Enemy" was the right word as far as Casper Yost
was concerned. In one letter to AT&T President Fish, he
spoke of Frank Bills as "the most active, able and
unscrupulous promoter in the west."

Even though the appearance of this independent company was a surprise, the groundwork had been laid years
earlier. And Nebraska Telephone had unwittingly played
a role.

In 1887 Nebraska Telephone's directors had voted to
raise rates in Lincoln, but only for new subscribers.
Nobody complained until 1893, when several newer subscribers refused to pay the higher rate. One sued, claim-
ing illegal rate discrimination. The suit finally was

decided against Nebraska Telephone in 1896.

But long before that, the company had asked its old subscribers to pay the higher rate. That provoked rebellion and 147 customers quit in 1893.

When this uproar was going full blast, Yost wrote to AT&T that "some of the people of Lincoln are after our company with a very sharp stick." A few months later, he wrote that he had never seen such bitterness, and that some people were trying to form an independent company.

During 1894, Yost wrote to AT&T saying "It has been in my mind for some time that it might be [good] policy to reduce rates in Lincoln . . . we are charging more than is charged in St. Joseph, Mo., and Des Moines, Iowa, and the people know of the fact." This plea was successful. Residence rates were reduced from $4 a month to $3 and business rates from $5 to $4.50.

The attempt to form an independent company was unsuccessful at that time, but the resentment of Bell rates lingered on. It was against this backdrop that Frank Woods made his decision to help organize an independent company nine years later. Soon he was up to his eyebrows in problems.

The Bills brothers were unable to meet their original commitment to have the exchange in operation by March 1904. Apparently some service was being given, but as Yost reported to AT&T, "their Strowger Automatic board has not worked satisfactorily and they are to commence collecting for service June 1." Along with the delay in getting started, the new company was pinched for cash.

On the brighter side, *Telephony* magazine devoted its main article in the May 1904 issue to "Lincoln's New Automatic System," calling it the "first large automatically operated telephone exchange west of Chicago." Features included an Italian marble switchboard, all metallic circuits and an underground distribution system that extended far into the residential districts. The dial wheel on the phone had 11 holes, the 11th marked "long distance." Pulling it connected the subscriber directly with a live operator.

This apparently was quite important to some customers. As *Telephony* put it: "Those subscribers who, from force of habit, mourn the loss of the silvery voice, and who do not consider a telephone message complete without [a

woman's] assistance . . . may call the information clerk*
and request her to operate the dial for him [sic] and
gradually taper off from his habit, thus becoming recon-
ciled to the inevitable."

One part of that *Telephony* article must have given
Casper Yost a wry chuckle. It described the "tell-tale
board," where signal lamps lit up, alerting an attendant
whenever one of the 3,000 automatic switches acted up.
Yost had had experience with automatics that required
constant attention.

The magazine also noted that the Lincoln
independent was probably the first large cable system to
use clamp seals to achieve watertight cable joints. The
usual method was to seal joints with molten lead.
Unfortunately, *Telephony's* enthusiasm for the new clamp
seals was premature — they worked only in theory. It soon
became apparent that the Lincoln Company badly needed
an experienced cable splicer. And Nebraska Telephone
had one named Mark Twain Caster. He was self-taught and
considered the best in that part of the country. Lincoln
Telephone promptly lured him away from Bell, even
though it required giving him the largest salary on the
payroll — $85 per month, plus a dollar a day for the use of
his horse. In 1906 Caster was promoted to general plant
superintendent and held that post for the next 32 years.

Leaky cable joints weren't the biggest problem the
new independent had. It needed more revenue. When it
had first announced that its monthly rates would be $3 for
business, $2 for residence,† Casper Yost said the com-
pany would have to raise rates or go bankrupt. Yost
probably had apoplexy later on when the independent
reduced its residential rate to $1.75 a month.

Before the new company had been in operation two
years, however, Frank Woods concluded that if it didn't

---

*The Lincoln information clerks offered many other services: they
would quote observatory time 24 hours per day, call a subscriber to
wake him whenever he wanted, and serve as a clearing house for
information on lost children, strayed horses, etc.

†The Lincoln Telephone rates were for metallic circuit service. When the
new company started, Nebraska Telephone was charging $5 a month
for business service, metallic circuit, and $4 for residence. Grounded
service rates were $4 business and $3 residential.

Frank H. Woods

change its course, it was doomed. Previously he'd been involved only in legal and promotional matters. Now he felt the company had to be reorganized. This was accomplished May 30, 1905. Woods replaced Charles J. Bills* as president, and was on his way to a full-time career as a telephone man.

He obtained an emergency loan from a Chicago financial firm to tide the company over while he tightened expense controls and hired experienced people for key jobs. By November 1906, he had accomplished all the efficiencies he could and the company announced rate increases: from $3 a month to $4 for business phones, from $1.75 a month to $2 for residential. This compared with $4 and $2.50 which Nebraska Telephone had started charging for metallic service in 1905.

The week that the announcement was made, Yost wrote: "The first day of their raise we secured 51 subscribers; the next day, 74; the next day, 102; and we are having a great deal of amusement at their expense."

Actually, Nebraska Telephone jumped on the situation with both feet. It publicly accused the independent of raising rates in order to pay unreasonable dividends. It published vicious cartoon advertisements. And within a few days, the Bell Company announced it would *reduce* its rates, making them the same as the Lincoln Company's new rates.

The Lincoln Company lost 20 per cent of its subscribers. Frank Woods made a personal plea to the Lincoln Commercial Club to examine the need for the new rates. When it found that the raises were justified, much of the furor died down. But the Bell people jeered that the report was a farce.

The Bell Company was now in the curious position of saying that $4 a month for business phones and $2 a month for residences was an exorbitant rate when

---

*Frank Bills was no longer involved. He had been a director only briefly during 1903.

THE AUTOMATIC ARM WILL ALWAYS WORK

One thing about the automatic telephone that will always work

ADVERTISEMENT

The Bell-Automatic rate war began with cartoons such as this in the *Lincoln Daily Star,* November 1906.

charged by the independent, but was perfectly proper when charged by Bell. And this when the Bell rates had been even higher a few months earlier.

It's no wonder the construction men of the two companies got into occasional fist fights. What is amazing is that there were so few battles and so little destruction of competitors' property.

There were plenty of ways for the two companies to harrass each other, however. Some of the original investors in the automatic company had received a $1,000 bond and a $500 stock certificate for a $900 cash investment. This wasn't unusual at the time. But national sentiment was crystalizing against the practice, particularly in the case of utilities which were just then coming under public regulation. Using the figures above as an example, such a company would be trying to pay interest or dividends on $1,500 worth of stock and bonds. But only $900 worth of plant would be available to earn revenue.

The phrase, "watered stock," came into the language, and Nebraska Telephone was quick to hurl the epithet at its Lincoln competitors. By 1908 the automatic people insisted they actually had $1,500 worth of plant to back up $1,500 worth of investment. But there was no defense against the charge that some investors had received a bonus.

Drawing again on his legal background, Frank Woods engineered a second reorganization. The old Lincoln Company was merged with the Western Telephone Company, a long distance company that Woods had organized in 1905. The latter had built an extensive network of lines in the Lincoln territory. In the process of this merger, Woods triumphantly announced that every cent of watered stock had been squeezed out. The date was January 1909, and the new company was called Lincoln Telephone and Telegraph. With a sounder financial structure and a long distance network, the Lincoln Company became one of the country's strongest independents.

Before the year was over, Frank Woods had been elected president of the National Independent Telephone Association. The stage was set for him to play a role in national telephone affairs that would have an important influence on both the Bell and independent companies for years to come. But one other major player in this drama needs to be reintroduced.

After an absence of 20 years, Theodore N. Vail had returned to the Bell System in 1907, this time as the head man.* By 1908 the Bell System had begun national advertising announcing the goal of "One Policy, One System, Universal Service." The text explained the close relationship between AT&T and the operating Bell companies. Because 1908 was an election year and antitrust sentiment was strong, some AT&T people feared the advertisements would invite politically inspired criticism.

---

*Vail had been president of AT&T during 1885-87 when it was only a subsidiary. Now it was the parent company of the Bell System.

One Policy
One System

Universal Service

THAT the American public requires a telephone service that is universal is becoming plainer every day.

Now, while people are learning that the Bell service has a broad national scope and the flexibility to meet the ever varying needs of telephone users, they know little of how these results have been brought about. The keynote is found in the motto—"One policy, one system, universal service."

Behind this motto may be found the American Telephone and Telegraph Company—the so-called "parent" Bell Company.

* * * *

A unified policy is obtained because the American Telephone and Telegraph Company has for one of its functions that of a holding company, which federates the associated companies and makes available for all what is accomplished by each.

As an important stockholder in the associated Bell companies, it assists them in financing their extensions, and it helps insure a sound and uniform financial policy.

* * * *

A unified system is obtained because the American Telephone and Telegraph Company has for one of its functions the ownership and maintenance of the telephones used by the 4,000,000 subscribers of the associated companies.

In the development of the art, it originates, tests, improves and protects new appliances and secures economies in the purchase of supplies.

It provides a clearing - house of standardization and thus insures economy in the construction of equipment, lines and conduits, as well as in operating methods and legal work—in fact, in all the functions of the associated companies which are held in common.

* * * *

Universal, comprehensive service is obtained because the American Telephone and Telegraph Company has among its other functions the construction and operation of long distance lines, which connect the systems of the associated companies into a unified and harmonious whole.

It establishes a single, instead of a divided, responsibility in inter-state connections, and a uniform system of operating and accounting; and secures a degree of efficiency in both local and long distance service that no association of independent neighboring companies could obtain.

* * * *

Hence it can be seen that the American Telephone and Telegraph Company is the active agency for securing *one policy, one system,* and *universal service*—the three factors which have made the telephone service of the United States superior to that of any other country.

American Telephone & Telegraph Company

National advertisements in 1908 began promoting Vail's goal of universal service.

When the problem was presented to Vail, he asked: "Are the statements in the advertisement true?" Yes, he was told. "Very well, then; let's print it and beat them to it."

Vail's dream was for anyone anywhere to be able to make a telephone call to any other telephone. Naturally he intended that the Bell System would make this possible. But the existence of competing phone companies in many locations was an obvious difficulty.

One of Vail's early efforts when he returned to the Bell System was to encourage interconnection between Bell and independent companies. During 1907, 450,000 independent telephones were linked to the nearest Bell exchanges. The following year, 250,000 more were added.

"Like the salvation it was, consolidation was offered practically free to those who would accept it," Vail's biographer wrote. "The Bell System was no longer regarded as an octopus to be destroyed. It had become a featherbed for tottering telephone companies."

Under Vail, the Bell attitude did become more reasonable and conciliatory. But the extravagant statements just quoted don't square with the record of hard-fought battles that took place in the next five years. Frank Woods certainly would have scoffed at the notion in December 1909 when he took the helm of the National Independent Telephone Association (NITA). The following year, AT&T bought control of Western Union Telegraph and the independents' fears of the Bell octopus were stirred up more than ever.

When Woods became NITA president, he was still firmly against any compromise or interconnection with Bell. "We know the benefits of competition," he said. "It's here to stay." His friend and ally, Theodore Gary,* an independent telephone leader from Missouri, was equally opposed to universal long distance service via Bell interconnections.

During Woods' term as NITA president, the association prompted antitrust actions against Bell companies in Michigan, Kansas, Missouri and Nebraska. Woods was actively involved, particularly in Nebraska. Early in the

---

*Years later, Gary was a principal owner of the Tri-State Company when Northwestern Bell purchased it.

summer of 1910, Nebraska Telephone engineered a transaction that gave Bell interests control of the independent telephone companies at Papillion, Nebraska City and Plattsmouth. The editor of the *Plattsmouth Journal* broke the story, stating that control of the Plattsmouth independent had fallen into the hands of "Eastern capitalists." The independents were convinced Nebraska Telephone was behind the move, and Yost admitted as much.

Woods helped persuade the Nebraska attorney general that the state's antitrust laws had been violated. The State Supreme Court issued an order restraining Nebraska Telephone from controlling or connecting with the companies. A summons was served on Yost soon after he had written Vail advising him of the Plattsmouth purchase. This suit hung over Yost's head for the next 18 months. It and the other antitrust actions against Bell companies gave the independents a strong hand in the negotiations that were about to begin.

By October 1910, despite his successes in twisting the Bell tail, Frank Woods had become convinced that the public had a right to demand the broadest possible system of telephone interconnection. This wasn't a popular stand for an NITA president to take, but Woods' experiences during the year had changed his mind. And he made it clear he wasn't speaking officially for NITA.

However, since some other independents, including Theodore Gary, had come to similar views, an NITA committee was formed to open negotiations with Bell representatives and with J. P. Morgan and Company. The latter had become involved both as owners of independent telephone properties and as a major source of telephone industry financing. The purpose of the negotiations was to explore the possibility of eliminating telephone competition through division of territory agreements, mergers and interconnection.

Frank Woods was chairman of this committee, called the Committee of Seven, and Tri-State President E. H. Moulton of Minneapolis, and Theodore Gary were among the members. N. C. Kingsbury, AT&T vice president, was chief of the Bell negotiators, and Henry P. Davison, a Morgan partner, represented that firm's interests. Davison was on record as believing that universal service and elimination of competition were essential to continued progress in the telephone industry.

According to the Lincoln Company's history, Woods found the Morgan man particularly hard to deal with. At one point early in the negotiations, Woods became convinced that the Morgan interests were allied with Bell.

The Lincoln history records that Woods shouted at Davison, "I can't do business with you, you're nothing but a hireling," and stalked out. One independent representative was so upset he ran after Woods crying, "You've spilt the milk." But Woods refused to return to the meeting.

Early the next morning, Woods was awakened by a telephone call at his hotel. It was Davison. He and Theodore Vail were in the lobby and wanted Woods to join them. At this meeting, according to the Lincoln history, Woods and Vail talked candidly and soon reached agreement on enough points that negotiations could continue. By January 1911, the two companies were exchanging data on which a division of territory might be based.

February of 1911 was a difficult month for Frank Woods. First there was the NITA convention where he and his Committee of Seven were called on the carpet. Angry delegates reaffirmed that their purpose was to perpetuate the integrity of the independent telephone system as a whole. They emphasized that they had not authorized any group to carry on negotiations with the Bell or Morgan interests.

February was also the month when Woods, in his sparring with the Bell people, came close to accepting a less favorable Nebraska settlement than he eventually won. At a conference with AT&T Vice President Kingsbury, Woods apparently gave tentative agreement to AT&T terms. These included Bell control of most of the long distance traffic, and, within two years, Bell control of a new company that would consolidate LT&T and other southeast Nebraska telephone properties. Woods wasn't too happy with the proposition, Kingsbury reported, and nothing was certain.

Meanwhile, Casper Yost was under the impression that the Lincoln people were going to control the consolidated company. He wasn't happy either. But he did have a big stake in two other factors that the settlement included: Woods was to help get the Nebraska antitrust law modified so that one telephone company could buy another, and he was to help the Nebraska Company purchase the property of the bankrupt Omaha Independent Company.

Yost wrote to Kingsbury saying that if it were not for the Omaha agreement and the antitrust law "and for the fact that Mr. Woods has worked so hard and faithfully to secure a combination of interests all over the United States, I should take the position that under no circumstances should they have control of the new Company." Yost also complained that Woods talked differently in New York than he did in Omaha. It was at this point that Kingsbury wrote back that Woods had more or less agreed to the Bell terms. That's how things looked for several months.

Meanwhile, at the NITA convention, after the delegates had spanked the Committee of Seven, they elected five of them to their board of directors, including Woods, Gary and Moulton. And the Committee continued to negotiate with the Bell and Morgan interests. Woods already had written authority from several major independents to deal on their behalf.

In April, the Nebraska Legislature did pass a bill permitting telephone companies to merge or sell out to each other, but it also required Bell to provide interconnection to all comers. Yost complained of having to take the bitter (interconnection) with the sweet. Despite the fact that the independents had supported the bill, public opinion saw it as more evidence that the Bell wanted to gobble up the independents. After all that, the governor vetoed the bill.

In May of 1911, Kingsbury wrote Yost discussing a proposal made by Woods. The proposition was for a new company to take over all the Bell property south of the Platte River, from one end of the state to the other. The independents were to control the new company, and the Bell System was to have a minority interest and provide the financing. The division of long distance traffic was not spelled out, but Woods was getting uneasy and was anxious for the new company to have all the long distance revenue possible.

Yost's answer was that "Mr. Woods' proposition is too ridiculous to merit any serious consideration." That's where matters stood when Yost, Kingsbury and Woods met in New York for more negotiations in mid-July of 1911. Surprisingly, they were able to agree on most issues. But Woods insisted that the new company had to have all the long distance revenues if it was to handle the heavy financial obligations of purchasing and consolidating the

A Problem in Navigation

Telephony had little faith in the Bell-Independent negotiations during 1911.

various properties. Bell negotiators weren't willing to give on that point.

Once again, Frank Woods spoke his mind angrily, promising the Bell men the competitive fight of their lives. Then he stomped out and took a train to New Hampshire where his wife and 6-year-old Frank Jr. were vacationing.

When Woods arrived in New Hampshire, a call from Vail was waiting. He told Woods he wanted him to have a satisfactory deal and persuaded him to bring his wife and son to Speedwell Farms, the Vail estate in Vermont. There, the two men talked and Vail finally agreed to let the new company have all the long distance lines in its territory. Perhaps he was influenced by memories of his own struggles with the giant Western Union Company years earlier, when he had held out for Bell control of all long distance lines.

Even after Vail and Woods reached agreement, Vail still had a problem. According to the Lincoln Telephone history, he didn't want his own negotiators to know he had overruled them. So he asked Woods to carry on further discussions at Speedwell Farms with the understanding that Vail would see to it Woods got what had been agreed to. In Northwestern Bell's files today, there is a copy of the agreement. It's buried in the back of one of four large binders marked "Lincoln Telephone and Telegraph Co." It looks just like several other proposed agreements except for one thing: In the lower left hand corner, it has two sets of initials penned in: "C.E.Y." and "F.H.W.," then underneath: "T.N.V., The House, Speedwell Farms, July 27, '11."

When all the details had been worked out,* the formal agreement between the two companies was finally signed Dec. 4, 1911. It was approved by the State Railway Com-

---

*The new company was to have all the territory in the 22 counties south of the Platte and east of the west boundaries of Adams and Hall counties, and operate all long distance lines. Nebraska Telephone was to buy the Woods' interest in telephone properties at Grand Island, Fremont and the Howard County Telephone Company. Nebraska Telephone agreed to accept 5 per cent preferred stock in the new company in an amount equal to the value of the Nebraska Telephone property sold to the new company. The preferred stock was to have no voting rights unless two successive dividends were missed. Finally, the new company was to make a sub-license agreement with Bell.

This canceled check represented the end of LT&T-Bell competition.

mission Jan. 8, 1912. Later that month, the antitrust suit against Nebraska Telephone was dismissed at the request of the attorney general. With Frank Woods' help, Nebraska Telephone was able to get together with the bondholders of the defunct Omaha Independent Company.

The day after the overall agreement was signed, Yost sent a copy to Kingsbury with a terse note that only hinted at the extent of his disappointment: "Whenever a man makes a deal of any importance, he always feels as if possibly he could have done better, and I have no doubt that is the feeling which Mr. Woods has as well as myself."

Actually, Woods and the Lincoln directors were well pleased with the agreement. But the strain of the long months of negotiation had taken its toll on Frank Woods' health. He was exhausted and had to take to his bed for rest. However, before 1912 ended, the Bell and Committee of Seven negotiators also reached agreements concerning Sioux City, Iowa, and Detroit, Mich. They were not able to resolve the competitive situations in Minneapolis-St. Paul, Kansas City or Buffalo, N.Y.

But something far more important had happened. Bell System leaders had accepted the fact that the independents were here to stay. Both the Bell and independent people had learned they could reach agreement in some areas. And each had been pushed into new attitudes by public opinion — the independents into accepting the idea of cooperation and interconnection with "the enemy," and the Bell System into responding to the public's fear of large concentrations of business power.

It was in this context that the Kingsbury Commitment was made toward the end of 1913. In a letter to the Attorney General of the United States, Vice President Kingsbury expressed the Bell companies' desire "to put their affairs beyond criticism." AT&T would give up control of Western Union. It would provide long distance connections to independents where there was no local competition. And it would purchase no more independent properties without regulatory approval. Now the truce was official.

Something of the sort had to happen sooner or later. But it's interesting to wonder how much longer the fight would have lasted if Frank Woods and Theodore Vail had not trusted and respected each other.

Vail expressed his feelings by sending his portrait to Woods with this inscription: "To the great Independent from his friend, Theo. N. Vail."

Frank Woods kept that portrait on his office wall for 30 years.

Chapter X

Tri-State Company

Twin service in the Twin Cities
— and elsewhere

IN THE LATE 1960S, the exclamation, "outasight," was a favorite. Hip teenagers using it would probably have been astonished to learn that at least one telephone manager had used the very same phrase 70 years earlier.

He was H. Vance Lane of Omaha, writing to J. W. Christie, the Minneapolis manager. Both were worried about the competitive threat posed by a wealthy and determined Keokuk, Iowa, man named J. C. Hubinger. Hubinger was a starch manufacturer and owner of some brand new telephone companies in eastern Iowa. Early in 1897, he had agents working in Omaha and the Twin Cities. Christie asked Lane about one of them.

"I can give you nothing relative to Mr. Collins' reputation," Lane answered, "except that he is a traveling salesman for Hubinger and as a starch man, he is 'out of sight.' As a telephone man, he himself admits he knows nothing about the business. And from [the things he says, I suspect] he is not misrepresenting matters . . . "

There was a certain amount of bravado in Lane's attitude. Hubinger was giving Lane and Yost quite a workout. Once the Omaha City Council unanimously refused

Hubinger a franchise, yet his agents kept right on working. They had 1,500 subscribers signed up when, on March 22, 1898, Omaha's Council turned them down again. However, early that same year, Hubinger did obtain franchises to operate in both Minneapolis and St. Paul. Only then did Hubinger give up in Omaha.

Northwestern Telephone Exchange had been operating in the Twin Cities since 1878 and had about 4,000 subscribers. According to a possibly biased report in *Telephony,* "Service was wretched; the plant was, with the exception of the underground work, in a decayed condition. The switchboards were old and the advent of the rival [company] was hailed with joy by [Bell] subscribers."

Hubinger's firm, the Mississippi Valley Company, began operation late in 1899. A little more than a year later, it had 2,700 phones in service — all one-party lines served by metallic circuits, as required by its franchise. The service of the company was exceptionally good, *Telephony* reported, and demand was strong.

The actual state of affairs wasn't really that cheery. Despite the 2,700 or so phones the company had operating in the Twin Cities, there were only 300 paying subscribers on April 1, 1901. Most independents gave some free connections to win friends; the Mississippi Valley people had gotten carried away.

As a result, the company was in deep financial trouble. Hubinger had nearly a million dollars invested, yet the firm was grossing only $16,000 annually. Hubinger had tried unsuccessfully to raise money by selling bonds. Finally he got some local people to help him, but he lost control of Mississippi Valley in the process.

This was to be the pattern for years to come. Between 1900 and 1934, control of this independent company was held by seven different men or groups. Some profited handsomely; others lost money. The history of the company was, to a considerable extent, a history of intricate financial deals.

The man who rounded up financial support for Hubinger in 1901 was Eder H. Moulton, an officer of the Farmers and Mechanics Savings Bank in St. Paul. The bulk of the financing came from a Chicago bond firm, Trowbridge and Niver, and all the Hubinger directors were replaced by men acceptable to the bond firm. The principal partners, L. A. Trowbridge and D. R. Niver, became directors and Trowbridge replaced Hubinger as president. Hubinger remained as a director.

The new directors arranged for an immediate financial transfusion — at a price. They voted to sell $375,000 worth of Mississippi Valley bonds (the same bonds Hubinger had been unable to sell) to Trowbridge and Niver for 80 cents on the dollar. The directors also voted to issue bonds to Hubinger as payment for $125,000 he had advanced to the company on a short-term basis. But Hubinger had to take his bonds at 100 cents on the dollar.

Seventeen days later, Niver resigned as a director and Trowbridge resigned as president. Moulton became a director and was elected president. The name of the company was changed to the Twin City Telephone Company. Trowbridge remained a director and his firm held 57 per cent of the voting stock. Hubinger now had less than 30 per cent.

After the company was reorganized in 1901, it resumed plant expansion work. By October of the following year, much had been accomplished. In a letter to a friend, President Moulton reported that the company now had 7,500 paying subscribers, compared to 300 at the time of reorganization. Its annual gross was $250,000, rather than $16,000. And the company published a brochure boasting of its accomplishments and criticizing Bell service.

There was justification for faulting Northwestern Telephone Exchange's operations in the Twin Cities. While it's difficult now to evaluate quality of service, we do know that dividends paid from 1890 through 1897 averaged nearly 12 per cent annually, and that no allowance for depreciation was made until 1902.

From 1883 until 1901, the Northwestern Exchange Company was operated as a subsidiary of Erie Telephone and Telegraph, an eastern holding company. Erie owned perpetual rights to use Bell telephones in Minnesota, and Northwestern Exchange remained nominally a part of the Bell System. But the American Company didn't control it.

In 1900 C. P. Wainman was promoted from general superintendent to general manager of Northwestern

Exchange. In 1901 the Erie directors resigned and were replaced by men representing the American Company. The next year, Casper Yost was elected president of Northwestern Exchange and the company finally began setting aside an allowance for depreciation before paying dividends. This knocked the dividend rate down to less than half what it had been. From 1902 through 1911, dividends averaged under 5 per cent.

C. P. Wainman

In 1903, two years after they had helped the Twin City Company get on its feet, Trowbridge and Niver sold their stock to Moulton. But not before they had bought another $200,000 worth of bonds at 82½ cents on the dollar and had paid $80,000 for preferred stock with a par value of $100,000. In the next 14 months, Moulton organized the Tri-State Telephone and Telegraph Company,* bought out Hubinger's interest in Twin City and gained solid control of both Tri-State and Twin City.

The Northwestern Telephone Exchange was also in the midst of transition. Under the Erie holding company, Northwestern Telephone Exchange and the Southwestern Bell Company had been operated as a unit. Apparently the American Company decided to return to that system. On January 1, 1905, Yost stepped down as president of Northwestern Exchange and H. J. Pettingill was named president of that company as well as Southwestern. About that time, Wainman's health failed and he gave up the general managership, though he was retained as a vice president.

By the spring of 1907, Theodore Vail was concerned about the Northwestern Exchange's competitive position. He asked his old friend, Yost, to check into it. On July 26, Yost reported back. His first recommendation was that residential rates be reduced to compete with Tri-State's lower charges.

Yost's second recommendation was that Wainman be

---

*The Tri-State Company was organized to build long distance lines and to establish local exchanges outside the Twin City area. Within a few years, it formally absorbed the Twin City Company.

made president of the Northwestern Exchange Company. He argued that Minnesota was too large and growing too fast to be under a president who had other territory to administer.

"Vice President Wainman is an able telephone man and a worker with good judgment. On account of overwork, his health failed about two years ago and he ceased to be general manager. He had for many years been virtually at the head of the company, and while that lasted, the company was a success. He does not blow his own horn, but is . . . very popular in the territory . . . knows all the leading men, and should be at the head of the company as he is again in good health. I know of no one thing which would so much strengthen the company as making Wainman its president . . . "

Vail bought only part of the recommendations. Rates were soon lowered. But Vail asked Yost to resume the presidency himself. And Yost, in turn, made Wainman first vice president and left day-to-day operation of the business to him.

Toward the end of 1908, both the Northwestern Exchange Company and Tri-State were interested in the purchase of the Zenith Telephone Company in Duluth. Sometime in the next year or so, two wealthy Pittsburgh, Pa., families — the Lockharts and the Masons — began to take an interest in the Tri-State Company. They loaned it large sums of money and also bought control of Zenith to keep it out of Bell hands.

In 1910 Yost reported to Vail that he had authorized Wainman to offer $5 million cash for the Tri-State Company. Tri-State people replied they had $8 million invested, and did not bother to make a counter offer.

Early in 1911, Yost reported to the American Company that he had not heard from Tri-State President Moulton "but by the end of this year he will want to sell to us and our offer should be one million dollars less . . . " During this same period, Moulton was a member of the Committee of Seven, headed by Lincoln's Frank Woods. Tri-State was one of the properties discussed in the committee's negotiations with the Bell System, but no agreement was reached. In its annual report for 1912, Tri-State reported that its plant had been evaluated by an Eastern consulting engineer and had been certified in excellent condition. That may have stiffened the Tri-State negotiating posture.

A more likely explanation, however, was a change in ownership that took place in June of 1912. By then, Tri-State had borrowed nearly $2.5 million from the Lockharts and Masons of Pittsburgh, all in notes payable on demand. The Pittsburgh people called attention to this. They also pointed out that they had purchased control of the Zenith Company when Tri-State had no funds and when "it was obvious no greater disaster could happen to the Tri-State Company than to have control of the Zenith Telephone Company pass into the hands of the Bell Telephone Company."

G. W. Robinson

Minnesota Historical Society

The Pittsburgh people wanted to exchange their $2.5 million worth of notes for Tri-State common stock of equal par value. They also wanted to exchange their controlling interest in the Zenith Company for $200,000 worth of Tri-State stock. The directors accepted the proposition. The directors also voted to issue an additional $400,000 worth of common stock to be divided proportionately among the stockholders, with the $400,000 to be deducted from surplus.

Once again, because of its constant need for more investment capital, the Tri-State Company had changed hands. The old owner lost control and the new owners realized immediate, sizable profits. In 1914 George W. Robinson replaced Moulton as president of Tri-State.

During 1915, Tri-State announced it was going to introduce automatic service in the Twin Cities the following year. It said the decision came after eight years of careful consideration.*

---

*Caster Yost had suspected something of the sort three years earlier when the Bell offer to purchase Tri-State was still being discussed. At that time, Yost wrote to the American Company:

"I have been wondering if Mr. Moulton wanted to sell his Tri-State Company and then start an automatic exchange in Minneapolis and also in St. Paul . . . I think the automatic proposition is about the only one that is left for the Independent people upon which they can hope to build exchanges to compete with us."

In its announcement, Tri-State said, "We believe automatic service to be the ultimate in telephony ... Automatic equipment has been installed, and is in successful operation throughout the offices and shops of the Great Northern Railway in St. Paul, Minneapolis and Superior, Wis.; and in the offices of the Burlington Railroad, the First National Bank, Northwestern Trust Company and the factory of Brown and Bigelow in St. Paul."

Dial service began May 28, 1916, in St. Paul and on Nov. 19 in Minneapolis. The report presented at the December directors' meeting said that service was excellent and customers were pleased. Automatic Electric representatives said the Minneapolis cut was the most successful they had ever seen.

The following year, both Tri-State and Northwestern Exchange appealed to the district court when the Minnesota Railroad and Warehouse Commission ordered the two companies to interconnect at Owatonna.* But the court appeal was only a rear guard action. Bowing to public pressure, and at the urging of the commission, the two companies began negotiations early in 1918 with the aim of eliminating competition entirely.

By July 1, the agreement had been worked out and the contracts signed. Northwestern Exchange withdrew from 37 counties in the southern part of the state. The larger towns where Bell property was sold to Tri-State were St. Paul, Winona, Faribault, Albert Lea, Austin, Stillwater, Owatonna and Northfield. Tri-State already had an interest in and connections with the independent exchanges at Rochester and Mankato.

In the other part of the bargain, Tri-State withdrew from all the rest of Minnesota. The larger exchanges sold to Northwestern Exchange were in Minneapolis, Bloomington, Brainerd, Thief River Falls, Litchfield, Cambridge, Mora, Princeton and Excelsior. The Zenith property at Duluth and the Stevens exchange at Morris also were sold to the Bell Company.

Tri-State President Robinson said the agreement gave

---

*In 1915 a state legislator named Frank E. Minette had successfully sponsored legislation that put telephone companies under the jurisdiction of the Railroad and Warehouse Commission.

Twin City Company's poles on left and Northwestern Exchange Company's on right. Minneapolis, 1902

the company a more compact territory and left it in a much stronger position. Another result was that both companies now had huge new engineering problems, particularly in Minneapolis and St. Paul, where manual and automatic systems had to be interconnected.*

In addition, vast quantities of new cable and central office wiring were necessary to connect what had previously been competing offices. Many phone numbers had to be changed and it was necessary to compile a new consolidated directory. It took two years to get all this done. The new system was put into service by both companies on Aug. 20, 1920.

On Dec. 17, 1925, Tri-State installed its 100,000th tele-

---

*The biggest difficulty was making it possible for customers with automatic service to call those with manual. Putting dial equipment at operator positions solved the problems of calling from manuals to automatics. But for calls from automatics to manuals, special operator positions were needed. These had to be equipped with display boards that translated dial impulses into illuminated figures — the proper figures for whatever number had been dialed. Upon reading the lighted number, the operator could then manually plug the call to its destination.

phone — in Gov. Theodore Christianson's office. The governor and other dignitaries then joined telephone officials at a luncheon at the St. Paul Athletic Club.

Early in 1928, Tri-State was again reorganized. The Pittsburgh interests sold substantial blocks of stock to Minnesota investors. Later that same year, Tri-State acquired control of the Dakota Central Company (headquarters in Aberdeen, S.D.). Both announcements were good news in St. Paul.

The purchase of a controlling interest in the Tri-State Company was carried out by a syndicate headed by St. Paul bankers. Apparently their intent was to retain control of the company in Minnesota. But in July of 1929, the word got out that Tri-State had been purchased by the Theodore Gary interests in Kansas City. Even that proved deceptive.

The bankers heading the syndicate had a chance to extend their interests in a chain of banks. They decided to sell their telephone stock and to recommend that their followers do so also — if the price was right. At the time, Tri-State stock was selling for around $150 per share. But at that price, there wasn't enough stock for sale to give anyone control of the company. The bankers proposed to furnish at least 51 per cent of the stock if the buyer would pay a premium price of $200 per share.

Gary executives heard about this and were quite interested. But as experienced telephone men, they felt that in order to provide efficient telephone service in Minneapolis-St. Paul, the two cities had to be served by the same company.

Meanwhile, news of the negotiations had reached Northwestern officials. They also were convinced that the Twin Cities should be engineered as a single telephone plant.

During June of 1929, Northwestern and Gary officials met several times. Out of these meetings came a general understanding that the Garys would purchase more than half of Tri-State's stock at $200 per share. Northwestern Bell would loan the Garys up to $16 million for that purpose, taking the stock purchased as collateral.

St. Paul and its small tributary exchanges were to be sold to Northwestern, along with the Tri-State and Dakota Central long distance lines that connected to points outside the territory.* The Garys were to retain the Dakota Central exchanges and also the Tri-State exchanges outside of St. Paul, along with long distance lines that connected points within the Tri-State and Dakota Central territories. Finally, the Gary people were to get a 10 per cent commission on all the Tri-State stock bought under the agreement.

However, no contract was signed until the following February. It followed the same general provisions except that it handled the Gary commission by raising the price Northwestern was to pay for St. Paul and the long distance lines. And it said that the deal could not be completed until regulatory approval had been obtained.

News of the contract became known in the industry during the summer of 1930. Later in the year, Tri-State President Robinson quit attending directors' meetings. He

---

*A Gary executive explained that he would never have considered giving up long distance lines five years earlier. But in 1929, with the Bell System engaged in a nationwide project of burying long distance cable, he was convinced long distance rates would eventually be reduced and that local telephone companies would have trouble providing equivalent service.

Tri-State installer-repairman, St. Paul, during World War I

Terminal room, Twin City Co., Minneapolis, 1904

had been upset earlier in the year and both the Bell and Gary people had made a special effort to reassure him.* But apparently the difficulties remained. In April of 1931, C. B. Randall, long time vice president and general counsel of Tri-State, was elected president.

By July, the Minnesota regulatory commission had approved the Northwestern Bell - Gary proposition and it was submitted to the Interstate Commerce Commission. There it hit a snag.

As a result of supplemental agreements, the Garys had purchased more than 99 percent of the Tri-State stock at that time and they owed Northwestern Bell $19.5 million. In the application presented to the ICC, total price of the Tri-State figured out to about $36 million, of which

*A familiar figure at Telephone Pioneer meetings during the 1930's, Robinson's career with Tri-State had started in 1904. He was hired as general auditor, was president for 16 years and was within a few months of being 65 when he retired. He headed a St. Paul investment firm for the next several years. In 1943 he moved to California where he died in 1947.

Northwestern's share was about $27.2 million.*

The ICC's examiner found that the proposed merger of the Twin Cities properties would likely result in cheaper and better service to customers there. Nevertheless, he held that Northwestern Bell would be paying almost $9 million more than the value of the property and recommended denial of approval.

The Bell and Gary people argued that the merger would benefit Twin Cities customers and would not result in higher rates; therefore the price paid should be left up to the companies. Despite the arguments, the ICC denied the application on Dec. 31, 1931.

This left the Garys in a difficult situation. They still owed Northwestern Bell $19.5 million secured by the Tri-State stock. Because of the nationwide depression, they were not able to finance the whole property for themselves. Bell and Gary accountants made several attempts to work out something that would win regulatory approval. But the best they could manage really did not do anything for the Garys. On the other hand, the new proposition was even better for Northwestern Bell than the original.

In a contract dated Feb. 21, 1933, the Gary people signed over all their Tri-State stock to Northwestern Bell in return for the surrender of notes worth about $12.5 million. The ICC approved this transaction in July and Northwestern took control of Tri-State and Dakota Central in September. The Garys had nothing to show for their efforts in the deal. They acquired no property, made no commission, and legally still owed Northwestern Bell nearly $9 million, including almost $2 million in accrued interest.

In December, Northwestern Bell's directors voted to write off this $9 million as a bad debt, deducting the amount from the Company's surplus. With that done, the actual cost of the Tri-State and Dakota Central properties came to almost $38 million. However, Northwestern Bell

---

*The $36 million total resulted from adding the $19.5 million cost of the stock to $16.5 million worth of Tri-State debt the buyer had to assume. Northwestern's share was $36 million minus the $8.8 million set as the price of the property the Garys were to keep.

NATURES MESSAGE DELIGHTS;
SO DOES THE SUPERIOR SERVICE OF THE TWIN CITY
TELEPHONE COMPANY.

Illustration from a 1902 Twin City Company brochure

controlled all the Tri-State and Dakota Central properties, instead of just St. Paul and some long distance lines.

From the ICC's point of view, it hadn't been simply an exercise in futility. By denying the original application, the ICC had forced Northwestern Bell to pay the excess $9 million out of surplus all at once. Thus there was no possibility this amount could ever be charged either to a capital account or to operating expenses. It could never become a cost to subscribers or a factor in demonstrating a need for higher earnings.

Because of abuses in other industries, particularly the power industry, new accounting rules were required for public utilities in 1933. Telephone companies were included. Under these rules, depreciable plant of a purchased company had to be entered on the parent company's books at "current cost new" or else, if sanctioned by the ICC, at the book value shown by the selling company. This was required even if the company was worth more because of customer good will and "going concern value." However, the excess paid for a business did not have to be written off all at once. It could be charged to surplus over a period of years.

If those rules had been in effect in 1931, it is possible NWB and the Garys might have worked out a transaction the ICC would have approved. And if that had happened, Rochester, Winona, Aberdeen, Huron and dozens of other Minnesota and South Dakota towns might still be independent company property today.

Chapter XI

Meanwhile, back at the office

The workaday world, Yost and the Northwestern Group

THE HISTORY OF TELEPHONY from 1893 to 1918 seems dominated by the struggle between the independents and the Bell companies. Even the development of the dial telephone appears as just a part of the competitive struggle.

But behind these events, there was a workaday world in which linemen still had to climb poles, operators had to complete calls and the company president had to solve all the problems nobody else handled.

Casper Yost's correspondence during the 1890s creates a vivid picture of what it was like to be a telephone company president then.

To a Chicago firm that had shipped a carload of inferior poles, Yost wrote: "Only two poles in the whole lot were up to specification . . . The party who told you they were a remarkably fine load of poles is either an awful liar or else no judge of poles."

To the company agent at Greenwood, Nebr.: "Some foul-mouthed, low-lived whelp called Ashland from your office last night and afterwards called Omaha. In both instances, he used language that no one but a contemptible cur would think of. If you cannot prevent that class of cattle from using our lines, we shall be compelled to remove the telephone from your place of busi-

Nebraska Plant men hauling poles from New Castle, Wyo., 1918

ness, even if we have to close the office. It was doubtless some drunken clerk of yours."

To a subscriber: "It is reported to me that parties other than yourself are using your telephone quite as much as you do. Your contract with us was for your personal use ... When [others] are using telephones they are liable to keep pay subscribers waiting* ... in plain English, it is stealing from us. Unless you stop outsiders from using [it] we must remove the telephone."

To a manufacturer who sent more conduit than ordered and then tried to collect for it: "I believe the American Tract Society furnishes, to certain classes of people, Bibles without charge. I would suggest that some be secured and that your company spend at least one hour a day reading same."

When American Bell insisted on knowing the intended use of transmitters that had been ordered, Yost answered: "Since it is impossible to deal with your company and be truthful, then truth will be smothered ... We cannot wait till we receive an order ... We must have some *in stock*. In the future, if you so desire, we will state what the instruments are to be used for [but we won't

---

*This was a real problem at the time. Of the approximately 85,000 people in Omaha, perhaps 80,000 had no phones.

really know]."

By September 1897, Yost had a new way of registering his opinions at headquarters in Boston. He could call.

The new long distance service to the East Coast was demonstrated in Omaha Sept. 15 with calls to Chicago, New York and other points. Special music was put on the line from the Schlitz Palm Garden in Milwaukee. A call to Chicago cost $5; Boston and New York calls cost $10.

Long distance service to nearby towns, even to those a few hundred miles away, had been available for some time. Nevertheless, long distance calls that skipped across several states were still a big thing in the late 1890s. Daisy McPherson,* the first operator in Valley City, N.D., had vivid memories of the first such call she placed . . . to Fort Wayne, Ind., in 1897. It had been a thrill for her to hear first Fargo, then Minneapolis and then Chicago, each say "Hello, Valley City," as the connection progressed.

One reason long distance lines were not constructed faster was the cost of the wire. To transmit calls over the longer distances, wires had to be quite thick. A pair of these wires used about 15 times as much copper per foot as an ordinary household lamp cord does today. The cost of the copper alone was a huge expense. It's no wonder that Omaha remained the western terminus of the long distance network for several years.

The long distance connection to the East wasn't the only big news of 1897. Nebraska Telephone installed a private branch exchange at the Cudahy Packing Plant, with 47 telephones connected to the switchboard. It was the first such installation west of the Mississippi River and the first use of common battery equipment in Omaha. Cudahy also signed a contract for a daily call to its Chicago office. Apparently this was one of the first such contracts executed by any telephone company.

During 1897, an Omaha lawyer named John O. Yeiser decided that $3 a month was plenty to pay for telephone service and demanded that a phone be installed at that rate. When the company refused, he sued, claiming the standard $5 rate was "unreasonable and exorbitant." The

---

*Later Mrs. J. W. Noxon, who died in 1960.

District Court agreed, and ordered the company to install a phone at $3 per month. Yost wrote Boston to report what had happened, adding: "I will send you a copy of the decision and you can then see what a Populist judge will do, and his reason for doing so."

A few days later, Yost wrote that he and other officers had been "served with notice to appear and show cause why we should not be punished for contempt in not having placed the telephone for Yeiser. My next letter may be written from jail."

Yost didn't go to jail. And within a few months, the Nebraska Supreme Court reversed the District Court decision, saying that it was not up to the courts to set rates for telephone service — that was a legislative function, not a judicial one. The Court suggested that grievances about rates should be taken to the State Transportation Board, which regulated telephone rates.

One of the strangest episodes of 1897 was one that Iowa Company officers came to in desperation. At the time, many local residents were stockholders in a competing independent company and anti-Bell sentiment was strong. The Iowa Company desperately needed to rebuild its plant in Des Moines, but the City Council had issued a directive that the Iowa Company not be allowed to install any new poles or wires.

Faced with that situation, the Bell people quietly planted the idea that they would be distressed if they had to put their downtown wires into cables. The Council reacted by passing a resolution ordering the company to do just that. As a result, the Iowa people were able to rebuild the plant enough to improve service "and fight the enemy."

In February 1898, Yost was again trying to educate the American Company to the facts of telephone life. "We have in our repair shop as skilled workmen as you have in Boston," he wrote. "To refuse to send us solid back transmitter diaphragms is worse than folly . . . the expense of sending a transmitter by express over 1,500 miles and [back] is too great . . . it takes about three weeks to send any article to Boston for repairs and again have same returned to us. We live in a community where low telephone rates prevail and make our money operating our plant at as small an expense as possible."

"Things I wish they would have told me . . ."

When Ella Crawford applied for an operator's job in South Omaha in 1902 she had no idea she'd be called on to handle a six-shooter or work under fire. All she knew was the $18 a month salary Bell offered was a darn-sight more attractive than the $3 a week she earned as a seamstress.

And so began a 45-year telephone career sparkled with tales of courage and dedication that Ella, and operators like her, considered to be more routine than heroic.

About that six-shooter. In those days, some customers would come to the telephone office to place their long distance calls and would pay for them on the spot. Working alone on the night shift, Ella revealed later in an article in *NWB* magazine: "To guard my cash box, I placed this revolver conspicuously on the desk. I couldn't have shot a thing with that battered old thing, even though it had been loaded. But my! It was a fearful object."

Another exciting moment came the night a nearby paint store caught fire. With just one wall separating the phone office from the inferno next door, the fire chief set up a ladder to one of the windows so Ella could escape on short notice. But with her switchboard deluged with calls, she stubbornly remained. "The light from the fire was so bright, even though the electric lights were out, I could see to operate from the glare of the flames."

And then there's every switchboard operator's old nemesis — lightning. "One time I was almost knocked off my chair," Ella remembered. "But I didn't have much time to think about it because I could smell insulation burning. Then, directly behind me, the main frame was on fire! That was in the days of shoe-top length skirts. Well, I just hoisted my skirt to my knees and kicked away, knocking the heat coils out. Then I called the wire chief and got him on the job — I wasn't too sure just how complete my job had been."

On her retirement in August of 1948, Ella fondly recalled: "Yes, if I had to choose all over again, I'd choose the telephone business."

His candor did him no harm. The next month he was elected president of the Iowa Company and he remained president of the Nebraska Company. By December of 1898, he was prodding Boston again. The Iowa and Nebraska companies each needed about 30,000 poles to carry out construction plans and the American Company was supposed to supply the money.

"There is snow in the timberlands of Michigan and Wisconsin," Yost wrote, "and parties needing poles for 1899 are now making their contracts . . . We should know at once if the two companies are to have the money. Many hundreds of dollars can be saved by contracting for poles at this time."

In 1899 AT&T became the parent company of the Bell System. AT&T had been organized in 1885 to build and operate long distance lines. American Bell had continued as the parent organization. The move in 1899 put both the long lines and the Bell operating companies under the AT&T's management.

At about the same time that AT&T became the headquarters company in 1899, Northwestern Telephone Exchange was in the midst of a fierce war with druggists in the Twin Cities. The druggists insisted on letting everyone use their telephones. The company maintained that these free-loaders were swamping the switchboards with calls, thereby delaying service to paying customers. The fight became so bitter that some phones were jerked off the wall. But finally a peace pact was signed in 1900. Pay telephones were installed in the drug stores, and an additional phone was placed for each druggist's private use.

During this same period, J. W. Christie, manager in Minneapolis, got what must surely have been one of the toughest assignments ever handed out. A bill had been introduced in the Minnesota Legislature calling for telephone rates to be cut in half. Christie's job was to get subscribers to sign a petition *opposing* the rate cut.

He was surprisingly successful, primarily because he got men like Charles A. Pillsbury, head of the flour company, to sign. Christie said Pillsbury roared at him at first. But after a discussion about what the rate cut would do to telephone service, Pillsbury put his name at the head of the list. Eventually, 70 per cent of Northwestern Telephone Exchange's customers signed the petition. The bill

The boomer

By Gil Brackett*

Probably the most romantic and, at times, the most cantankerous individual ever to don a pair of hooks and mount a telephone pole was the boomer lineman. This gent was a salty fellow, a nomad of the telephone industry from its birth until somewhere near 1918. Like the geese, when the first sign of frost brought a chill to the night air, Mr. Boomer was in a dither until he was on his way south, canvas "tote" bag in one hand, a pair of hooks slung over a shoulder as he waved farewell and shouted, "See you next spring!"

I saw a lineman stop suddenly in the act of swinging his hand-axe and bellow, "Hear them geese? I got their message!" He came down the pole in three jumps to greet the foreman with, "I'm on my way, Boss!" . . .

Mr. Boomer was a rugged sort of a man . . . tractable with a foreman he admired as a master, but became feisty and hard to handle under one less knowledgeable than himself.

Few ever married but that didn't mean they weren't interested in the fair sex. Sometimes it meant trouble. In the small town of West Point, Nebr., during the early 1900s, the local gallants rose in force and drove the amorous raiders from the town and in such a hurry they had no time to get their tools or duffle bags. A new crew was brought in under a stern warning . . . an armistice had been signed and the battle of West Point was over.

The boomer has been gone now for more than a half century. I wonder what he would say about the elimination of his beloved toll leads, replaced by Telstar, television, radio, shortwave and other means. I can hear him complain: "Gee, Boss, they done ruined the phone business. No poles to climb? It jest ain't human!"

---

*Mr. Brackett retired as traffic results supervisor in Des Moines in 1953. Subsequently he wrote hundreds of articles including the above, which was reprinted by *NWB* magazine in 1968. Mr. Brackett died April 1, 1975, at age 86.

to cut rates was dropped.

A fire the night before Thanksgiving 1902, destroyed the telephone office in Yankton, S.D. As soon as Manager N. E. Gibbons realized that nothing could be saved, he immediately rerouted long distance lines and set up a make-shift long distance office in the Vanderhule & Sampson Drug Store on 3rd Street.

While the fire was still burning, Gibbons got a call through to Minneapolis. C. P. Wainman, superintendent of Northwestern Telephone Exchange, had left strict instructions he was not to be disturbed during the night. But Gibbons was able to persuade the Minneapolis operators that he had a real emergency.

By the morning of Thanksgiving Day, Wainman was on a train headed for Yankton. He had with him a new switchboard, a supply of cable and other materials, along with a switchboardman, cable splicer and carpenter. Meanwhile, Gibbons had located space for a new office in another building. Within a few days, service was back to normal for Yankton's 150 subscribers.

As late as 1903, when exchange service was still relatively new in Eveleth, Minn., many local housewives refused to have phones. F. E. Lister, manager then, recalled that of the first 100 phones, about 40 were in saloons.

While Lister was still trying to crack the residential market, the local banker's wife arranged a concert to be given by an opera singer. The day before the concert, the banker's wife sprained her ankle and was laid up in bed.

Manager Lister seized the opportunity. He set up a transmitter on the stage, connected it to a line to the banker's house and loaned the banker's wife an operator's head set. Then he urged the singer to sing into the transmitter as often as possible. The banker's wife was delighted and, shortly afterwards, orders for residence telephones began to come in from women who had originally refused.

In April of 1903, 150 Nebraska Telephone linemen went on strike for higher wages and formal recognition of their union, the International Brotherhood of Electrical Workers (IBEW). Western Union and Postal Telegraph linemen also went out. At the time, the *Omaha Bee* reported that the IBEW had planned a similar strike a year earlier but it had not materialized because Nebraska Telephone had raised wages.

The 1903 strike lasted almost two weeks. Then the telephone linemen went back to work without an agreement. While it lasted, however, the strike caused quite a stir. Yost wrote to the American Company that he had met with 200 leading businessmen and they had overwhelmingly supported Nebraska Telephone's position.

Yost's mood varied from whimsical to desperate. In one letter, he said that it might be necessary to close the Omaha exchange, "but it will give the officers time to go fishing." However, in letters to telephone officials in Iowa, Illinois and Missouri, he pleaded: "Can you send us any linemen?"

Records are sketchy, but the Omaha strike was at least the fourth in a two-year period. In July of 1901, linemen in Duluth were in the midst of a prolonged strike against both Northwestern Telephone Exchange and the Zenith Company. One of their demands was for an eight-hour working day; the companies were offering nine.

In the spring of 1902, the Northwestern Telephone Exchange Company apparently signed an agreement with the IBEW granting, among other things, time-and-a-half for overtime and for work on Sundays and holidays. C. P. Wainman, general manager of Northwestern Exchange, wrote President Fish of the American Company to reassure him that the company had *not* agreed to hire only union men. Wainman also emphasized that it was understood that no employee would be fired simply because he belonged to a union.

Some 75 operators went on strike against the Iowa and the Mutual telephone companies in Des Moines in June of 1902. They wanted wages of $25 to $30 per month instead of the $18 to $25 they were getting and demanded time-and-a-half for overtime and double time for Sundays and holidays. The *Des Moines Register* said the "girls' " union was the first of its kind in the country, and that other unions in town were pledging their support.

Linemen and electrical workers did go out in sympathy, both in Des Moines and in Davenport, where Iowa Telephone still had its headquarters. But the men went back after two months. The women returned to work sometime in the fall, but the available records do not indicate whether or not an agreement was signed.

The last quarter of 1903 saw these developments in Yost's continuing struggle against what he saw as short-sighted policies: he made a strong appeal to AT&T President Fish for permission to install an independent manufacturer's one-piece telephone set in the home of an influential Omaha family. "I do not want the leading people of Omaha advertising a desirable telephone apparatus which we have not supplied."

In another letter to Fish, Yost argued for permission to interconnect with farm lines, even though the farmers were using telephones manufactured by the independents. He reasoned that if he could just do business with them for a while, he could convince them that "we are fair men." Then, when their telephones inevitably went on the blink, they would likely replace them with Bell instruments. Perhaps because of letters like this, interconnection policies were relaxed gradually the next few years.

For several years, Yost had a running battle with Western Electric officials, too. He repeatedly accused them of not sending materials when promised, of not relaying information as requested and of frequent billing errors. Obviously with past gripes in mind, he wrote Western Electric in December of 1903 to say that since their contract allowed either party to terminate it by giving a year's notice, he was giving notice. He did the same thing two years later.

The headquarters of the Iowa Company were moved from Davenport to Des Moines in 1904. And Omaha customers received common battery service.

The following year, 1905, Walter S. Rowe sold the Pierre and Fort Pierre, S.D., telephone properties to Dakota Central for $20,000. Only 31, Rowe had already crammed a lifetime of difficulties into 10 years. A telegrapher, he fell heir to the uncompleted Pierre phone system when George Holmes died while building it.

Rowe worked night and day, sleeping at the switchboard so he could handle night calls. He built what he claimed was South Dakota's first underground cable system and also managed to string a steel wire across the treacherous Missouri River so Pierre and Fort Pierre could be connected.

1902 photograph of the first common battery board in Iowa, located in Davenport

To buy the wire, Rowe borrowed $75 at 24 per cent interest. He worked all the next fall at a government rock works, at $1.52 per day, to pay it off.

Western Electric set up a distributing house in Minneapolis in 1907. Similar installations had been established at Omaha and Des Moines in 1904. Previously, supplies had been stored at various locations "and when an order came in," old-timers recalled, "we had to hitch up a team and pick up cross arms here, and wire there, and a switchboard, perhaps at some other location."

Casper Yost was elected president of Northwestern Telephone Exchange again in 1907, which once more made him the head of the three companies operating in what is now Northwestern Bell territory. Even AT&T was confused by this. Yost finally promised AT&T that when he wrote them on behalf of a particular company, he would use that company's letterhead.*

---

*Unfortunately, the letterheads don't show on Yost's file copies.

At about the same time Yost and AT&T were fretting with the letterhead dilemma, a Black Hills foreman named H. H. Wright was worrying about how to keep his linemen alive. Because the terrain was so rugged and the frequent snows so deep, Wright kept records of where each outlying settler lived in relation to pole lines. This paid off one winter when a lineman's horse collapsed in deep snow. The exhausted man barely managed to get to a pole and climb it so he could phone for help. He gave Wright the number of the pole and Wright called the nearest settler, who went out on skis. The rescuer not only saved the lineman from freezing to death, he even got the horse to shelter.

Meanwhile, AT&T was struggling, too. The fight against competition had required immense amounts of money. The companies that later made up Northwestern Bell were only a small part of the Bell System, yet even they had required huge sums of money. The Iowa Company had to be bailed out of virtual bankruptcy. Long distance lines had to be built in sparsely settled territory. Emergency plant improvements had to be made in locations where competition was most threatening — the early installation of common battery switchboards in the Twin Cities, for instance.

As a result of demands like these, multiplied all across the country, AT&T was financially overstretched. And this came at a time when the whole country was battling inflation. People were nervous and hanging on to their money. Telephone bonds were not selling well and bankers were worried about AT&T's financial condition. It was their idea to bring Theodore Vail back, and to move AT&T headquarters from Boston to New York.

In the years since he had left the Bell organization, Vail had regained his health and his zest for living. He had lost one fortune trying to set up a company to heat urban buildings with superheated water piped in underground ducts. Then he had gone to South America and made a new fortune building electric street railways and a hydroelectric plant.

Vail kept in touch during these years, and had even been offered the AT&T presidency in 1901 before Frederick P. Fish was asked. Now he was in a position to accept. But before he did, he summoned three trusted old friends, including Casper Yost, and discussed the situation at length.

When he did take the presidency in 1907, Vail's work was laid out for him. He had to resolve the financial crisis quickly. Since telephone bonds were not selling well, Vail proposed a $20 million stock issue. He sensed that even with all the competitive difficulties the Bell System was having, the public still had faith in it. He was right; the stock was grabbed up almost immediately. That, in turn, reassured the bankers and other bond buyers. Within a few months, the company was able to sell more bonds.

From then on, Casper Yost had a sympathetic friend at the head of the Bell System. Much has been written about the impact of Vail's character on the course of telephone history. One reason he was so successful is that he relied on men like Yost to counsel and support him. Yost's integrity and business judgment were qualities Vail could count on.

An example is an early 1908 letter from Yost to Vice President Wainman in Minnesota:

"When in Minneapolis," Yost wrote, "I learned that some of the Contract Department solicitors were going to special-line subscribers and, without telling them of the reduction in rates, were saying to them that if they desired an extension telephone, they could have same without any charge over what had been previously paid. When the subscribers find out — as they surely will — that they have been taken advantage of, there will be all kinds of trouble . . . Instead of the rate reduction helping us, it will, by reason of not dealing fairly with [customers], make them unfriendly to us."

Yost asked Wainman to stop the practice immediately. "Tell the subscribers of the rate reduction, and then try to induce them to take the additional service."

In 1909 a formal general office staff for all three companies — Nebraska, Iowa and Northwestern Telephone Exchange — was established in Omaha. At the time, the Bell System was in the process of consolidating its various operating companies into larger units.

Previously, while Yost had been president of all three, their operations had otherwise been entirely separate. Now, the top officers of all three were to be the same, down to the department level. George McFarland was

W. B. T. Belt   A. A. Lowman

named general manager of all three companies; Thomas Cotter* became general superintendent of traffic; and C. P. Wainman, general commercial superintendent.

Two future presidents of Northwestern Bell were given important responsibilities. W. B. T. Belt was named general superintendent of plant, and A. A. Lowman was put in charge of the Nebraska Division Plant.

Belt had started in January of 1889 as a door-to-door collector of electric power and telephone bills. He attracted favorable attention very soon.

Because a bad sleet storm had tangled telephone and electric power lines, fuses in many residential phones had burned out. When Belt tried to collect bills, customers refused to pay because their phones were not working. Belt discovered that by carrying a bit of gold foil (the fuse material) and a screwdriver, he could restore service quickly and then make his collections.

Belt became manager at Omaha in 1899, superintendent for the Nebraska Company in 1904 and general manager in 1907. George McFarland left Omaha to accept the presidency of the Pacific Company in 1913 and Belt became vice president and general manager of the North-

---

*Cotter and his boss, Thomas B. Doolittle (See footnote, Ch. III, p. 36) were traveling traffic experts for AT&T in the early 1900s. Casper Yost credited their activities with having "saved hundreds of thousands of dollars" for those companies. Doolittle, Cotter and associates did the first Toll Traffic Engineering for the Northwestern Group Companies in this period. In 1909 Mr. Cotter was hired by the Northwestern Group. He retired in 1919 and died in 1924.

western Group the following year.*

Lowman had started his telephone career as a night operator while visiting at Wahoo, Nebr., when he was only 12. Most of the calls he handled were either for the Union Pacific Railroad or for the bawdy houses, he recalled.

Lowman started full-time work as a repairman at Clarinda, Iowa, in 1894. After serving as district manager at Shenandoah, Iowa, and wire chief in Council Bluffs, Iowa, he was put in charge of installation and maintenance in Omaha in 1906. He succeeded Belt as general plant superintendent in 1914 and then as vice president and general manager in 1919.

Shortly after Lowman became plant superintendent for the Nebraska Division in 1909, a major storm hit. Two inches of sleet knocked down hundreds of poles on the 50-wire long distance route running west from Lincoln. Then a foot of snow fell and it kept snowing and blowing for a week, making restoration doubly difficult.

Every morning, Lowman would start out with a two-horse buggy loaded with overshoes, mittens, tobacco and whatever else the construction men wanted. Snuff was particularly important to some of the linemen of Swedish descent. The first day, Lowman's supplies only lasted about two miles, but he went on another 11 miles, to the end of the damage area, taking orders.

One man at the end of the line desperately needed overshoes. Every day, Lowman would be out by the time he got there. On the fifth day, Lowman fought off all intermediate marauders and proudly delivered a package to the long-suffering lineman, who opened it eagerly.

Sure enough, there were two brand new overshoes — both for the left foot.

It was also in 1909 that Yost began dreaming of a new headquarters building in Omaha. He explained to New

---

*McFarland's old partner, Charles E. Hall, was Northwestern Group vice president and general manager for a year after McFarland left. Then he was Group officer in charge of independent companies that were Bell controlled but that had not been consolidated. At one time or another, Hall was president of 14 of these companies and general manager of two more. Later he was tax commissioner for Northwestern Bell until he was elected secretary in 1924. He retired in 1930 and died in 1941.

York that his three companies already had their headquarters in Omaha; he was sure it was only a matter of time until they would be consolidated. The new headquarters building was erected in 1911, on the south side of Douglas Street between 18th and 19th Streets.

Even while he was looking ahead to a large consolidated company, Yost was also trying to keep his empire within bounds. In April of 1909, he wrote a friend that he was sorry the telephone company could not hire the man's niece. "I have been recently complaining that we are using too many stenographers and typewriters, and have insisted that the force be cut down."*

---

*Another belt-tightening campaign a few years later produced this story: The Nebraska Division construction superintendent was in Norfolk to supervise force reduction. He and H. E. McKown, district plant chief, were going down the list of construction crews with a ruler, haggling over which men to keep, which to lay off. Then the construction superintendent was called to the phone. McKown quietly moved the ruler down the page, thereby keeping one whole crew intact.

The Nebraska Telephone Company occupied the first three buildings (from the left) at 18th and Douglas, Omaha.

The record does not show how successful this particular economy drive was. But another personnel policy which was developed at this time is still having a profound effect on Bell System employees. Theodore Vail felt very emotional about his fellow telephone workers. He wanted to create a system that would give them security in their old age, or when they were ill or injured during their working years. Vail was corresponding with Yost and others about details of the plan as early as 1910.

The result was the Employee Benefit Program which was put into effect by the Northwestern Group and other Bell System companies at the beginning of 1913. It was a pioneering effort. At the time, most business and industrial workers did not have either a pension plan or sickness and accident benefits.

What that meant is made clear in the anecdotes of old-timers. H. H. Cockrell, retired General Office accountant, recalled that in the early 1900s, most employees would struggle to work even when barely able to hold up their heads. In one instance, a man named Fiala, who worked in Omaha Accounting, kept plugging away at his ledger book and never complained, Cockrell said. No one thought anything about Fiala's health until one day when he went home at noon and died.

Another time, a frail man named Pike came to work with a bad case of the flu. Since he was chilled, he kept his overcoat on. Unfortunately, his seat was near the window, and passersby could see him. Because of this, the supervisor told Pike to take off the coat or leave. He took it off.

At one point, Dan Hegarty, an Omaha Plant man, fell from a pole and fractured his kneecap. In that instance, Hegarty swore that his boss, John Wicks, had his name off the payroll before he hit the ground.

Scattered incidents such as these did not mean that telephone officials were callous. In that era's economy, most businesses simply could not afford to pay for work they weren't getting.

What Theodore Vail and a few other industrial leaders did was introduce the concept that providing for pensions, and paying salaries to the sick and injured, were legitimate costs that should be included in a company's expenses.

If the Employee Benefit Program was the best news of

1913, a killer tornado that sliced through the heart of Omaha was the worst. The tornado hit about 6 p.m. on Easter Sunday, March 23. It left 99 dead, 322 injured, 618 homes demolished and almost 2,000 other homes damaged. Some 6,000 telephones were knocked out and 120 long distance lines were cut.

The Webster exchange building, on the city's northeast edge, was in the middle of a severely damaged area. Every window and door was blown out, operators were hit by splintered glass and some were blasted from their chairs. The roof was leaking and the power was out.

Even so, the building was about the only shelter left in the neighborhood and hundreds of people, some of them hysterical, sought refuge there. In the midst of this panic, and with a chill rain blowing in on them, the operators were trying to handle the flood of calls. Some of the women were bleeding from face or hand cuts, and their switchboard positions were littered with broken glass. A temporary hospital was set up in an adjacent room and the operators could hear the moans of the wounded and dying all through the long night.

Fortunately, off-duty telephone people were streaming in along with the refugees. Mrs. May Gamble, a former operator, found someone to care for her baby, walked two miles through the rain, and stayed at the board 20 hours after she got there. Plant men quickly rigged temporary covers over the windows and began disconnecting shorted customer lines at the main frame. These shorted lines had caused hundreds of permanent signals on the switchboard, making it almost impossible for the operators to find the live calls.

The Webster office had a standby generator in the building. It provided power there during the 10 days commercial power was off. A portable generator, kept for such emergencies, was taken to the Benson branch exchange. Getting electricity to the Florence branch exchange was more of a problem, since no other generator was available.

However, the Webster and Florence offices were connected by a trunk cable. One cable pair couldn't carry enough current to do much good. But a lot of cable pairs could. By rearranging circuits, the engineers were able to make 50 pairs available in this trunk. At one end, these were hooked up to the Webster battery, and at the other, to

Aftermath of 1913 Easter Sunday tornado at 24th and Lake Sts., Omaha

the Florence battery. That kept the Florence exchange in operation for the duration.

Since all long distance lines were knocked out, messengers were sent east and west on the first trains available. As soon as they got to towns where communications were possible, they sent out the call for help. At Nebraska outstate points, the Plant chiefs had already figured out some major disaster was involved, since they couldn't reach Omaha by any route. They had begun gathering men and equipment before the call for help arrived.

Grand Island had a contingent of men into Omaha before dawn. Men from Norfolk, Lincoln and Hastings arrived a little later. And by 7:30 that morning, 95 men were on a train headed for Omaha from Minneapolis. By Tuesday morning, 500 extra Plant men were on the job — 130 from the Northwestern Exchange Company, 125 from Norfolk and Grand Island, 90 from the Iowa companies, 40 from Lincoln Telephone and Telegraph and 115 picked up locally.

Omaha Plant men had three AT&T circuits to Denver working by dawn Monday. By the following Sunday, they had most of the other long distance lines and local cable systems repaired. All station trouble was cleared 10 days after the storm. The restoration job was perhaps the first in which Northwestern Group workmen used automobiles and trucks. General Plant Manager Belt reported to Yost that they had been a big factor in speeding the work.

The restoration of the AT&T circuits to Denver had been a high priority item because the Bell System was busily pushing its long lines westward. After 14 years of being the western terminus of the long lines, Omaha lost that distinction in 1911 when the circuits reached Denver.

Two years later, the lines were extended on to Salt Lake City. Meanwhile, Dr. Lee De Forest, a native of Council Bluffs, Iowa,* had invented the audion vacuum tube. With improvements made by Bell Labs engineers, these tubes made it possible to build amplifiers (repeaters) reliable enough for use in long distance transmission. The first vacuum tube telephone repeater in commercial long distance use was installed at Philadelphia in 1913. It was on the New York-Baltimore line. By 1914 an experimental transcontinental line, using the repeaters, was in operation between New York and San Francisco.

The line was put into commercial service on Jan. 25, 1915, with much fanfare. Alexander Graham Bell in New York talked to Thomas Watson in San Francisco. Visiting easily over the 3,400 miles separating them, they reminisced about their first telephone conversations nearly 40 years earlier. Iowa's George McFarland, then president of the Pacific Company, took a turn speaking. And Casper Yost was chosen to represent the associated company presidents among the dignitaries gathered in New York.

The transcontinental line wasn't the only major long distance project in the Northwestern Group's territory during this period. An unsatisfactory line connecting Pierre and Rapid City was replaced by a copper circuit built to Nebraska Telephone specifications by Western Union in 1911. It was carried on Western Union poles. In a letter to President Zietlow of the Dakota Central Company, which

---

*The elder De Forest was a Congregational minister, and the family lived in several Iowa towns while Lee De Forest was a boy.

operated the Pierre telephone system, Yost said he doubted the line would earn much, but that it was to the advantage of both companies to demonstrate that they were prepared to offer top quality service.

This line had to be replaced in 1916, apparently because the 1911 circuit had to be removed from the railroad right of way. An unusual amount of information is available on that particular project. R. W. Mason, later an auditor in Des Moines, wrote a detailed account of the job for the Pioneer Historical Committee in 1951.* Mason shared the clerking responsibilities with a newcomer from the East, Dud Colby, who later became secretary-treasurer of the Company.

The project involved setting 6,572 poles over a 182-mile distance. Besides the two clerks, the crew consisted of six foremen, 10 linemen, 45 groundmen, two powdermen (for blasting pole holes in rocky terrain) and five cooks.

The equipment included seven teams of horses, one Garford truck, one Ford open roadster and a gasoline-driven well digger.

It was Mason's opinion this was the first job in the Nebraska Area in which motor equipment was used. This might be because in 1915, just a year earlier, Arthur Lowman, general plant manager, made a special study for W. B. T. Belt, vice president and general manager. In it, Lowman reported that experimental use indicated that purchase of one truck for the Minneapolis District would save the company money, but that he could not recommend use of trucks in Omaha, St. Paul or Des Moines.†

The use of the Ford roadster on the Pierre-Rapid City job had its amusing sidelights. Once Mason and Colby got lost, spent the night at a rancher's, and had to face the irate general foreman, W. J. Duffy, when they finally drifted in. Duffy needed the roadster to make his rounds since the work was strung out over many miles.

---

*A souvenir Mason kept, a 58-x25-inch sheet of wrapping paper with a day-by-day account of the job's progress, is in the Pioneer Museum in Omaha.

†Apparently the use of trucks in the 1913 tornado restoration work in Omaha had involved rented vehicles.

The crew for the Pierre to Rapid City line used a gasoline-driven well digger for pole holes. 1916, near Phillip, S.D.

On another occasion, a traveling auditor showed up. One of his duties was to deliver all paychecks personally, to be sure the payroll records were not padded. But it was a cold day, the auditor had no overcoat and the men were scattered over a 70-mile area. After a few hours of frigid traveling in the open roadster, the auditor gave it up and told Mason to complete his own audit.

The crew camped in tents, which were moved weekly at first, but every four days toward the end of the project. Once the wind blew so fiercely that all the tents had to be taken down except the mess and office tents. Despite the difficulties, the job was completed late in November 1916. It was nearly on schedule, with 996 poles set the final seven days.

In less than six months, America was at war and telephone men were helping fight it. That made the Pierre-Rapid City project a nostalgic adventure never to be duplicated. By the time telephone men came back from the war, they had been thoroughly indoctrinated in the use of trucks and automobiles in their construction projects.

Chapter XII

Northwestern goes to France

Stringing lines wasn't enough; the Cats saved a town, too

THEODORE VAIL was an old man in 1916 and there were times when he acted it. He would play solitaire for hours, whistling softly. He reminisced a lot about bygone days and particularly enjoyed visiting with old friends.

One of his favorites was Harry B. Thayer, then president of Western Electric. He and Vail were the kind of friends who didn't always have to talk. As Vail put it, "Sometimes old Thayer comes and we just sit and look at each other."

Vail was 71 years old then and still very much the president of AT&T. He was slowing down, but he retained a keen sense of what was happening in the world and how it might affect the telephone business. He was a staunch Republican, but still thought it foolish of his Republican friends to expect that Justice Hughes would defeat President Wilson. Nor did Vail share the prevailing optimism that the threat of war would go away.

At the time, the Bell System needed extra capital. Vail proposed a sale of stock and bonds to raise $130 million, much more than previously considered. "But why do we need all that money now?" one director asked.

"Well," Vail replied, "I believe when you go sleighing

it is a good plan to go when there is plenty of snow. Something tells me that snow is going to be pretty scarce."

He even urged pricing the bonds more attractively than the directors thought necessary. He wanted them to sell quickly. They did, and the Bell System was in sound financial condition when America was drawn into World War I. Many other companies were caught short in the suddenly tight money market.

While Vail was making sure that AT&T was financially sound, a few other key men like John J. Carty, AT&T's chief engineer, were discussing with military leaders how telephone people and know-how could best be used if war came. Little did they know that before the war was over, the government would actually take over the telephone companies. But that story comes later.

In November 1916, the presidents of the Bell associated companies met in New York and Carty told them of possibilities that had been discussed with the Signal Corps. Carty wanted to be sure that, if necessary, military needs could be met without crippling basic service. That meant careful planning.

Sioux Falls Preparedness Day, 1916

A blank telegram started friendship

Bernice Vail, an Arlington, Nebr., high school girl, was fascinated by the name on the blank telegram form: Theodore N. Vail, president of Western Union. (For a time, AT&T owned Western Union, and Vail was president of both.) Bernice probably wasn't related to this Vail, but she wanted to know the man anyway. Finally, one day in 1913, she wrote him a note. It was the start of a correspondence that would last six or seven years.

Despite their age differences (Vail was nearly 70 when he started writing), the two pen pals got along beautifully. They called each other "cousin" even though it was never established that they were related to each other.

Vail's involvement with young people was always apparent in his notes. Once he wrote, " . . . the other day I was invited to lunch by the sophomore class in domestic science and they gave me a good lunch, too; 14 or 15 girls prepared it and waited on us. And I am ashamed to say I was very greedy and ate too much."

He always took a special interest in Bernice's activities. "It is a long time since November," he wrote in March of 1914, "and since then, the Christmas you were planning has come and gone and probably your girl friend has come back from California and you have gotten used to your new principal."

In one letter, Vail apologized for his bad writing habits: "Now, when I don't answer your letters at once, keep on writing. Sooner or later you will get an answer."

Bernice later became the wife of Robert Page, who retired from Northwestern Bell in 1964 as a commercial representative.

Early in 1917, the Northwestern Group made studies to determine how rapidly messages could be transmitted to Chicago and Washington, D.C., from military posts and major factories in Northwestern territory. Large stocks of wire, cable, switchboards, telephones and pole line materials were stored near military posts.

On April 5, 1917, the day before Congress declared war, W. B. T. Belt, vice president and general manager of the Northwestern Group, sent a letter to all telephone men. He asked for about 200 volunteers to serve in a telegraph battalion of the Signal Corps Reserve. Out of 3,650 male employees, 974 volunteered.

The applicants were carefully screened, and the men started training. They were in France before Christmas.

Officially, they were the 408th Telegraph Battalion, U.S. Signal Corps. But in French, the 408th translated as Le Quatre Cent Huit. To Midwestern ears, it sounded like "The Cats on Wheat," and that's what they began calling themselves. It was an elite outfit, and it's had a lot of well-deserved publicity in the years since. But 800 other Northwestern people also served during the war.

Some 25 Northwestern volunteers were in the 405th, another of the 12 battalions staffed by Bell System people. Over 60 Plant men were in the National Guard and were called up as soon as war was declared. All told, 1,005 Northwestern employees were in service. Some came home heroes. Seven did not come home.*

Two who are known to have been cited for bravery were Herschel V. Lane of Minneapolis and Oscar A. Bondelid of Grand Forks, N. D.

Lane, son of H. Vance Lane, former vice president and general manager of Nebraska Telephone, was awarded the Distinguished Service Cross for carrying messages through heavy artillery and machine gun fire.

Bondelid was cited for conspicuous gallantry for "maintaining under heavy shell fire" a vital communication line for his machine gun company at Cantigny. The

---

*The Northwestern dead: William D. Brainerd, Minden, Nebr.; Herbert Derome, Sioux Falls; Daniel E. Dowd, Des Moines; R. L. Harris, Grand Island, Nebr.; Ralph C. Hiatt, Minneapolis; S. C. Sorenson, Deadwood, S.D.; and Leo H. Wendt, Des Moines.

line ran through a valley straight to the front. "It was the worst place to make a man work that I ever saw," Bondelid said. "It was valuable as a communication line. The Boche knew it and shelled the deuce out of it." At first, there was only enough wire for a grounded line. For ground rods, Bondelid and his partner stuck a bayonet into the ground at one end and a hand ax at the other. Soon they got enough wire to make a metallic circuit, and later used eight reels of wire patching breaks. Bondelid was hit by shell fragments several times and had a hole in his helmet by the time the area was secure.

On the home front, Northwestern and the other Bell companies had to restrict new installations. However, there was no letup on military installations. At Camp Dodge outside of Des Moines, an Army city sprang up. Northwestern installed a PBX at the camp and placed 42,000 feet of 100-pair cable, 24,000 feet of 300-pair, 175 poles and nine miles of underground cable ducts. Some 30 of Iowa's best operators were recruited as post operators.

In the Plant Department, 224 women started handling such jobs as caring for storage batteries, repairing switchboard cords and adjusting relays. Scores of women moved into accounting jobs formerly held by men.

Industries aiding the war effort were given priority in the handling of long distance calls. And alert operators soon discovered there were people who would pose as government aides in order to get calls through. A potato farmer once demanded preferred service because he was raising food for the war.

One of the reasons long distance service had to be handled on a priority basis was that so many telephone operators were needed in military installations. Operators who could speak French were particularly in demand overseas. Marie Gagnon of Grafton, N.D., a Northwestern operator-volunteer,* handled many of Gen. Pershing's calls. He had the highest priority, she recalled. "We were

---

*Other Northwestern operators who volunteered for overseas service were Delta E. Hagan, Monticello, Minn.; Estelle Russell, St. Cloud, Minn.; Anna A. Kinney, Davenport, Iowa; Nell Wilkins, Omaha; Georgette Schaerr, Fremont, Nebr.; Margaret Olker, Duluth, Minn.; and Cordelia Dupuis, Rolla, N.D.

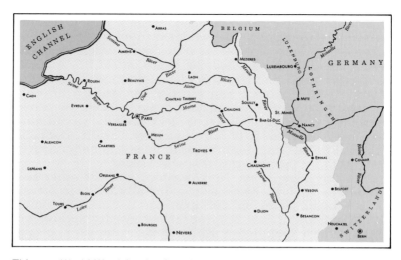

This was World War I for the Cats. Troyes is located just south of the Seine River. Nevers is near the Loire River, south of Troyes.

allowed to cut anyone else off if he needed the line."

Some of the American officers had problems communicating with French operators. That explains the response one American operator got when she first arrived at an Army post in France and said, "Number, please." "Thank God, you're here at last," the officer on the line blurted.

American methods sometimes grated on French sensibilities. The French were accustomed to running their wires along lines of least resistance. Americans bulled their way over hills, through swamps, whatever was necessary to take the most direct route.

An American general, just arrived in France, wanted to get in touch with Gen. Pershing immediately. When he found he'd have to wait his turn behind 22 other people placing long distance calls at the French telephone office, he canceled the call and ordered his men to begin stringing four wires to Paris immediately.

"Use the French poles," he told them. Within five minutes the work was started. Soon, French officials were in a dither. Such things couldn't be done without the proper authorizations. "Get them, get anything," the general ordered, "but meantime the work will go on."

While overseas, The Cats on Wheat installed more than 300 miles of telephone-telegraph lines, working much of the time in knee-deep mud. One 30-mile line from Chaumont to Souilly crossed the Marne River four times.

In July 1918, 10 trucks and 10 motorcycles from the 408th were transferred to the 1st Army for use in the St. Mihiel offensive. Soon after, 15 of the battalion's heavy trucks and their drivers, under the command of Lt. Fred Butt,* were detailed to haul ammunition during the Aisne-Marne offensive. The drivers, all telephone men, often drove from 40 to 50 hours without rest, through the congested rear areas during the day, up to the front over shell-torn roads at night. They proved they could do more than string wire if the occasion demanded.

When the Germans started their drive on Chateau-Thierry, the 408th Battalion was stationed at Troyes. This place became a haven for thousands of refugees.

A German advance had surprised local peasants, many of whom stayed until the Germans were within shooting range. These peasants had survived four years near the front and had begun to think they'd be spared.

Now as refugees, they were hauled to Troyes in freight trains. City authorities there were unprepared and turned in desperation to the men of the 408th for help. One Northwestern man who was there described what happened:

"The Red Cross provided free soup, bread, and wine which the Signal Corps men served over a counter set up in the depot. A rushing business was carried on 24 hours a day. Arrangements were made to house the visitors in the Cathedral and its court. But that was a mile away, so the 408th used its trucks to provide day and night bus service for more than two weeks. The men rigged makeshift beds which were spread out on the floors of the buildings around the courtyard.

"Many came with tears in their eyes to give their thanks for 'les Americans' and the wonderful work they were doing, not only at the front, but all through the country wherever help was needed."

---

*Officers of the 408th were Maj. F. W. McDougal, commander; A. A. Gieriet and Paul Bunce, captains; and Fred B. Butt, A. W. Huntzinger, P. M. McCullough and W. C. Hutchinson, first lieutenants.

RÉPUBLIQUE FRANÇAISE

A.M.

VILLE DE NEVERS

Nevers, le 13 Août 193 8.

LE MAIRE DE LA VILLE DE NEVERS félicite

les survivants du 408e Bataillon Télégraphique

de l'Armée Américaine stationnant à NEVERS en

décembre 1917, et s'associe au geste de

M. W.E. RYAN commémorant le bon souvenir que

la population nivernaise a conservé d'eux.

Le Maire,

Ed Ryan, one of the 408th Telegraph Battalion veterans, brought the above letter with him to the 1940 reunion of The Cats on Wheat in Des Moines. Attached to a bottle of champagne, the letter was given by the mayor of Nevers upon a visit by Ryan with his wife, who is French.

The mayor gave instructions that the champagne was to be drunk by the last surviving members of the battalion.

The letter, dated the 13th of August 1938, reads:

"The mayor of the village of Nevers congratulates the survivors of the 408th Telegraphic Battalion of the American Army stationed at Nevers in December 1917, and joins Mr. W. E. Ryan in commemorating the good memory that the people of Nevers held of them."

For years after, an American visitor to Troyes had only to say, "Le Quatre Cent Huit" and the grateful people would provide him food and lodging for as long as he wanted to stay.

When the armistice was signed on Nov. 11, 1918, everyone was thinking, "When do we go home?" But for the Cats, the hardest jobs were still to come. They built lines into Luxembourg as the Germans withdrew.

In February, the 408th joined other Signal Corps groups in the staggering task of taking inventory of all the telephone and telegraph facilities in a 15,000-square-mile territory. They listed every line — German, French or American; military, railroad or civil, including descriptions of the type of construction and current condition.

The Cats started home in April, traveling by way of Gibraltar. They arrived in Des Moines on May 22, 1919, and were greeted with a celebration that included a banquet at noon, entertainment in the afternoon, and a reception and dance in the evening.

The return of the Cats came just a couple of months before another "end of the war" ceremony. On July 30, Postmaster General Albert S. Burleson signed an order

The 408th Battalion was honored in an Armistice Parade, Grand Island, Nebr., 1920.

returning the Bell System to private ownership. For exactly one year, the U.S. Government had controlled all telephone and telegraph properties in the country as a wartime emergency measure.

In an interview after the war, Burleson told how surprised he had been at his first meeting with Vail and the other telephone officials. He had expected "public-be-damned" autocrats, furious at having to submit to government control. Instead, "every word that Mr. Vail said showed an entirely unselfish point of view, a desire to serve the government and the public at whatever cost."

Soon Burleson asked Vail to be his confidential advisor and operate the Bell System. The two men continued to work harmoniously in what could have been a difficult situation. The *New York Times* commented editorially:

"Mr. Vail was never a believer in the right of big business to go its way unhindered. No big businessman ever submitted to control more loyally."

For years, there had been people in and out of government (including Postmaster Burleson) who thought the government ought to control the nation's wire communications. Naturally, Bell System people were uneasy that the temporary wartime situation might become permanent. Undoubtedly the mutual respect and spirit of cooperation that developed between Bell officers and postal officials helped prevent that.

Return of the telephone properties to private control closed out a unique wartime episode. But the emotional (and official) end had come months earlier ... on Armistice Day. In a nostalgic story in 1928, *Northwestern Bell* magazine told how various Northwestern servicemen had reacted that day when the French began shouting, "Fini — la guerre est fini!"

A. R. Smith, Plant Department, Des Moines, captain in 16th Infantry, 1st Division: "The men threw their caps in the air, but they stayed in the trenches. We were dug in near Sec in the St. Mihiel sector. No one ran around in the open. They had seen too much of war to take chances."

Martin Carlson, Plant, Omaha, runner with 355th Infantry, 89th Division: "That day would have been the end of us, for we were to cross the Meuse, and judging by the German machine gun nests and their strong position which we later inspected, I don't see how one of us would have lived. We had taken Stenay the night before. To us the armistice meant just one thing — life."

F. O. Caldwell, Plant, Sioux Falls: "We were at Napoleon's barracks, Brest, building more barracks when we heard all the French yelling their heads off, but we did not know what it was all about until afternoon. That evening some of us went AWOL."

T. J. Bolger, Plant, Fargo, 423rd Telegraph Battalion: "The bells of Winchester Abbey in England told us that something had happened, as we marched past. That night we sailed for France, nevertheless."

H. P. Bertelson, Commercial, Fargo, 30th Service Company, Signal Corps: "Aching feet is my recollection, for we paraded from 137th St., to 76th St. and then back again, in New York."

E. E. Greeling, Commercial, Minneapolis, *USS Gulfmaid:* "I was on watch in the lookout station searching for that telltale periscope which marked the presence of a U-boat. One of the prettiest sights was soon after when a ship passed fully lighted."

Two of the former Cats on Wheat, John McAlpin, left, and Tennis Coash, display the standard of the 408th Battalion. Both were linemen, but McAlpin also ran the company office, while Coash was a cook. Coash retired from Northwestern Bell in 1956 and McAlpin in 1957.

The Flivver

A Company vehicle in operation in Waverly, Iowa, in 1924 might have been the forerunner of today's economy car. The flivver, as telephone men called it, had the best service and repair record of all motor equipment owned by the Company. Yet it was nearly four years old.

The Ford delivery car traveled 18 miles on a gallon of gasoline, while most automobiles of this type averaged only 12 miles. And it was just as easy on tires as it was on gas — "rubber" costs were about half those for other vehicles.

Although the flivver had been driven 36,000 miles, its motor had never been overhauled and was still in good condition. W. J. Dempsey took good care of the car, and repairs were few and far between. As one writer put it, "the bolt in time saved nine."

Chapter XIII

The telephone grows up

Calling London, talking to crowds

and sending pictures

become realities

THEY CALLED THEM THE ROARING TWENTIES, and, for the most part, they were good years for Northwestern Bell. But they began on a somber note. Theodore Vail died April 16, 1920, and Casper Yost died Nov. 22, six weeks before the Northwestern Group of Companies officially became Northwestern Bell Telephone Company.

That merger was something that Yost had worked toward for more than a decade. There had been a common link among the companies ever since he had become president of the Northwestern Telephone Exchange Company in 1907. At that time he was already president of the Iowa and Nebraska companies.

Yost stepped aside May 1, 1919, when W. B. T. Belt became president of the Northwestern Group. Yost's health wasn't good, but it was hoped that as chairman of the board, he'd live to see the birth of Northwestern Bell.

Louis Korty died next, in May of 1921. Of the four men from Northwestern territory who'd been in Philadelphia to see Professor Bell demonstrate his telephone in 1876, Korty was the only one to stay in the telephone business into the '20s. He was secretary-treasurer of the Nebraska Company until 1899, and remained a director and executive committee member until February 1920.

After all the years of struggle and consolidation, the final merger that created Northwestern Bell was almost an anticlimax. On Dec. 10, 1920, the Iowa Company changed its name to Northwestern Bell Telephone Company. And on Jan. 1, 1921, the Nebraska and Northwestern Exchange companies were merged into the new company, which remained an Iowa corporation. However, since Chairman Yost, President Belt and the General Office staff were all operating out of Omaha when the decisions were made, Omaha remained the corporate headquarters.

Actually, the main change was that bookkeeping, billing and accounting would be simpler with just one company. Otherwise, things went on much the same. *Northwestern Bell* magazine had already been publishing monthly for a year. With tongue in cheek, the editor suggested that the new company was called Northwestern Bell so the magazine's name would not have to be changed.

A sense of humor was a handy thing to have at the time. Telephone supplies and equipment were more scarce in 1920 than they had been any time during the war. Telephone people were collecting bits of rope that could be sent in to make insulation for cable. Out-of-style telephones were being installed for lack of newer models.

Even tools were hard to get. In the spring of 1920, the Iowa Plant had had pliers on order for a full year and needed at least 144. Whenever Western Electric got a shipment of tools, a few were doled out to each operating company. Poles might arrive anywhere from 30 days to six months after they had been shipped.

Of course, not everything was so frustrating. Omaha employees had been in their brand-new headquarters building* since early in 1919 and plans were under way to install a large machine-switching (dial) central office there. When the Atlantic office was converted to dial Dec. 10, 1921, Omaha became the first city to have the Bell System's newly developed panel switching equipment.

---

*Located on the northwest corner of 19th and Douglas, this building was the first segment of "The Block that Talk Built." These buildings now house Omaha District, Nebraska Area and General Headquarters offices.

Northwestern Group headquarters building under construction at 19th and Douglas, Omaha, 1918

Because this was the world's first cutover to panel, the engineers took it in easy stages. After the ATlantic cut, the new JAckson office was put in service gradually throughout 1922. By November, the old Tyler and Douglas manual offices were shut down and the exchange names honorably retired. By then, almost half of Omaha's 56,000 phones were dial.

Having the first panel equipment wasn't Northwestern's only first in 1921. A new high-speed style of long distance service got its start at Altoona, Iowa, that year. The secret was simplicity itself: keep the customer on the line while putting the call through. Previously, long distance operators took down the information necessary to make a call, then called the customer back when they had the distant party on the line.*

Originally, this made sense. Long distance calls often had to be plugged through various intermediate points. Frequently this involved delays.

But as long distance service became more dependable and direct circuits were available to many cities, calls were going through faster. That was the situation when W. F. Cozad, general traffic superintendent, and G. A. Drew, Iowa division traffic superintendent, visited the Altoona office where Kittie Jeffers was chief operator.

Some versions of what happened say Miss Jeffers first suggested keeping the customer on the line. Others say it was Cozad. Either way, Kittie Jeffers was encouraged to experiment with the idea. It worked so well, the idea spread. And studies showed that customers started talking in about 1½ minutes compared to the eight-minute interval previously considered good service.

By 1923 the procedure was being pushed throughout Northwestern Bell. And, of course, it had been given a telephonese acronym: CLR (for "combined line and recording"). Wherever it was tried, customers were both astonished and delighted. By 1926 the Bell System was recommending the method to all companies.

While Traffic people were pioneering new methods, Plant forces were fighting old enemies. Repairs from sleet storms in February and March of 1922 had not yet been completed when a surprise storm hit in April. Damage, which totaled $1 million, was concentrated in Nebraska from Holdrege to South Sioux City. But it included parts of Iowa, Minnesota and South Dakota.

The million-dollar price tag for that storm was double the amount the Company had been spending per year on storm repairs. Some 22,000 poles were down, most snapped off at the base. The damage was so heavy and

---

*In large city offices, the process was even more specialized. "Recording" operators made out the call tickets; more experienced "line" operators put the calls through. Sometimes elaborate mechanical systems carried the tickets to the line operators.

The covers of the first two editions of *The Northwestern Bell* magazine featured "The Spirit of Service" and Casper E. Yost.

the area so large, that telephone officials had to deploy crews and map strategy like generals planning a battle.

Supplies in Western Electric's Omaha warehouse were soon exhausted, and 13 carloads of materials were hurriedly dispatched from Kansas City, Chicago and other cities. The transcontinental long distance circuits were back in service within four days, and most other lines had been restored within three weeks.

Also during the early 1920s, the Bell System introduced public address systems. It was a logical telephone by-product. The principal parts were a high-energy telephone transmitter (the microphone), a scaled-up version of the "repeater" units developed to boost the strength of telephone signals on long distance circuits (the amplifier) and an overgrown telephone receiver that could boom out huge volumes of sound (the loudspeaker).

The most dramatic of the early demonstrations was when 125,000 people heard President Harding's inaugural address March 4, 1921. In September of 1922, 25,000 heard Vice President Coolidge speak at the Minnesota State Fair. William Jennings Bryan spoke to 20,000 at a convention in Des Moines, in July of 1923.

But where 125,000 heard Harding's inauguration in 1921, something like 20 million heard Coolidge take office four years later, by means of a Bell System network radio broadcast. WHO in Des Moines and WCCO in Minneapolis were two of the 21 stations that received the program via AT&T Long Lines circuits.

Bell scientists had been experimenting with vacuum tube amplifiers and radio broadcasting almost from the time the vacuum tube was invented in 1906 by Lee De Forest, a Council Bluffs, Iowa, native. Western Electric held basic patents on broadcasting equipment and was selling radio transmitters. In 1922 AT&T began operating station WEAF in New York to learn more about broadcasting and how it would affect the industry.

In the next few years, WEAF and the Bell System pioneered network broadcasting and the concept of commercially sponsored programs. But by 1926, Bell officials had decided that entertainment broadcasting was too far removed from the company's role as a common carrier. WEAF was sold to RCA for $1 million, and thus began the National Broadcasting Company.

WEAF's network stations, including WOC in Davenport, Iowa, and WCCO in Minneapolis, were the original Red Network. Stations previously operated by RCA, General Electric and Westinghouse were soon connected by

Williams Jennings Bryan, left, nearest camera, listens to brother Charles using the new public address system at Des Moines.

other Bell System circuits to form the Blue Network. The names came from the original circuit map drawn by Long Lines engineers. WEAF's affiliate stations were connected with red pencil lines. The new network was drawn in with blue pencil.

Other milestones in the early 1920s: Northwestern Bell joined in the nationwide moment of silence honoring Alexander Graham Bell's memory. Bell died Aug. 2, 1922, and on Aug. 4, telephone service throughout the country was suspended between 6:25 and 6:26 p.m., the only time the entire network has ever been shut down. Another pioneer, J. L. W. Zietlow, founder of the Dakota Central Company, died Nov. 14, 1922.

Northwestern Bell was becoming increasingly safety conscious as the 1920s began. Plant first aid courses were offered in Minneapolis, Omaha and Des Moines and there were more volunteers than openings. The 37 Minneapolis men who graduated March 29, 1921, were the first to complete a Northwestern course conducted with the Red Cross. *NWB* magazine had a whole how-to-do-it page on artificial respiration in 1922.

Because of the derring-do flavor of the business in the early days, old-time linemen were particularly scornful of such things as safety straps which they felt "tied them to the pole." In the early days, it wasn't unheard of for a rotten pole to break when a man climbed it. He was better off if he could jump clear. But by the 1890s, when more and more telephone lines were near the new electric power lines, the threat of electric shock created a more urgent reason for using straps. A shock could knock a man backwards before he knew what had happened.

Although safety straps were coming into use around the turn of the century, they weren't required by Company policy until around 1925. And then some of the old-timers wouldn't go along. D. J. Hegarty recalled that his father, Mike, retired in 1928 with 48 years' service and he'd never worn a safety strap.

But with safety consciousness growing, the Company decided to ask the Plant men themselves to help write a safety code in 1924. At the local level, rules were suggested and discussed. Delegates then took the suggestions to division meetings and finally, division representatives met and hashed out the Company-wide version.

The proper way to crank a motor vehicle, as shown in a 1924 Northwestern Bell safety manual, was to keep the thumb alongside the crank. This allowed the crank to slip easily from the hand if the motor backfired. When the crank was gripped too firmly, a backfire could spin the crank in the opposite direction and could inflict an injury ranging from a skinned finger to a broken arm.

A number of other safety methods were explained in the booklet and illustrated with photographs. Although the clothing of the men in the pictures is now out of style, many of the practices are still valid.

In 1923 *NWB* magazine passed along the information that the United States, with only six per cent of the world's population, had 64 per cent of its telephones. And Iowa, with 21.7 phones per 100 population, had the highest telephone development in the world. In comparison, Northwestern Bell states had 18.9 phones per 100 population and the United States figure was only 13.1 per 100. Iowa had more phones than Italy, Belgium, Austria and Switzerland combined. This apparently continued the pattern started in the earliest years when Iowa had more exchanges than the other states combined.

But less than half were Bell phones. In Iowa, the ratio was 186,000 Bell to 350,000 independent. For the five states, it was 543,000 Bell, 880,000 independent.*

In May of 1926, Northwestern's first carrier equipment was installed on the long distance line between Minneapolis and Hibbing, Minn., via Duluth. This made it possible to send four simultaneous conversations over a single pair of wires. Each conversation was sent on its own "carrier" frequency. Three radio-like units at each end were tuned so that each one would receive only one of the conversations. The fourth conversation traveled along the circuit in the normal way. At distances of more than 250 miles, installing carrier equipment was cheaper than stringing additional wires.

At the beginning of 1927, Northwestern was able to complete the merger of the Sioux City Telephone Company and its 17,000 dial phones into NWB. Also in 1927, 7,500 phones of Minneapolis' HYland exchange were converted to dial. With some 3,000 DUpont phones cut the previous year, and the 28,000-phone ATlantic and MAin cutover in 1928, Minneapolis had a total of nearly 75,000 dial phones and Tri-State had another 20,000 in St. Paul.

President Coolidge's decision to establish his 1927 summer White House at the Game Lodge in Custer State Park, S.D., catapulted Northwestern Bell into a crash construction program. Facilities which telephone engineers had originally planned to install over a five-year period had to be rushed to completion in weeks. To get things

---

*At the beginning of 1975, there were 4,790,000 Bell-operated phones in the five states and 1,740,000 independent.

The Hegarty saga:
Five generations with NWB

In 1879 three years after Bell's telephone transmitted its first coherent sentence, a 16-year-old Irish boy named Michael C. Hegarty arrived in America, looking for a job. The one that he found really started something for Northwestern Bell.

Hegarty, an adventurous youngster, left home when he was 11. By the time he came to the United States, he'd been in many foreign countries. His first job in America was working as a construction man for a telegraph company. Linemen were in great demand then, and they jumped from job to job. Hegarty soon found himself traveling throughout the East and South. Like most other linemen, he went by train. "A pair of hooks was a pass on any railroad," he later recalled. "A lineman could ride any train and go anywhere he wanted."

In the course of his traveling, Hegarty came to Dubuque, Iowa. When the telegraph crew he was with ran out of supplies, Hegarty joined the town's newly organized telephone company.

After working for several Bell companies, Hegarty moved to Omaha in 1889. He stayed in Omaha the rest of his life, and was a vital force in the town's telephone expansion. For 10 years he was on double duty — running a construction crew in the day and answering fire calls at night. (When a call came in, he would jump out of his bed at the telephone office, rush to the scene of the fire, and disconnect telephone wires so firemen could work safely.) Hegarty helped build one of Omaha's early day switchboards and had a part in stringing the first metallic circuit to Nebraska City.

Mike Hegarty gave the telephone business something else, too — his family. All five of his children went into telephone work. In succeeding generations, 14 more Hegartys entered the business. Seven of them still work for NWB. Altogether, the five generations of Hegartys have over 400 years of service.

When old Mike retired in 1928 with 48 years of service, the second generation was well entrenched in the business. But he was confident that tradition would be carried on. To him, telephones and Hegartys were inseparable.

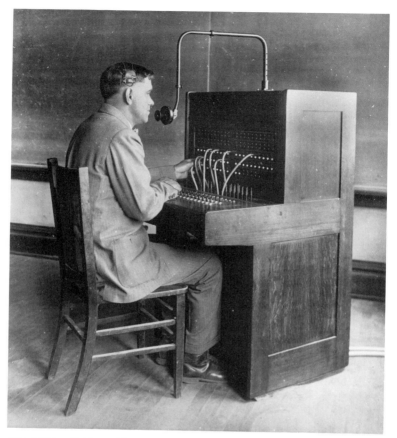

The PBX switchboard installed for President Coolidge

rolling, the engineers worked around the clock to get an estimate ready.

By the time the President arrived, a PBX had been set up in the temporary presidential offices in the Rapid City High School. Extensive carrier and repeater equipment had been installed not only in the Rapid City exchange but also at Sidney, Nebr., on the cross-country cable. One of the toughest parts of the job was to build a new line from Custer to the Game Lodge, more than 15 miles through rugged terrain. This provided reliable modern circuitry between the Lodge and the presidential offices 32 miles away in Rapid City. In addition, experienced operators were brought to Rapid City from nearby states to help handle the extra calling load.

The story has two happy endings. The new telephone system performed flawlessly, meeting every demand the presidential party placed on it. And the President's visit stimulated so much tourist interest in the Black Hills that soon the extra facilities were fully utilized. Mt. Coolidge Lookout and Grace Coolidge Creek are two momentos that today's Black Hills tourist will find.

Northwestern Bell was a part of two other notable events of 1927. Early in the year, the Bell System's third transcontinental line was opened. Minneapolis, Fargo, Bismarck and Dickinson were on this northern route. The middle route already passed through Davenport, Des Moines, Omaha and North Platte.

Then on Feb. 19, 1927, NWB President Belt placed the first transatlantic call ever made from the Upper Midwest. In a ceremony opening commercial radiotelephone service to England, he talked with Col. Herbert E. Shreeve, a Bell engineer who had been involved in transatlantic radio experiments ever since the first successful

The Northern Transcontinental long distance line, St. Cloud, Minn., 1927

NWB President Belt placed the first transatlantic call from the Midwest.

transmission in 1915.* After Belt's call from Omaha to London, three other commercial calls were completed from Northwestern Bell territory to England that day. (The three-minute rate was $27.)

The year 1927 was also the first time the handset, or "French" phone, was available in the Bell System. This combination of receiver and transmitter proved far more popular than anticipated. NWB expected orders for 3,000 the first year, but wound up installing 10,000.

And 1927 was the year AT&T decided to sell its telephones to the associated companies. Previously, the phones had remained AT&T property. With this decision, which Casper Yost had urged 29 years earlier, the American Company also announced the license contract fee would be cut from four per cent to two per cent of an associated company's gross revenue. It was reduced to 1½ per cent the next year.

A new Northwestern Bell service order plan went into effect in 1927. This was the first time Business Office

---

*In fact, the first words heard across the Atlantic, on Oct. 15, 1915, were "Hello, Shreeve. Hello, Shreeve," spoken by another Bell engineer, B. B. Webb. The Navy's transmitting tower at Arlington, Va., was used on this side, the European antenna was on Paris' Eiffel Tower.

procedures had been standardized in a Company-wide practice. More important, this was the first service order plan backed up by an interdepartmental practice. Plant and Commercial teams worked six months developing it. Newly developed AT&T recommendations were the guide.

In 1928 the growth of Northwestern Bell led to a new organizational plan. The four divisions — Iowa, Minnesota, Nebraska-South Dakota and North Dakota — were renamed "areas" with a general manager for each.

In Omaha, A. A. Lowman's title was changed from vice president and general manager to vice president in charge of operations. The four new general managers reporting to him were H. G. Conger, Iowa; Frank Bracelin, Minnesota; W. F. Cozad, Nebraska-South Dakota; and L. D. Richardson, North Dakota. The division superintendents for the operating departments became "managers," and instead of reporting to department heads in Omaha, they now reported to area general managers. Harry I. Dodson was appointed assistant vice president in charge of Lowman's staff of operations supervisors.

Late in 1928, the Bell System's main long distance cable route reached Davenport. This gave the eastern edge of Northwestern Bell territory direct cable access to Chicago, St. Louis, New York and other eastern points.

Interstate long distance rates were reduced in 1926, 1927 and 1929. By 1929 long distance traffic had grown so much the Bell System was designing a nationwide network. While most telephones in the United States could be interconnected, some had to go through so many intermediate points that people had trouble hearing.

Under the network plan, there were to be eight regional switching centers which would be fully interconnected with each other. Within the regions, there were to be primary outlets. Each of these would have long distance circuits to smaller communities in its area, plus outward connections to one or more of the regional centers. Primary centers for Northwestern were Des Moines, Davenport, Waterloo, Mason City and Sioux City in Iowa; Minneapolis and Duluth in Minnesota; Omaha, Grand Island, Sidney, Rapid City, Aberdeen and Sioux Falls in the Nebraska-South Dakota Area; and Fargo, Bismarck and Minot in North Dakota.

In October of 1929, 1,200 Telephone Pioneers from all parts of the United States and Canada came to Minneapolis for the first Pioneer General Assembly held in Northwestern territory. This was just seven years after Northwestern's three Pioneer chapters — Hawkeye, Casper E. Yost and C. P. Wainman — had been chartered. Prior to 1922, there had been only a national Pioneer organization.

Late in the year, the Minnesota Area adopted a rotation billing plan and also started using machines to prepare customer bills. Previously, amounts due had been entered by hand. Under the rotation plan, customers received their bills at different times during the month. This spread the work more evenly, and the Nebraska-South Dakota Area adopted the plan the next year.

Color television was demonstrated at Bell Labs in 1929. Herbert Hoover, while secretary of commerce, had helped the Labs demonstrate black and white TV two years earlier. In Connecticut, operator dialing of long distance calls was being tested between Hartford and Man-

First long distance TV transmissions by wire. Secretary Hoover's voice and image were sent from Washington, D.C., to New York City, April 1927.

Walter Gifford

"The best possible service"

Bell System policy is "to furnish the best possible telephone service at the lowest cost consistent with financial safety," AT&T President Walter S. Gifford told National Association of Railroad and Utilities Commissioners at their convention in Dallas, October 1927.

The statement was widely quoted at the time and Bell System leaders still say it is the yardstick against which today's decisions are measured. Following are excerpts from Gifford's talk:

"The fact that ownership [of AT&T stock] is widespread and diffused imposes an unusual obligation on management to see to it that the savings of these hundreds of thousands of people are secure and remain so.

"The fact that the responsibility for such a large part of the entire telephone service of the country rests solely upon this Company and its Associated Companies also imposes on the management an unusual obligation to the public to see to it that the service shall at all times be adequate, dependable and satisfactory to the user.

"Obviously, the only sound policy that will meet these obligations is to continue to furnish the best possible telephone service at the lowest cost consistent with financial safety ... This policy is bound to succeed in the long run and there is no justification for acting otherwise than for the long run.

"Earnings must be sufficient to assure the best possible telephone service at all times and to assure the continued financial integrity of the business ... The margin of safety in earnings is only a small percentage of the rate charged for service, ... it is essential that this margin be kept adequate. Cutting it too close can only result in the long run in deterioration of service ..."

chester. And Northwestern people were pushing a new concept for builders — concealed telephone wiring.

When the decade started, NWB had 413,000 telephones in service. During the 10 years, 214,000 had been added to make a total of 627,000. Almost 24 per cent were dial, compared to less than five per cent on Jan. 1, 1920. The conversion of 30,000 Des Moines phones to dial in July of 1929 gave the total a big boost. In addition, 900 phones at Hopkins, Minn., and almost 500 at South Sioux City, Nebr., were converted to dial in 1929.

Theodore Vail's goal of universal service had almost become a reality in NWB territory. Of the 865,000 phones operated by independents at the end of 1929, 99.5 per cent were connected to Bell lines. In 1915 it had been only about 85 per cent.

As the decade closed out, Des Moines telephone people had been in their new 10-story headquarters building for months. In Omaha, a 1929 addition to the headquarters building changed it from an L-shape to a U-shape. And plans were well along for a 24-story building in downtown Minneapolis to house equipment and offices. Times had been good in the 1920s. Few could foresee how bad the next few years were going to be.

A 1926 version of the snowmobile was used by Foreman George Gleason and his crew during restoration of storm damage north of Minneapolis.

Ice and Fire,
Fire and Ice

Dial conversions, "no delay" long distance service, overseas calling, new buildings and a new system of management organization — these were among the highlights of the 1920s. But as always, the real telephone story was a story of people. Again and again, Northwestern employees showed their bravery, determination, ingenuity and sense of humor as they provided service, no matter what.

• After a 48-hour blizzard in Duluth, Minn., operators plowed through 20-foot drifts to get to work. Several came on skis. With snow blocking doors and windows on the first floor, Esther Swedberg climbed out a second-story window and slid down a drift so she could head for the telephone office.

• When golf ball-size hail shattered skylights over the Rapid City, S.D., switchboard and drove the operators out, Manager T. J. Bolger and Combinationman H. T. Hill dragged a canvas over the board, crawled under with flashlights and answered calls.

• Construction men cut through ice 30 inches thick on the St. Louis River between Duluth, Minn., and Superior, Wis., to bring up a faulty cable in 1925. They started at the river bank and worked their way out, laying the cable on the ice. They found the trouble exactly where Tester A. M. Koefod had said it would be. The damaged section was cut out and the ends spliced back together. But then the cable was too short to go back through the opening. The men had to cut a new, straighter slot in the ice so the cable could be lowered back to the river bottom.

• A rash of fires gave operators a bad time in 1926. In March, dense smoke from a department store fire filled the operating room at Fort Madison, Iowa, for six hours. Operators tied wet cloths over their faces but could stand the smoke only a few minutes at a time. All operators were called in and they worked 15-minute shifts. A doctor opened his office on the other side of the building and gave the women eye wash and other first aid while they were off duty.

• In December, the smell of smoke awakened Carrie Wahl, Company agent at McClusky, N.D., and her relief operator, Clara Redlinger. They called firemen, warned a nearby hotel of the danger and were then driven out by smoke. After getting their breath, they went back in to save Company records, the cash drawer and furniture. While firemen brought the blaze under control, Combinationmen M. K. Rauk and William Baillie covered the switchboard with blankets and kept most of it from getting wet. But the main frame and much of the building's interior were coated with ice in the 28 below zero temperature. The two combinationmen patched a hole burned in the roof, built a fire in the stove to thaw things out, and worked all night to get the exchange back in service by 8 a.m.

• William Mockel, a combinationman at Williston, N.D., had a long hike in January of 1925. The testboard showed a break on the Minot circuit, east of White Earth, so Mockel shouldered his equipment and caught an eastbound freight train. When it slowed down at White Earth, Mockel jumped from the caboose into a snowbank. He found the break a couple of miles on further east.

By 6:30 p.m., when he had the trouble cleared, it was snowing again and the wind was coming out of the west so fiercely that Mockel couldn't walk into it. So he told the Williston testboardman he'd keep walking east to a box car siding called Manitou. If he couldn't hole up there, he'd walk on to Ross, about eight miles away.

As he slogged on, the dark got darker and the snow came harder. He kept straining to see lights, but couldn't. When it got to be midnight, Mockel knew he'd missed both Manitou and Ross in the storm. He quit looking at his watch and started telling himself that as long as he was walking, he was still alive.

At 3:30 a.m., he finally staggered into the station at Stanley. The dumbfounded stationmaster stared at him and blurted, "My God, man, where'd you come from?" When Mockel told him he had walked from White Earth, the man said: "That's nearly 20 miles from here! In that blizzard? You should have been dead hours ago!"

Mockel called his boss, who'd been pacing the floor, and told him what had happened. When the 4 a.m. train to Williston pulled into Stanley, Mockel collapsed into a seat and fell asleep immediately.

He got back at 8 a.m., just in time to report for work.

Chapter XIV

First the Depression, then another war

A test of strength for Americans and the telephone business

THE ONE EVENT that most dominated American life in the early 1930s happened 64 days before the decade actually began. The bottom dropped out of the stock market Oct. 29, 1929. By the end of the year, stocks were worth $15 billion less to their owners than they had been on Oct. 28. The Great Depression was under way.

But the full impact didn't hit the Upper Midwest right away. Businessmen expected difficulties, not disaster. In his New Year's message, NWB President Belt sounded an optimistic note and urged employees to give customers top quality service — the kind that would convince them they had to have a telephone even when times were bad.

Belt's positive words reflected the Bell System's philosophy in the face of national financial calamity. As it turned out, 1930 wasn't a bad year for NWB.

During the year, ground was broken in downtown Minneapolis for a $3 million, 24-story telephone building. NWBers in Rapid City, S.D., also moved into a new building. While Bell Labs was impressing New Yorkers with a two-way television, operators at the new Minneapolis long distance switchboard were trying out a pneumatic tube that distributed their call tickets.

Minneapolis telephone building under construction, 1930

But none of these signs of progress in 1930 could hide the fact that Northwestern Bell was in for tough times. While the 1930 Annual Report was encouraging, Belt's year-end words held some warnings, too. Additions to plant and equipment cost about $16 million, highest in the Company's history. A net gain of 16,000 phones included 5,500 added as a result of completion of the merger of the Marshall Telephone Company at Marshalltown, Iowa, into NWB. Belt's appraisal: NWB's territory suffered less than most of the country but a "slowing up of business" had come.

It was just the beginning. During the next three years, nearly 110,000 Northwestern telephones were taken out of service, almost one of every five. The Company lost one-third of its long distance traffic.

NWB had to put a new emphasis on sales efforts that could result in new business.

This was reflected in the Company's first off-the-job training courses for Commercial employees, held in Nebraska and South Dakota. *NWB* magazine began to carry an increasing number of stories on how employees could increase sales. The Minnesota Area began mailing ads directly to customers.

By this time, employee associations had sprung up in a number of cities in NWB territory. (Some, in fact, had been in operation as early as 1918.) Most were loosely knit social groups, organized by departments and with the help of management. Still, they served as a good meeting ground for the Company and its people.

During these depression years, Upper Midwesterners were plagued with floods, heat and drought. Farmers were especially hard-hit. In North Dakota, a rural "work-for-credit" plan got under way in 1934. Farmers helped repair telephone lines, and the money earned was credited to their bills. The plan helped farmers, and it also kept rural telephone plant in service for better years.

Northwestern Bell's construction program helped others throughout the territory. Where it could, the Company tried to go on with scheduled improvements, betting that the new facilities would be needed when better days returned. And the pay checks from these jobs were a lifesaver to a lot of families. At Davenport, Iowa, for example, a $1 million NWB improvement program provided jobs for over 125 persons for nine months in 1935.

In 1933 owners of the Tri-State Telephone and Telegraph Company wanted to sell to Northwestern Bell. The transfer was made after the Interstate Commerce Commission approved the sale. The purchase included the Tri-State subsidiary, the Dakota Central Company.*

At the time, Tri-State and Dakota Central were operating 167 exchanges, including St. Paul. Northwestern officials believed that if they could coordinate planning for the entire Twin Cities area, they could save money and provide better service, too. They anticipated similar benefits from consolidation of the long distance plant.

President Belt and his officers added the Tri-State and

---

*Chapter VI tells the Dakota Central story; Chapter X is devoted to Tri-State.

Dakota Central operations to their other responsibilities. But the consolidation itself was worked out gradually over several years. However, one immediate result was the addition of 2,500 new employees.

Meanwhile, the push was on to bring together employee associations and make them more than just social groups. Finally, in 1934, Plant, Traffic, Commercial and Accounting people formed Company-wide organizations. Each association had its own constitution and by-laws and negotiated an agreement with the Company. NWB no longer participated in their activities but still provided financial help. A year later, with the advent of the National Labor Relations Act,* the groups would start charging dues and be completely on their own. For employees, it meant the start of real unionizing.

Also in 1934, President Belt told employees that sales and public relations efforts were paying off. "I believe," said Belt, "there are signs pointing to better times."

In the first half of the year, the Company did gain 12,000 phones and employees initiated half of those sales. Still, it wasn't easy. To gain that 12,000, installers had to put in 65,000 phones. (The other 53,000 were moves rather than new customers.) The year-end gain was 18,000.

Company officers, however, recognized that with a strong push on sales, there had to be an increased concern for the customer's point of view. In 1933 public relations committees were set up in each area "to help employees of all departments gain and maintain the good will and cooperation of customers." Also in 1933, service representatives began using standardized memos in their customer contacts to evaluate "how customers felt about all phases of their telephone service, and how they reacted to the Company and its employees."

But factors like the weather continued to cause setbacks. In the summer of 1935, great dust storms affected service in Nebraska. The winter brought a blizzard to Minnesota and the Dakotas which dropped temperatures

---

*The National Labor Relations Act, commonly known as the Wagner Act, granted employees of a company the right to organize and bargain collectively without interference from their employer. Among other things, it made it illegal for companies to provide any kind of financial assistance to employee groups.

to 56 degrees below zero, piled 20-foot snow drifts and took 10 lives in North Dakota alone. Although one of the worst storms in the Midwest's history, the blizzard did less telephone damage than an earlier 1932 North Dakota sleet storm that left 199 towns isolated from long distance service and wrecked 12,000 poles.

During 1934, President Franklin D. Roosevelt approved the Communications Act, bringing interstate telephone business under regulation of the Federal Communications Commission instead of the Interstate Commerce Commission. One of NWB's first contacts with the FCC was filing new tariffs for a night and Sunday discount period on station-to-station interstate calls.

On the day the tariffs were filed — Dec. 16, 1935 — Arthur A. Lowman was named president of Northwestern Bell and Horace G. Conger became operations vice president. W. B. T. Belt, who had guided the Company through some of the most crucial years of its history, became chairman of the board and retired the next year after nearly 48 years of service — 16 as president.

That same year, Omaha service representatives began using desks instead of counters to visit with customers about telephone needs. The year 1935 also saw

Omaha public office, 1935

the nation beginning to struggle out of the depression. Total wages and salaries were up, even farm income improved substantially. And Northwestern Bell ended the year with a gain of more than 20,000 phones. The gains continued in subsequent years, slowly and steadily for the most part, but with an occasional dramatic surge. In Minneapolis, installers worked 5,353 service orders during a 13-day period in September 1937. However, not until mid-1939 did Northwestern have as many phones in service as it had on Dec. 31, 1930.*

With the gradual economic recovery, Northwestern Bell's construction program perked up. The Company started the decade with 24 per cent of its phones dial and ended with almost 49 per cent. With Tri-State and Dakota Central phones included, the figure was 52 per cent dial at the end of 1939.

From 1936 through 1939, 148 offices were converted to step-by-step dial and six others got panel dial equipment. But the really big conversion year was 1940, with 110 new step-by-step offices (106 conversions, four new offices). The following year, 57 more were added.

The late '30s also saw a push towards a national organization of telephone labor groups. At least one Northwestern Bell association joined the bandwagon, sending representatives to a national convention in St. Louis in 1937. By June of 1939, a constitution had been formally adopted for the National Federation of Telephone Workers.

In 1938 Northwestern's name became well-known even in New England. The Company sent nearly 200 Plant men to Keene, N. H., to help New England Telephone repair damage caused by a hurricane. It took a freight train to haul trucks, tools and men to the area. Here's how a *Keene Sentinel* story read Nov. 11, the day after the men left: "Approximately 200 telephonic Lochinvars from the West have come and gone — leaving behind them in Keene and surrounding towns a host of new friends (and, in some cases, new sweethearts of Yankeeland).

---

*Figures here and in previous paragraphs do not include Tri-State and Dakota Central phones acquired in the 1933 purchase.

Loading equipment at Council Bluffs, Iowa, for the trip to Keene, N.H.

"Final impression which the telephone men from Minnesota, South Dakota, Iowa and Nebraska got from Keene was a mass expression of gratitude and good-fellowship in a spontaneous turnout of between two and three thousand persons, headed by the American Legion drum corps, who thronged the station platform."

In 1940 NWB customers were introduced to a phone equipped with six buttons that would permit easy pick-up and transfer of calls.

With the beginning of the 1940s, Northwestern Plant men could feel they were making headway against their traditional enemies — sleet and wind. The Bell System was laying twin underground telephone cables from Omaha to Sacramento, Calif. Storm protection was a side benefit; the main motive was national defense. Under way in early 1941, the 1,600-mile cable project cost $20 million.

Europe had been aflame with World War II since 1939. France had fallen in 1940. England was desperately embattled. The United States was struggling to avoid being drawn into the war but the President and the Congress were agreed that the country had to be prepared.

This was the atmosphere when NWB was called on to provide telephone facilities for companies with defense contracts at Burlington, Iowa (a shell-loading plant), and the Martin Bomber Assembly Plant near Omaha. Telephone facilities to accommodate 5,000 men had already been provided at Ft. Meade, S.D.

Uniformed watchmen were standing guard at NWB's headquarters building in Omaha; Nebraska State Highway Patrolmen were watching telephone lines for sabotage attempts. By May 1941, NWB had coordinators for Army and defense projects. The Company was giving four Army Signal Corps wire chiefs a 200-hour special training course and a popular pastime among NWB's women was knitting garments for "Bundles for Britain" and the Red Cross.

On Dec. 8, 1941, the day after the attack on Pearl Harbor, long distance calls rocketed 50 per cent above normal in some NWB-served cities. Company newspaper ads that month urged customers to curtail personal long distance calling — especially around Christmas — because of heavy military demands on circuits. This would be the main theme for the war years.

Long distance calling and extension service had been promoted vigorously in the late 1930s. Now the Company had to apply the brakes and head in the other direction.

High demands from the military were accompanied by acute shortages of materials for telephone lines and equipment. There were, too, substantial increases in taxes and other telephone expenses. A special excise tax on telephone service — an "emergency war measure" — was one of the added burdens. In 1941 NWB earnings per share dropped to $5.64 from $6.41 in 1939. Telephone revenues during the same two-year period were up 9.37 per cent, while telephone expenses and taxes were up 12.15 per cent. War caused an unprecedented demand for service, but NWB's earnings were suffering.

Among developments not related to the war, representatives of the four Northwestern Bell employee associations met in the fall of '41 and established the Northwestern Union of Telephone Workers, the first Company-wide, interdepartmental union. In December, it was recognized as the official bargaining representative of all non-supervisory employees. From then on, it was in close contact with the National Federation of Telephone Workers and sent delegates to all of the national conventions. By February of 1942, the new union had signed its first contract and agreement with Northwestern Bell.

During the summer of 1942, the Tri-State and Dakota Central properties were fully consolidated and formally merged with NWB. In July, there was a reduction in long distance rates — the 10th in 15 years; experimental use of a "leave-word" service for dial telephone users began in Cedar Rapids, Iowa — for a small charge, operators answered and took messages for customers who were away.

Starting March 3, 1942, wall or desk-type upright phones could no longer be replaced with hand telephones; after Labor Day, residence extensions couldn't be installed at all. In some towns, party lines were the only kind of service available for new customers and those who moved. Replacements and improvements in facilities were deferred. These were among the restrictions imposed by government's General Conservation Orders. A later order limited the telephone industry's use of critical war materials and stringently limited how existing stocks of telephones and equipment could be used.

Telephone materials weren't the only scarce items. Meat, canned goods, sugar, butter, shoes and gasoline were all rationed. Cigarettes and many other articles were hard to get. Community-wide drives were held to collect scrap metal. Tin cans and old razor blades were recycled.

The telephone center at the Sioux City army air base handled personal calls for service men.

In NWB territory, there were 44 new military or government establishments in operation by mid-1942. All needed telephone facilities, many on a rush basis.

Meanwhile, telephone people were helping in their spare time, too. In the summer of 1942, the newly organized Women's Army Auxiliary Corps set up its headquarters at Ft. Des Moines, Iowa. Hester Peters, an NWB personnel assistant from Omaha, assisted in the selection of candidates seeking WAC commissions. By the end of 1942, Northwestern had instructed nearly 100 Signal Corps men in telephone and teletypewriter work.

Early in the war, 86 Plant men volunteered for the Signal Corps. Eventually, more than 1,550 Northwestern Bell men and women served in the Armed Forces. Twenty-four didn't make it home.*

There were big jobs for employees at home, too. NWBers were cautioned to keep military secrets because, as one poster warned, *"Loose Lips Sink Ships."* Employees cooperated with the security program and also helped conserve scarce materials. Uncle Sam wanted "10 per cent of our pay for War Savings Bonds." Thousands of NWBers responded to the plea: during the first three years following Pearl Harbor, they bought bonds worth $8 million at maturity.

NWBers collected books for the USO, and boxes of goodies were sent to servicemen. NWB women attendants at military camp telephone centers doubled as train-meeters, bridesmaids and apartment-finders. Telephone women were nurses' and dietitians' aides, Gray Ladies and bandage-rollers. In Minneapolis, Northwestern

---

*The 24 Northwestern Bell employees who died while in military service were: Richard C. Cherry, Valentine, Nebr.; John F. Dahl, Nebr.-S.D. Area; Harry L. Davis, Minneapolis; William J. Fenton, Nebr.-S.D. Area; John E. Fogarty, Omaha; Frederick C. Hoagland, Mitchell, S.D.; Tom F. Kenny, Iowa Area; George W. Knauer, Fargo; Harry F. Knight, Omaha; John A. McCallum, Minneapolis; Richard P. McDonald, Minneapolis; Charles J. McGill, Minneapolis; George B. McGovern, Shakopee, Minn.; Jack F. Meyer, Omaha; Ralph J. Pettitt, Nebr.-S.D. Area; Stanley A. Roese, Minneapolis; John H. Shipley, Des Moines; Douglas L. Smith, Minneapolis; Theodore R. Tucker, Iowa Area; Robert W. Turner, Minn. Area; Harold A. Watkins, Duluth; Clarian C. Wysocki, N.D. Area; Noreen A. Yarger, Clarion, Iowa; Robert P. Young, Omaha.

employees made frequent trips to the blood bank, one of 18 set up around the country to donate blood to wounded servicemen overseas. Back yards were dug up for Victory Gardens to boost the wartime food supply.

On Oct. 1, 1942, Russell J. Hopley became NWB's president, and A. A. Lowman moved to chairman of the board. Former President W. B. T. Belt died Feb. 8, 1942, at age 70.

The war year 1942 also saw the new cross-country buried telephone cable in use. Northwestern plant investment had increased to $200 million, $40 million more than 1933. Revenues from long distance service were back up to pre-depression peaks.

Lowman, who had done much to raise long distance and other revenues, retired from the board chairmanship on Aug. 31, 1943, but continued as a Company director and member of the board's executive committee.

In spite of curtailments in telephone installation, the Company's millionth phone was installed on Sept. 17, 1943. Only a small *NWB* magazine item acknowledged it. "No new telephones, except for war orders, have been made for about a year, but we had a considerable reserve of telephone instruments on hand, and we have repaired telephones that ordinarily would have been taken out of service as obsolete, and in every way we have endeavored to do 'the most with the least.' "

An example: phones left in vacant dwellings were at a bare minimum — three for every 1,000 in service. The figure for 1934 had been 150 "left-ins" for each 1,000 phones in service. Northwestern Bell's 1944 Annual Report showed 1,033,000 telephones in service at year's end. Some 38,600 orders for service couldn't be filled.

Switchboards were jammed when news came of victory in Europe. V-E Day — May 8, 1945 — put such a load on NWB circuits that extra operators had to be called in. Many more came in voluntarily. On Aug. 14, 1945, when President Truman announced Japan's surrender, long distance volumes broke all records.

NWBers began to return home from military duty. Their help would be needed. In 15 years, Northwestern Bell had successfully made the transitions from prosperity to depression to recovery to war. Another transition — to peace — would be one of the hardest.

North Dakota blizzards & other stories

THE DEPRESSION AND THE WAR years placed special demands on NWBers, but they still remained alert to the importance of every call. If fires, floods and windstorms threatened service, or a caller was in trouble, telephone people responded.

To jump off a train during a blizzard in the middle of nowhere sounds like a good way to commit suicide. But for early-day North Dakota Plant men, it was just one of the ordeals they sometimes had to endure while trying to clear trouble. Since telephone lines often paralleled railroad tracks, it made sense to ride trains to where the trouble seemed to be. If there was a blizzard at the time — tough!

Many such stories weren't even recorded. Some got only laconic mention. In 1944, when he was jotting down his experiences at Crosby, N.D., Emil Nelson recalled how, years earlier, he'd hopped a train when called out on a case of trouble one Christmas Day.

"A blizzard descended, stalling the train," he wrote, "so I walked 12 miles in order to be home and eat my Christmas dinner."

Frank Stone, the manager at Carrington, N.D., didn't make it home for dinner at all one bitter day in January of 1936. The telephone circuit north to New Rockford had gone dead. Late in the afternoon, Stone hitched a ride with a Northern Pacific engineer. About six miles out, he located the trouble.

He unloaded his heavy tools, told the engineer he'd go to a nearby farmhouse when done, and watched the train chug away into the darkness. He got the line repaired just as the wind and the snow were starting up again.

When Stone reached the farmhouse, he found that the phone was dead. Since he wanted to let his wife know he was OK, he set out for another farm two miles away. By then the blizzard was screaming. And he kept breaking through the crust into waist-deep snow. Fighting an almost overwhelming urge to lie down, Stone hung his heavy tools on a fence and floundered on.

By the time he got to the farmhouse, he could barely talk. The next morning, he woke up in an upstairs bedroom. His clothes were missing and he couldn't remember what had happened. The grandma of the house had gotten him to bed and had taken his clothes to dry them. She fed him a big breakfast and he hiked back to Carrington, just in time to call off the search party. The tools were still on the fence the next spring.

• When a snowstorm blocked roads around Reeder, N.D., NWB Agent Blanche Puariea still got help for a seriously ill woman. Within minutes after the call for help, Mrs. Puariea had located the doctor in another town and persuaded him to attempt the trip by train. She then arranged for the train to make a special stop near the ailing woman's home.

• After a giant research balloon took off near Rapid City, S.D., then burst and came down near Loomis, Nebr., telephone men played a big roll. C. A. LeMasters, wire chief at Lexington, Nebr., saw the balloonists parachute to safety. LeMasters took them to a farmhouse and called other NWBers who manned special connections to broadcast the story to the nation.

• Hard times made temporary telephone men out of a lot of rural people. An example was the building of the Sugar Lake, Minn., line in 1930-31. Bill "Highpockets" Higholt, the Grand Rapids manager, had explained that Northwestern Bell couldn't afford to build 12 miles of line for 12 customers. But the Company would install the lines and phones if the customers would furnish the poles and set them. First the men cut 500 cedar poles. Then resort owner Arthur Otis put chains on his Model A and pulled a sleigh to distribute the poles. Finally the community put on a big dance to raise the $300 needed to hire 500 pole holes dug, each five feet deep. The line was operating by the opening of the walleye season May 15.

• In 1935 NWB employees in southwest Nebraska received a Vail Medal after they were credited with saving dozens of families from a devastating flood. Operators at Stratton, Trenton, Culbertson, McCook and Oxford notified customers living near the swelling Republican River. Telephone people worked day and night to restore service and help with rescue operations.

• In reporting the story of a serious accident, the Decorah, Iowa, *Journal* said that Mrs. Elmie Dalen, night operator at Calmar, "handled all the emergency calls for physicians, ambulances and other needs rapidly and efficiently, though she knew that her son was one of the victims.

• Omaha telephone men wore special masks and gloves for a new kind of trouble-shooting in the summer of 1938. Their job was to eliminate thousands of wasps and hornets which were nesting in terminal boxes on telephone poles.

• Among the many stories of devotion to duty during a storm, one cited as "typical" during a 1942 blizzard was that of Foreman A. W. Serres and his crew. Driving 220 miles from Medora, N.D., to Isabel, S.D., the crew became stuck some 20 times in huge drifts. Several times they drove steel stakes into the ground and pulled the truck out backwards with a winch line. They drove cross-country to avoid drifts; they had only brief periods of sleep on farmhouse floors; they dealt with wet spark plugs, a frozen gas line and a dead battery. After three days, they reached Isabel and restored service.

• That same year, L. F. Steele and John Rayburn of Cedar Rapids were repairing lines over the swift Cedar River when their boat capsized. By gripping the wires, the men were able to edge to shore where they dried their clothes and went back to work.

• Several times, Northwestern Bell loaned men to help with telephone problems outside the territory. Iowa Construction Foreman L. J. Anderson and nine other NWB men helped the Army build a 442-mile line from Edmonton, Canada, to Fairbanks, Alaska, *in eight days.* The period included the worst snowstorm in 40 years and temperatures of 72 below, but they made it.

• Edward Wren, wire chief at Iowa City, Iowa, helped design and install a special telephone for a friend who had no arms. The special set had the receiver mounted on an accordion-type holder, and a switchhook that the friend could operate with his knee.

Chapter XV

Building the network

From postwar shortages to
direct distance dialing

THE END OF WORLD WAR II unleashed a demand for service greater than telephone people had ever seen. It caught the Company desperately short of manpower and supplies.

In early 1946 a lack of telephone sets had helped produce 59,000 held orders.* Even as phones became available, they could not always be hooked up. In many locations, central office equipment wasn't available, or central offices were all in use. Some customers had to wait, or settle for party line service. In the central offices, normal margins for growth and overload were eliminated to give more people service.

Northwestern Bell had only 454 construction people in the five states as 1945 began. By the end of 1947, the construction force had more than quadrupled. More than 6,000 employees were added during 1945-46, bringing the Company total to 20,000. On Sept. 2, 1945, V-J Day, the Company had only 274 passenger cars and 1,006 trucks. By the end of 1947, it had 441 cars and 1,570 trucks. More heavy trucks were needed but weren't available.

---

*Held orders are customer requests for service the Company was unable to fill. The reference here is to orders where the customer has no service at all.

During 1946, those held orders were reduced to 23,500, most of them new. By the end of 1949, held orders were down to 11,000 and 87 per cent of all orders for main telephone service were worked on a current basis.

In the interim, the Bell System had experienced its first nationwide strike.

The National Federation of Telephone Workers had a hand in local bargaining in 1945. In 1947 a national policy committee was established to represent Federation affiliates, and given authority to call a Systemwide strike.

The strike started on April 7, 1947, and lasted about six weeks. Management people were assigned to switchboards or Plant jobs to keep service as normal as possible. The strike ended inconclusively and, before the year was out, the Northwestern Union of Telephone Workers was negotiating for affiliation with the Communications Workers of America. The CWA was recognized by the Company as bargaining representative for its craft employees early in 1948. The following year, the union was chartered as a member of the Congress of Industrial Organizations (CIO) which later affiliated with the American Federation of Labor to become the AFL-CIO.

Another task facing the Company as 1945 began was conversion of 346 manual offices to dial. By Dec. 31, 1959, 231 had been converted and 111 new dial offices had been added. NWB started 1945 with 60 per cent of its phones dial, ended 1959 with more than 90 per cent.

Besides dial conversions, construction work of the period included introduction of new services and equipment. Spidery towers began punctuating rural horizons as new microwave routes hopscotched across open spaces. And heavy tractors crawled across the land burying cable, although the big push to go underground would come later.

One of the most unusual jobs of 1946 was construction of a line terminating at a pole in the middle of a North Dakota wheat field. The pole had a phone on it and was the first construction at the site which eventually became Garrison Dam. That phone was in the middle of what became the town of Riverdale, home for the engineers and workers who built the dam. (A dial office for Riverdale went into service in December 1947.)

In 1947, in the Twin Cities, NWB introduced its first mobile telephone service. And the Company's first No. 1

As manual offices were converted to dial a new form of headgear was adopted for protection from falling heat coils. Jamestown, N.D., 1958.

crossbar office was installed for Omaha's Pleasant (now 451) exchange. Crossbar was faster and more efficient than the panel equipment previously used in large urban offices. Northwestern Bell and Long Lines embarked on an ambitious $13 million cable project that same year. The main feature was a coaxial cable* placed between Des Moines and Ames, Iowa, and completed to Minneapolis in 1949. New (non-coax) cable tied in Sauk Centre, Wilmar, St. Cloud, Mankato, Rochester, Albert Lea and Austin in Minnesota and Fort Dodge and Waterloo in Iowa. While

---

*This was not the first. In June 1941, the first commercial installation of coaxial cable in the Bell System, known as the type L1, went into full-time service between Minneapolis and Stevens Point, Wis. In November 1940, a snow storm disrupted open wire service in the Minneapolis area for four days and the as yet unfinished coaxial system furnished enough channels for emergency service.

coaxial cable was the backbone of the project, economics dictated that the link from Sauk Centre to Fargo, N.D., be an open wire pole line with carrier equipment that put up to 16 circuits on each pair of wires.

On June 30, 1950, U.S. troops entered the Korean War and NWBers began leaving for training camps. The Korean action did not stymie Company growth but there were cutbacks in such materials as copper, and recycling efforts were intensified. Lead was scarce and polyethylene was used increasingly as a protective coating for telephone cable. The Bell System was already recycling wire and other scrap. Western Electric's subsidiary, Nassau Smelting and Refining Company, was the Bell System's official "scrap agent."

The underground Command Post at Headquarters, Strategic Air Command

As world tensions continued, the nation became more aware of the need for a communications system which enemy action couldn't disrupt. The Strategic Air Command asked for millions of dollars worth of communications equipment and later ordered the famed "red telephone." Centered in SAC's underground nerve center at Offutt Air Force Base near Omaha, these facilities became a demanding responsibility for Northwestern Bell.* As SAC's vice commander, Major General Francis H. Griswold, put it a few years later: "In case of an attack against this country, our ability to survive and retaliate would be no better than our ability to communicate immediate instructions to our retaliating force."

On Sept. 30, 1950, six TV stations in Northwestern Bell territory joined nationwide television networks. They were KSTP-TV and WTCN-TV in the Twin Cities; WOW-TV and KMTV in Omaha; WOC-TV in Davenport, Iowa, and WOI-TV in Ames, Iowa. This was made possible by linking a new Bell System microwave route from Chicago to Omaha with the existing coaxial cable from Des Moines to Minneapolis. This route — extended to California via Denver — was carrying network television coast-to-coast by September 1951.

A year later, NWB's first No. 5 crossbar office was installed at Bellevue, Nebr., south of Omaha next door to SAC Headquarters. An armistice ended the fighting in Korea in July 1953 and that same month, a new microwave route opened between Minneapolis and Chicago-Milwaukee via Rochester, Minn.

Among the hundreds of buildings or additions constructed in the period were these major projects: 1948 — an addition to the northwest corner of the Des Moines Headquarters building adding six floors above the old fourth level; 1955 — 54 new buildings or additions completed, and construction started on the Tenth Street building in Des Moines; 1957 — completion of a 12-story addition to the Omaha Headquarters building adjacent to

---

*The responsibilities at SAC grew to the point that a separate Northwestern Bell SAC District was established in 1962. In the spring of 1975, there were 35 Northwestern Bell and 35 AT&T people assigned to SAC.

the 38-year-old Douglas building.*

During 1948, Northwestern Bell and AT&T collaborated to celebrate the installation of the Bell System's 30 millionth phone at Marshalltown, Iowa. In five postwar years, Northwestern Bell alone added 492,000 telephones, much of the growth due to population increases and booming commercial activity. But once past the postwar equipment shortages, the Company could plan for and meet the growing demand for service.

But not all the growth was predictable.

Early in 1951, a drilling crew near Tioga, N.D., pulled a drilling bit from the 10,000 foot level, swabbed off a pint of oil, and launched a scramble for leases that prompted one oilman to observe that that single pint of oil had "cost more people more money than any other pint in the world." Other drillings in the area hit oil and the boom was on.

In Williston, the nearest large town, long distance traffic jumped 40 per cent. The single circuit between Williston and Tioga was hopelessly clogged. Northwestern Bell quickly installed carrier equipment to add three more circuits. Fortunately, conversion of Williston to dial was underway. Engineers increased equipment estimates and the cutover took place in July. With 30 producing oil wells in the area and furious drilling continuing, Williston's population was expected to double in five years.

Oil had been discovered near Kimball, in southwestern Nebraska, in June 1951, and two years earlier near Gurley, Nebr., 12 miles north of Sidney. In both Kimball and Sidney, demand for phones and long distance boomed, though not on the same scale as at Williston.†

---

*Another 12-story addition to the Omaha Headquarters was completed in 1964. And in 1970, a third 15-story addition was occupied, thereby completing "the block that talk built."

†The Williston Basin ranked 14th in production and 15th in reserves in a 1973 Department of Labor compilation. Population comparisons tell the story, too: Williston jumped from 7,378 in 1950 to 11,866 in 1960 and still had 11,280 in 1970. Sidney jumped from 4,912 in 1950 to 8,004 in 1960, then dropped back to 6,403. The energy crisis brought new activity to both fields in 1975.

Tragically, storms and floods ravaged Northwestern Bell territory during the same period, forcing the diversion of precious money and manpower into restoral work. But not all the storm stories focused on costly damage. Some were about grit.

An example: May floods in 1945 put a forbidding sea between Chief Operator Beryl Cox and her office in Broken Bow, Nebr. But when she learned that 85 phones were out and the exchange basement was rapidly filling with water, she started out anyway. She waded a mile and a half through knee-deep water to a road where she could catch a ride. Then, she and the other operators kept the calls going through . . . by lantern light part of the time.

When an April 1948 flood backed the Park River into Grafton, N.D., Manager Hap Fridlund sandbagged entrances to the telephone building. Then, with electric power out, he and four others manned hand pumps for 17 hours to keep ahead of seepage water. At one time, water rose 21 inches on the outside of the building, but vital telephone equipment stayed dry. Meanwhile, E. J. Fox, conversion foreman at Grand Forks, was struggling to bring a portable generator to Grafton. When water got too deep for his car, he carried the generator across a flooded section of highway and hitched a ride. Blocked a second time, he carried the generator again. At one point, where a train was standing on a siding, Fox persuaded the conductor to back it up so the generator could be hauled part way by rail. Finally, he got the generator to the telephone building. Meanwhile, Grafton's telephone service had continued without interruption.

Other storms and floods were more costly. The preceeding decade, storm restoral costs had averaged under $300,000 per year. Then the damage totals began to climb.

In January 1949, a blizzard struck western Nebraska, both Dakotas and southern Minnesota. Cross-country trains were stalled, stranding thousands. Twenty people died in Nebraska. More storms late in January prompted President Truman to order out the Army. Northwestern Bell rushed communications for Major General Lewis A. Pick at his "Operation Snowbound" headquarters in Omaha. "Snowbound" coordinated the efforts of thousands of rescue workers, 1,200 snowplows, bulldozers and trucks plus 350 planes as roads were opened and sup-

Vital partner — good neighbor

When Western Electric opened its new distribution center in Minneapolis in 1949, Geddes, S.D., residents took no notice. Geddes soon had reason to be thankful.

Fire at NWB's dial office in Geddes knocked out all 362 of the town's phones Aug. 24. Almost before the fire was out, Manager M. J. Houlihan rented hotel rooms and hooked up three lines for emergency long distance service. By the next day, Western Electric had an installation crew and a manual PBX in Geddes. NWB sent in operators and by the second day, most townspeople had manual service. Western shipped equipment from Chicago, Philadelphia and Lincoln, Nebr. Twelve days after the fire, dial service was restored.

In the same year, Western began overnight truck runs to Omaha to deliver equipment needed in NWB's rush to catch up with postwar needs. In 1963 Omaha got its own distribution house and NWB assigned 25 people there to expedite order handling. Outlying NWB locations began ordering supplies from Omaha and Minneapolis via Dataphone® the same year. In 1971 a branch of the Omaha distribution house was opened in Des Moines.

In 1972 Western opened a regional warehouse (Material Management Center) northwest of Council Bluffs to supply the distribution houses and give better support to Western's own installation crews.

Through it all, Western established an amazing record of holding costs down. In 1974 *Business Week* magazine reported that Western's prices for its products (except cable) were at about the level they'd been in 1950 and were substantially lower than those for comparable equipment. Transmission equipment was 28 per cent lower. Cable, sensitive to copper costs, was 10 per cent lower.

One of the manufacturing plants responsible for Western's good record was also a good neighbor. In 1958 Western began production at a plant on a 390-acre tract at Millard, Nebr., near Omaha. Eventually, the plant provided thousands of jobs as it produced cable and switching equipment for the Bell System.

Iowa crews from Guttenberg and Iowa Falls assisted in 1951 sleet storm repair work north of St. Peter, Minn.

plies rushed to stranded people and livestock.

Telephone people volunteered for rescue work after their regular jobs; operators slept in telephone buildings, sometimes working 16-18 hour shifts. As General Pick put it: "Without the telephone and the fine cooperation of telephone people and switchboard operators, our task would have been much less speedily accomplished and relief longer delayed."

In 1950 a March blizzard hit all five states, isolated 566 towns, and cut 2,200 long distance circuits. Damage totaled $1 million, and was worst in the Dakotas. Six hundred local construction men were joined by 1,000 more from Iowa, Minnesota and Nebraska in the restoral work. Like most storms, this one had its curious stories. At Sioux City, Iowa, operators slept on tables, desks and even the floor. Stalled on North Dakota's Highway 81, two men in a transport truck rigged a makeshift telephone from a radio and other material. One man shinnied up a pole and tapped the wires. Flabbergasted operators at first refused to believe the men. Finally convinced, they sent aid.

In April of 1952, the Mississippi, Missouri and other swollen rivers roared through the Upper Midwest. Flood waters drove thousands from their homes in Bismarck-Mandan, N.D., the Fargo-Moorhead area; St. Paul and Shakopee, Minn.; Davenport, Dubuque, Muscatine and other Iowa cities. Fort Pierre, S.D., was inundated and virtually all of South Sioux City, Nebr., too. In Pierre, S.D., nearly all the business district was under water.

One of the most dramatic chapters in the flood history was written in Omaha and Council Bluffs.

On April 10, 1952, the forecasters warned that the two cities had a week to prepare for the biggest flood in history. Some 50,000 people, including volunteers from hundreds of miles away, worked night and day to make the miracle that saved the cities. When the flood crested, the river sprawled a dozen miles wide across bottomlands to the north. Between the cities, 30 miles of hastily raised dikes confined the torrent to a foaming chute a quarter mile wide.

Just as the flood crested, a huge sewer broke. Millions of gallons of water spurted up behind a levee near downtown Omaha. It was the greatest threat of the week-long struggle, and a Northwestern Bell mobile telephone car played a key role in averting disaster. While Omaha Service Engineer Ray Dodendorf sped a flood control official to the scene, the official sent out call after call for men, machines, steel, stone and sandbags. Minutes were crucial; the mobile phone made them count.

Other hastily installed phones along the levees had brought help rushing to danger points previously. Telephone people had joined others in building dikes, and, during the tense crest period, Northwestern Bell employees constantly patrolled a long stretch of levee in north Omaha. The odds were so against the effort, two-thirds of Council Bluffs was evacuated. While residents hauled belongings to high ground, telephone men removed thousands of phones. Through a massive effort, all were reinstalled four days after the "all clear."

On Monday, June 8, 1953, the usually quiet Floyd River cut a mile-wide path of destruction through Sioux City. By Tuesday, 14 were dead; property damage totaled $60 million; 5,000 of the city's 37,000 phones were out, plus 120 long distance circuits. Telephone damage came to $225,000, the worst at the Leeds central office. A five-foot wall of water had poured over dial machinery and power units, leaving muck behind. It first appeared the switches would have to be replaced. But the last telephone men in the building had pulled the main fuse before leaving in a boat; damage from electrolysis was less than expected. All the Leeds equipment was dismantled, cleaned and back together by Saturday. Most of the office's 1,100 telephones were working again a week after the flood.

On March 15, 1954, President Eisenhower spoke via telephone to dignitaries on hand for the hydroelectric power plant opening ceremony at Fort Randall Dam, Pickstown, S.D. Ike's phone hook-up had taken some doing. Four days before the ceremony, a killer storm hit South Dakota (and Iowa, Nebraska and North Dakota). The normal long distance route out of Pickstown — via Wagner, Mitchell and Sioux Falls — was too badly damaged to be restored in time. An alternate link via Yankton and Vermillion was connected with Omaha via Sioux City, Iowa. To speed the work, snapped poles were lashed to their broken stumps where possible. When the line was almost ready the night before Ike's talk, a truck slid on ice near Yankton and snapped a pole on the improvised line. That prompted another frantic night's work.

The 1952 flood in the coulee area of Moorhead, Minn., looking southwest into Fargo, N.D.

R. J. Hopley   E. J. McNeely   S. B. Cousins   A. F. Jacobson

Worse, storm damage cost the Company $1.3 million.

Four men led Northwestern Bell through these difficult years of shortages, storms and growth.

Russell Hopley, named president in 1942, guided the Company through the postwar years of shortages. His career was cut short when he died of a heart attack in November 1949, but not before he had further distinguished himself. While the nation was preoccupied with national defense in 1948, Hopley spent much of his time in Washington as Director of Civil Defense planning. For his efforts, he earned a National Military Establishment Certificate of Appreciation, the first ever presented. Northwestern Bell's second in command while Hopley was in Washington was Fred Kappel, the Company's vice president-operations, who would go on to become the Bell System's top man during the 1960s.

Eugene McNeely, Hopley's successor, joined Northwestern Bell as vice president-operations in early 1949. He was named president December 6, 1949. A Missourian, McNeely began his telephone career as a Southwestern Bell student engineer in 1922.

Sanford B. Cousins became Northwestern Bell's new president in September 1952 when McNeely moved to an AT&T vice presidency.* Cousins had joined AT&T as a traffic assistant in 1920. Before coming to Omaha, he was a vice president and general manager at the Bell Telephone Laboratories.

Early in 1955, Cousins became an AT&T vice president and on February 1, A. F. Jacobson succeeded him.

---

*McNeely went on to become AT&T president in 1961 succeeding Kappel, who became chairman of the board.

Making headlines

Next to typewriters and printing presses, the telephone may be the newspaper's most indispensable tool. It's inevitable, then, that telephone people sometimes end up in the newspaper business. Two such events:

When heavy rains and hail knocked out 1,500 phones and the Watertown, S.D., municipal power plant about 5 p.m. July 7, 1950, the telephone office switched to its emergency generator. Repairmen worked most of the night and had nearly all damaged plant back in service the next afternoon. Commercial employees kept the business office open until midnight so townsfolk could make long distance calls. When a new storm knocked out 175 more lines, repairmen had them restored by midnight the second day.

Early in the emergency, Manager M. D. Morris suggested moving the daily *Public Opinion's* newswire teletypewriter to the telephone office so it could use NWB's power. When the Northwestern Public Service Company made power available for emergency use, the paper was able to publish without missing an issue.

The *Public Opinion* praised both the power and telephone companies: " . . . the telephone company and its personnel, as usual, threw schedules and convenience out the window and pitched in to restore communication as swiftly as could be done. There are those . . . who . . . argue that big corporations have no souls, but a lot of Watertown people now know otherwise . . . "

Late in 1951, during remodeling work at the St. Paul *Dispatch-Pioneer Press* building, a workman with an air hammer cut all 200 of the telephone lines serving the paper. The PBX went dead at 4:45 p.m. At 5 p.m., Northwestern Bell proposed transferring the newspaper's calls to the telephone company's PBX so they could be answered in the district office. By 5:20, Traffic and Commercial people were temporarily in the newspaper business. Newspaper personnel arrived shortly to turn the office into a makeshift "City Room." Meanwhile, Plant men rerouted four vacant circuits in a nearby building to restore service to two newswire teletypewriters and two switchboard trunks. By 7:30 p.m., normal service was restored at the newspaper.

Jacobson had served as vice president-operations for Illinois Bell, as director of operations for Long Lines and as assistant vice president of AT&T before he became Northwestern Bell's sixth president.

But "Jake" was a home-grown product. He started his career in Omaha as a Commercial clerk in 1925. While attending the University of Nebraska in Lincoln he worked for Lincoln Telephone and Telegraph Company and then, during the summers, for Northwestern Bell. After graduation in 1925, he joined NWB full-time and worked his way through the ranks to vice president-operations before he joined Illinois Bell in 1951. Jake would serve longer than any other Northwestern Bell president since Belt.

In the first few years of Jake's 15 years as top man for Northwestern Bell, the Company would make two Areas out of one, add a new department and a major new service.

After eight years of gradual transition, the process of establishing full staff operations in Sioux Falls was speeded up in 1956 and completed in 1957. A general manager had been appointed for South Dakota in 1949 but most staff support came from department heads in Omaha and was shared with the Nebraska general manager. In 1956 South Dakota's general manager, R. A. Devereaux, and the general manager for Nebraska, J. B. Moore, both became vice presidents as well as general managers. In the following year, about 100 Northwestern Bell employees transferred to Sioux Falls, including Traffic, Plant, Engineering and Commercial Staff personnel. Only Directory and Accounting remained as joint Nebraska-South Dakota operations.

During 1958, the Commercial Department turned directory matters over to the new Directory Department. Growth on the Directory side was illustrated in Minneapolis the next year. For the first time, that city's directory was printed in two sections, regular listings and Yellow Pages. Growth had made a single book unwieldy.*

The most significant moment of the decade, however, came earlier, on August 18, 1957, when customers in

---

*Minneapolis was the 10th city in the nation to require a separate Yellow Pages directory.

Minneapolis, St. Paul and 12 other communities began dialing their own long distance calls.*

The planning to make *customer* long distance dialing a reality started long before. As early as 1943, Philadelphia operators were dialing long distance calls in that region. World War II postponed further work.

It was a good thing planning had started early. In 1946 long distance calling volumes were running 30 per cent ahead of the previous year's and double 1940. In some Northwestern Bell offices, extra people were hired to handle paperwork so operators could complete more calls. New operators trained at dummy positions† because there were no spare switchboard positions. Old PBX cabinets were adapted for extra switchboard positions and two dozen Army surplus switchboards were pressed into service even though they required considerable modification.

For Northwestern Bell, the first taste of the new era came at Davenport, Iowa, in 1947. Operators there were the Company's first to start pressing buttons ("key pulsing" instead of dialing) to ring up local numbers.

A major change came in Minneapolis in 1951 when a $4 million A4A long distance switching system was cut into service in February.‡ This tied the Twin Cities into 12 other similar machines in the Bell System's long distance dialing network.

---

*Lake Minnetonka, White Bear Lake, Mahtomedi, Forest Lake, Stillwater, St. Croix Beach, Red Wing, Anoka, St. Cloud, Virginia, Eveleth and Gilbert.

†Large photographs of switchboards mounted on wood frames and with a few keys and circuits for training.

‡One of the features of the A4A was that it was designed for later expansion into the No. 4A machine. A4A stood for "Advance 4A." The A4A provided alternate routing of calls when first choice circuits were busy. And, where only A4A machines were involved, operators could reach any dialable number with just one three-digit code. The earlier No. 4 machine did not provide alternate routing and operators had to dial a separate three-digit code for every intermediate switching point the call went through. Conversion to the 4A machines later in the 1950s enlarged the switching centers' "brain capacity" to provide more flexibility in call routing, capacity and increased speed.

"Big business"

"The town of Rugby [N.D.] can thank its lucky stars that there was "Big Business" in the form of Western Electric and the Bell Telephone Company," the editor of the *Pierce County Tribune* wrote after a fire destroyed three buildings in Rugby, including the telephone office, in 1954. The chronology:

March 25, 7:25 p.m. — Fire discovered; 7:31 p.m. — Telephone building evacuated, facility records rescued; 7:40 p.m. — Emergency long distance station established; 9:30 p.m. — An eight-position switchboard ordered from Western Electric in Minneapolis; 11:59 p.m. — More long distance circuits in operation with telephone operators taking calls and sending messengers to bring customers to temporary office. March 26, 1:30 a.m. — New switchboard leaves Minneapolis; 5:30 a.m. — Cable splicing to replace burned-out section underway; 9:30 a.m. — Auto batteries powered two new switchboard positions connected to 16 phones strategically located about town. March 27 & 28 — Western installers rush connections to the new board while emergency service continues on two positions. Rescued records prove invaluable. March 29 — Rugby's telephones back in service.

Other excerpts from the newspaper editorial: "We are not so naive as to believe there are not times when 'Big Business' should have its claws clipped . . . [but] who but 'Big Business' could step to a phone and summon its best brains; its trained hands and its specialists from all over . . . and have them respond so quickly?

"If you watched the operation from the time the first move was made; to order supplies from Minneapolis; set up emergency toll stations in parts of town; the obtaining of the new temporary quarters and the speed with which infinitely complex equipment was assembled and 'activated,' you would find the word 'miracle' popping up in your mind . . . Thank the Almighty for that kind of 'Big Business.' "

Then Twin Cities operators could complete many calls by dialing directly to customers in distant cities. Previously, the calling operator relayed the number to an inward operator in the distant city. If there were no direct circuits, the calling operator had to go through operators in intermediate locations. Now the operator had to dial only a routing code and the customer's number.

Building on the start made at Philadelphia in 1943, other switching centers went into service at New York, Chicago and Cleveland* during 1949. Coast-to-coast operator dialing arrived late that year with the completion of a switching center at Oakland, Calif.

Omaha operators began dialing long distance in 1952 and that same year, one of the last of NWB's former boy operators retired in Des Moines. He was Ted D. Dreyer, chief clerk in the Plant engineer's office and a long time officer in the McFarland (now Hawkeye) Pioneer Chapter. Dreyer had 51 years, 7 months service when he retired. He

---

*When the Cleveland center was completed in June of 1949, Des Moines operators became the first in Northwestern Bell who could dial customers in distant cities, but they were able to dial only Cleveland numbers until September 1949.

Long distance operators in Omaha

died in 1969. A 1947 *NWB* magazine article about Dreyer told a bit of what it was like to be Iowa City's night operator when you were a 13-year-old schoolboy:

"The high-pitched voice of the young boy, and the fact that distant operators thought him a girl, enabled him to have considerable fun at nights when he would converse with girl operators at eastern offices, and sometimes exchange stories that were not intended for masculine ears. The night operators at points in eastern states would ask him in all seriousness about the Indian situation and the kind of log cabin he lived in."

With the installation of an A4A switching center in Omaha, not only could operators there dial many of their long distance calls, Omaha customers could also receive operator-dialed long distance calls. Calls went through faster, particularly those that had to go through intermediate points. When coast-to-coast long distance was introduced in 1915, the average call required 20 minutes for completion. In the early 1920s, the Bell System's average long distance completion time was seven or eight minutes. Improvements such as keeping the customer on the line, and reorganizing the long distance network around manual switching centers, brought that average down to little more than two minutes by the early 1940s.

With the new A4A machines, the average dropped to under one minute. (And with the introduction of the No. 4A machines late in the 1950s, average completion time dropped to 24 seconds.)

Installation of the new switching machines and operator dialing were necessary preparations for NWB's 1957 introduction of *customer* dialing of long distance calls. That began when the A4A switching machine in Minneapolis was expanded. (The Bell System had first tested direct distance dialing in 1951 at Englewood, N.J., and was offering the service in other locations by 1957.) As revolutionary as it was, customer long distance dialing needs to be understood in context. It was a logical outgrowth of operator dialing, and a major milestone in the realization of a dream that began with Alexander Graham Bell, who first visualized the possibility of anyone anywhere being able to talk to anyone else.

The switch to long distance dialing required millions of hours (and dollars) of planning, but it was only part of

The 10-story Des Moines Tenth Street building built in 1955 later had five floors and a 15-story wing added on as shown in this 1965 picture.

NWB's postwar construction costs. Nearly 350 dial offices were installed. New cable and microwave routes were constructed. Not only had the Company caught up with the spiraling demand for telephone services, it had spent huge amounts to make its operations more efficient.

In 1959, for example, operators in Omaha began using new "mark sense" cards to record long distance calls. Instead of writing down the details on paper tickets, operators used special pencils to mark appropriate locations on the cards. As the name implies, machines "sensed" the marks and translated them into holes punched in the cards. Other machines automatically processed the cards to create long distance billing statements for each customer. With the new system, Traffic's ticket filing desks were no longer needed. And the pneumatic tubes that carried tickets from switchboard to rate desk were removed. As the year progressed, the Company introduced mark sense in other offices.

But while this progress had been taking place, other storms interrupted the work. Early Thursday evening, June 20, 1957, a tornado hit Fargo, N.D., killing 11 and injuring 100.

Mrs. C. O. Leverson, wife of Northwestern Bell's Fargo construction supervisor, saw the funnel coming. She and her son, Dick, rushed from their car to a nearby house but were swept from the porch, landing in rubble 50 feet away. Mrs. Leverson was seriously injured. Doreen Anderson and her family huddled under tables in their basement. Emerging, they found the roof and front porch gone, a stranger's photo in Doreen's bedroom.

Damage totaled $20 million, $500,000 of it to telephone plant. In Fargo, 3,900 phones were out, 100 more in Moorhead, Minn. By 9:30 p.m., all positions on the Fargo long distance board were filled. Off-duty operators showed up; former operators volunteered. Two vacationing Traffic people (Thelma Patterson, traffic clerk, Grand Forks, and Chief Operator Bertha Justice, Minot) walked in and stayed several days. They were badly needed; more than 11,000 outgoing calls were placed the following day, compared to 4,100 the previous Christmas.

Aftermath of the Fargo tornado

Manager Jim DuBois kept the business office open until 2:30 a.m. so people without phones could make long distance calls. His staff served hot coffee to those in line. While Fargo engineers were surveying damage in the dark and making equipment estimates, Western Electric crews were being called to work in Minneapolis. They loaded three trucks before morning; the first arrived in Fargo at 9:30 a.m. Twelve construction and 33 splicing crews came in from Minnesota and outstate North Dakota.

They worked all day, some continued all night. All work was interrupted by drenching rain at 7 a.m. Saturday. It dumped nearly three inches before quitting around midnight. Nevertheless, all 297 long distance circuits were restored Sunday night. Most local service was restored by the following Friday. Enough outside plant to serve a city of several thousand had been installed.

A 20-inch snowfall one day in March 1959, didn't keep Waukon, Iowa, Combinationman Robert S. Burrett from having a race with the stork. At 5:30 a.m. Burrett arrived at work just as the night operator received a call from an expectant mother requesting an ambulance. Since the ambulance driver was snowed in, as were local police cruisers, and the woman's husband was out of town, Burrett plowed his truck through the snow to the woman's house, shoveled 30 feet to her door and headed for the hospital. The snow stopped them within a half block of their destination so Burrett shoveled another path to the hospital door. They made it in time and mother, daughter and telephone man were all reported in good condition.

All the while the Company was fighting storms and tackling mammoth construction projects, inflation was eating away at telephone earnings. As early as 1952, *NWB* magazine dramatized inflation's cost by picturing a set of six installer's tools that had cost $8.02 ten years earlier. In 1952 the price tag was $13.57.

The combined effect of inflation, plus the construction effort, can be seen in the statistics. Net addition to plant in 1946 came to $17 million, more than the total for the five prewar years. It was only the beginning. In three years, the Company added nearly $100 million worth of plant, almost half again as much as the total plant in service when WW II ended.

In 1949 NWB's construction spending reached $1

Cable plow train laying the Twin City-Duluth toll cable in 1951

million every 10 days. By 1959 it had grown to more than $86 million — or $1 million every three days.

The Company's investment per telephone emphasized the problem. At the end of 1944, NWB had $198 invested in plant for every telephone in service. The figure dropped to $182 in 1946, as telephones were rushed into service without corresponding central office expansion. Then the figures started a relentless climb. At the end of 1959, NWB had $322 of plant invested for every phone in service and was making a new investment of $577 for every phone added.

Those were the reasons why NWB had been forced to seek rate increases off and on throughout the postwar years. In 1957 the Company had rate requests pending in all five states. New rates went into effect in Iowa and Nebraska that year. The North Dakota Commission refused any increase. The South Dakota Commission also refused a general rate increase, but did allow reclassification of some towns into higher rate brackets where growth justified it.* Early in 1958, the Minnesota Commission approved a general rate increase.

All in all, the rate increases had been modest. Best of all, the effort and money that had gone into increasing operating efficiencies were about to pay off.

------

*South Dakota did get a general rate increase in 1961, then went eight years without another.

Chapter XVI

The information explosion

Transmitting data and voice: new uses for the network

A YEAR-END BLIZZARD battered eastern South Dakota and bordering areas off and on for a week, beginning Dec. 27, 1959. It caused $400,000 damage to telephone plant even though buried cable did provide uninterrupted service between Sioux Falls and major towns in the area. The storm started Sunday with freezing rain, then snow and sub-zero weather. Two inches of ice clogged the area by Monday. Tuesday brought new snow and 50-mile-an-hour winds. Friday, another foot of snow fell, accompanied by heavy, shifting winds. Through it all, 500 men drawn from all five operating areas struggled to restore 5,000 phones and 700 long distance circuits. At one time or another, 100 towns were isolated; all were restored before the blizzard ended.

It was a tough way to start a decade, but before the year was over things were looking up.

Late in 1960, millions watched a man-made "star" move across the heavens. Echo I, a National Aeronautics and Space Administration satellite, was demonstrating the feasibility of communication via satellite. Bell Labs helped design the communications equipment and furnished the principal ground station. In 1955, two years before any satellites had orbited, Dr. John R. Pierce of Bell

Labs had suggested a satellite communications system. The fragile Echo I balloon itself was made at Northfield, Minn., tucked into a metal sphere two feet in diameter. In orbit 1,000 miles above Earth, the sphere split open and Echo I ballooned to its full ten-story size.

It was only the beginning. Telstar, financed entirely by the Bell System, was launched early in July 1962. Within two weeks, Europeans watched a live telecast from the United States, relayed via Telstar. Part of that broadcast originated in South Dakota's Black Hills. With Mt. Rushmore as a background, the Mormon Tabernacle Choir sang "America the Beautiful." Later a buffalo herd thundered past in Custer State Park.

The buffalo scenes reached Europe in these jumps: from portable microwave equipment in Custer via similar equipment atop Mt. Coolidge, in the Mt. Rushmore park-

Glenn N. Thorgrimson, toll service foreman from Minneapolis (left) and Larry E. Jackson, toll terminalman from Ottumwa, Iowa, align a corner reflector antenna.

ing lot, and on trucks parked near Hermosa. There it joined a television relay system into Wyoming for transfer to AT&T's transcontinental network and on to the Bell System's giant $15 million horn antenna at Andover, Me., which beamed the signal to Telstar for relay to Europe. "The picture looked great in Brussels," jubilant television men reported.

A three-foot sphere, Telstar was crammed with 15,000 miniature components designed, tested and assembled by Bell Labs. The job would have been impossible without such Labs inventions as the tiny transistors which used so little power; solar cells which transformed sunlight into electricity; the frequency-modulation feedback receiver, ruby maser and traveling wave tube which provided ultra-low noise transmission and reception. A *New York Times* feature listed 10 other Bell inventions essential to Telstar's success.

In 1965 a communications satellite named Early Bird was launched into a stationary orbit 22,300 miles above the Atlantic Ocean between the United States and Europe. Despite AT&T's pioneering role in space communications, Congress created a special agency called Communications Satellite Corp. (Comsat) to handle satellite communications. Early Bird was its first satellite. Soon it was carrying telephone and television signals between the continents.

Other changes were taking place on earth.

Northwestern Bell, with the rest of the Bell System, was building a nationwide telephone network more versatile than Prof. Bell ever imagined — and offering its use to the public at bargain prices.

NWB's last magneto toll center (handling long distance for nearby towns) was converted to dial in 1960. Many Correctionville, Iowa, people weren't anxious for the change even though they'd been kidded about their old-fashioned phones. They knew they'd miss the personal service of Chief Operator Leila Goodman and the other operators. The next year, two small magneto offices that had just been acquired (Bondurant and Polk City, Iowa) were converted and that was it. The long, colorful hand-crank telephone era had come to an end.

In September, Omaha became the first major city in the United States to have All-Number Calling. Previously, Omaha phone numbers had been two letters and four digits. The nationwide direct dialing network required two-letters — five-digits, or seven digits. (Switching machines don't care whether you dial PEnnsylvania 6-5000 or 736-5000.) Ninety per cent of the Bell System already was on the 2-5 plan. But the change to all numbers would provide more central office designations.*

When Twin City customers began dialing long distance in 1957, they could reach only about 9 million phones. When Omaha's 228,000 phones were hooked into the network in June of 1961, about half of Northwestern Bell's 2.5 million phones could dial 46 million of the 70 million phones in the U.S. Omaha also became the first major Northwestern Bell city where Automatic Number Identification (ANI) equipment recorded the calling number so that no operator had to come on the line.

One outgrowth of the long distance dialing network was Wide Area Telephone Service (WATS), a private line access to the dialing network. By paying a monthly fee, a customer could dial unlimited long distance calls within a selected geographical area and time limit. NWB gained its first customers in February of 1960, and within a year, had 135.

Another new network service was Dataphone®. When Northwestern Bell's first Dataphones went into service early in 1961, Omaha and Minneapolis branch offices of Hardware Mutuals insurance firm could transmit policy information faster and more accurately than before. All the information needed to issue a car insurance policy could be transmitted in 30 seconds via phone to the home office in Wisconsin.

For some time, business machines had been processing information on punched cards, punched tape or magnetic tapes. Dataphone made it possible for one machine to send information to another at high speed via long distance circuits.

In 1962 the same company† became the Bell System's

---

*Using all numbers, a total of 800 three-digit central office codes are possible, compared to only 500 using letters and numbers.

†That company is now Sentry Life Insurance Company.

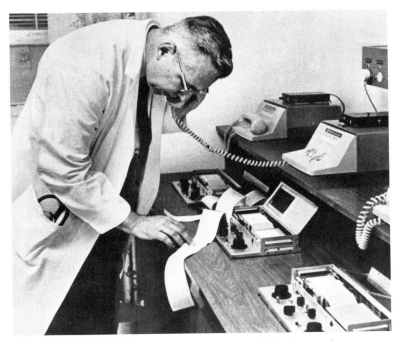

Physician receiving an electrocardiogram over a Dataphone set

first Dataspeed® customer. Minneapolis was one of ten locations from which the firm could send data at the rate of more than a thousand words per minute.

In 1963 NWB and heart specialists at St. Joseph's Hospital in Omaha began testing a medical data transmission system designed by Bell Laboratories. Although many physicians can make a limited heart diagnosis from an electrocardiogram, a specialist can be much more precise. Previously, outstate doctors mailed cardiograms. Now they could transmit them by phone. First outstate users were the Community Bailey Hospital in Chamberlain, S.D., and a Spalding, Nebr., physician who had a portable cardiograph. He could take cardiograms in his office or the patient's home.

Technological innovations weren't the only changes facing the Company. When the postwar demand for basic service had been satisfied, customers became more demanding. They wanted new conveniences and distinctive styling. Color phones had been introduced as early as 1955 and since about that time, the Bell System had been shifting from a policy of providing a basic service to one of determining customer wants and satisfying them.

A separate Marketing Department had been established in 1960. And by 1961, Northwestern Bell had nine major account managers on the job. The concept grew out of the recognition that 20 per cent of all System revenue came from .02 of one per cent of its business customers, yet they didn't always get the kind of service they wanted. Bell System routines had been established to handle thousands of similar orders efficiently. Now, in addition, NWB and other System companies were hustling to assure more flexibility and sensitivity to customer preferences.

Throughout the '60s, the Bell System introduced many new services, new ways to supply them and new uses for the network.

Clifford L. Sampson, vice president-operations, caught the spirit of what was happening in a 1963 *NWB* magazine article titled "Change." "Never before has man been asked to absorb so much change so suddenly," he noted. "When we think of all the new services we have launched recently and the improvements in methods, techniques and operations, we must conclude that we are facing an era that will call for the best efforts of all of us."

Sampson pointed out that Northwestern Bell had three times as many phones as it had 20 years previously and was spending 10 times as much annually on construction. It had a plant investment of $35,000 for each employee, three times what it had been 20 years before and more than twice the average for firms making up the Dow Jones Industrial Index.

Construction totals that seemed huge in the '50s were dwarfed in the '60s. The 10-year construction cost came to $1.3 billion. Dial conversions, long distance dialing, new cable, new buildings, Electronic Switching Systems (ESS) and a host of lesser achievements contributed to the immense total.

The First National Bank of Minneapolis became, in May of 1960, the first commercial institution in Northwestern territory (and the fourth in the nation) to have the Bell System's new direct inward dial PBX (later called

The Gergen Gadget

When you can save six hours on an installation that normally takes eight, that's something. And in this case, that particular something was named "The Gergen Gadget," after its originator, Des Moines Equipmentman Ted Gergen. He suggested the device and Engineer Ellis Wicker designed it. Then Gergen built a model in 1960, according to a November 1961 *NWB* magazine story.

The Gergen Gadget was a new arrangement of Key Telephone Unit equipment, used in conjunction with four-wire, high-quality service, used by many business customers for data transmission.

Explaining the Gadget's advantages, Gergen says, "It used to take eight hours to make a four-wire installation; the Gadget can be installed in under two hours. Removing the equipment took about four hours; this new equipment comes out in about 30 minutes. Under the old wiring procedures, it was easy to cut the wrong phone out of service when you were removing a line — components were scattered all over.

"Trouble-shooting used to be a nightmare," Wicker interjects. "The Gadget has cut our maintenance time."

The first Gadget made the rounds through Des Moines Plant and Engineering. Finally it was sent to Western Electric, accompanied by an order for "50 things just like this thing," Wicker says through a broad grin. "When they arrived we tested them the only way we could — on the job. They worked."

"Since the unit is pre-wired at Western Electric," Gergen continues, "we're saving all the time we used to spend putting components together. The Gadget, costs only $2 more than the separate parts cost before."

Ted Gergen explains what motivated him and Wicker to produce the Gadget: "You might say we found a bottleneck and weren't satisfied with the old crutch, 'It's always been done that way.' Besides, when we first started talking about it, a lot of folks said we were nuts. We had to see if they were right, now didn't we?"

Centrex). Customers were able to dial directly to any of the bank's PBX extensions. The same year, NWB and Omaha University were pioneering Tele-Lectures in which distinguished scholars could speak to a class and answer questions, via long distance.

In the summer of 1962, Minnesota Accounting began using 1401 computers to store customer account records, calculate long distance charges, print customer bills and keep customer payment records. The 1401 consolidated and speeded up operations previously handled with punched cards, and made new statistical data available. Des Moines and Omaha Accounting switched to the 1401 later that year.

The Minneapolis Gas Company and the *Omaha World-Herald* want ad section became Northwestern Bell's first customers to have a new Automatic Call Distributor in 1963. It automatically distributed calls equally to the answering staff and, when all were busy, held the call while continuously searching the circuits until an open line was available.

The same year, because a customer balked at having a cable terminal box attached to a walnut-paneled wall, Minneapolis Service Foreman Huey Jennings designed an alternative that pleased both the customer and Western Electric. He put a hinged frame on the back of a 756A PBX, then installed on the frame all the components that had been in the terminal box. The hinge allowed easy access to the PBX. Western soon started putting the hinged frame units on all its 756A PBXs. Installation time was cut from two or three days to about three hours.

A call from U.S. Attorney General Robert Kennedy to Aberdeen, S.D., during 1963 helped celebrate the first commercial installation of a Tele-Braille attachment that enabled a blind person to operate a PBX. The Tele-Braille Unit had been invented by two Pacific Northwest telephone men and tested in the State School for the Blind at Portland, Ore. NWB's Jack Vostad, a communications rep, and Vernon Williams, a blind attorney in Aberdeen (and brother of C. M. Williams of General Office Accounting in Omaha), flew to Portland to check it out. Back in Aberdeen, they persuaded the city commissioners to install one at City Hall. NWB's Dorothy Nultemeier trained Velma Schultz to operate it. The third day on the job, Miss Schultz confirmed everyone's faith. A four-inch rain flooded parts of the city. As hundreds of calls came in to City Hall, Miss Schultz handled them rapidly and smoothly.

Nebraska became the second state in the nation to have a statewide Educational Television Network as a result of work begun in 1963. (North Carolina was first in 1960.) The plan was to have studios in Lincoln and Omaha and transmitters at seven locations around the state, with NWB and independent companies providing facilities. In Iowa, closed circuit television linked the State University of Iowa College of Medicine and University Hospital.

One night in February 1964, customers in Alliance, Nebr., leapfrogged over almost all others in the United States. From being among the few still having manual service, they became third in the nation to have Touch-Tone®. (The Alliance cutover was to dial, but Touch-Tone was available for a modest extra charge.)

The Touch-Tone phone has pushbuttons instead of a dial. And the impulses that make the switching machines operate are musical tones instead of the circuit-breaking pulses of a dial. Because Touch-Tone is faster than dialing, Strategic Air Command Headquarters, in June, became the Bell System's first customer to have a Touch-Tone PBX. The SAC PBX handled 9,000 calls per

Northwestern Bell and University of Omaha (now University of Nebr. at Omaha) pioneered Tele-Lecture in October 1960.

day; the seconds saved were important. Because extra equipment had to be added to regular dial offices to translate Touch-Tone's musical signals, the service was introduced gradually. By year's end, it was available in 16 central offices throughout Northwestern's territory; 8,000 customers were using it.

In 1965 another new telephone — the Trimline® — was available. An all new design with the dial in the handset, it was popular immediately. Northwestern offered it early; it didn't become available throughout the Bell System until 1967. In 1966 NWB people in Bismarck, N.D., and Clinton, Iowa, helped test a new residential sales concept — the Touch-Tone package: three Touch-Tone phones, any style, any color, with a choice of cord length, at a reduced rate. Reaction was so favorable, the offering became standard.

Late in 1965, Omaha operators could obtain rate quotations from a talking computer, the first such system in the world. To quote charges on coin phone calls or those from hotels or motels, operators previously consulted rate sheets, or called "rate and route" operators.

Now, by key pulsing the computer's access code, then 11 more digits, the operator got an immediate voice answer giving the three-minute rate for the type of call, time of day, day of the week and any holiday rate in effect at that moment. (In fact, the computer's response was so immediate a slight delay had to be built in so the operator would be ready for the answer.) The service was made available to other operators throughout NWB territory early in 1966. (In 1968 the rate computer was reprogrammed to give total charges, including tax, on all calls when the operator keyed in the minutes talked.)

In the spring of 1967, because of the growing complexity and size of the Company's Minnesota operation, a new post of general manager-operations was created, reporting to Vice President W. L. Huffman. Bruce G. Schwartz was appointed and assumed responsibility for Commercial, Marketing, Plant and Traffic.*

---

*In 1969 Minnesota's operations were divided into Northern and Southern Divisions, each headed by an operations manager who reported to the general manager-operations.

Starting September 1967, students at the new Southwest State Minnesota College at Marshall could dial the college's tape library whenever they wished and listen to the assigned lecture on earphone sets in their rooms. Class time was freed for questions and discussions. With nothing to go on but ingenuity, NWBers had used Centrex and ordinary switching equipment to build the system, unlike any in the world.

The same year, the Minnesota Area took the first step in a three-year program to eliminate message unit charges in the 1,375-square-mile Twin City vicinity. Eventually customers would be able to make local calls to some 622,000 telephones in an area 50 to 55 miles in diameter. The result was the largest local calling area in the nation.*

When a night fire destroyed a Des Moines radio supply company, the manager rented a nearby building, called Northwestern Bell at 3 a.m. to transfer service, and went to bed. When he arrived at 8:15 a.m., installers were already at work. Then a truckload of new supplies arrived. By 9 a.m., he was back in business, with phone service. "We could have gotten the phones in quicker," one NWBer said, "but the firemen kept turning us away."

Late in February 1967, Rochester, Minn., became the fourth city in the country to have the Bell System's new Electronic Switching System (ESS). Some 2,000 man-years of Bell Labs and Western Electric work had gone into developing ESS — one of the most massive research and development projects ever sponsored by private enterprise. (St. Paul's Cottage Grove office became NWB's second ESS installation in October 1967.)

ESS was radically different from previous switching systems, even crossbar. With electromagnetic systems every task to be performed has to be wired in. Changing a customer's number requires disconnecting a pair of wires, reconnecting them at another spot. In contrast, ESS func-

---

*Subsequently, competitive pressures have forced telephone companies and regulatory authorities toward pricing policies that more nearly reflect the actual cost of providing a service. As a result, it is unlikely there will be any more local calling areas the size of the one in the Twin Cities.

Electronic Switching System office

tions are controlled by the program stored in its memory. Brief, coded instructions typed in via teletypewriter are all that's needed to change a customer's number. Another difference: older systems are inactive except when processing a call. ESS keeps checking itself. If it finds trouble, it switches to a back-up part, types a message telling where the trouble is.

ESS offices are capable of providing services "that nobody has ever dreamed of yet," Bell Labs engineers said. In Rochester, Speed Calling, Three-Way Calling and Call Forwarding were offered as customer options.* Any

---

*Speed Calling — a customer dials only three digits instead of seven or eleven to reach frequently called numbers; Three-Way Calling — a third local party can be added to an existing call; Call Forwarding — a customer can have his calls automatically transferred to another number; Call Waiting — a signal notifies the customer, while he is talking, that another call is waiting. The customer can hold the first call, answer the second, return to the first.

Rochester was not the first Northwestern Bell exchange to have Custom Calling Services. That honor goes to the Morningside area of Sioux City, Iowa. The Bell System test-marketed the customer options there and in Wellesley, Mass. Eventually, electronic offices will make Custom Calling Services available to every customer, but the Sioux City and Wellesley trials were unique in that they utilized crossbar rather than electronic switches.

can be discontinued, or new services added, by changing the ESS program. In fact, Call Waiting and certain special business services have since been added. One enables major business customers to make best use of their long distance facilities. If the customer dials a branch office in a distant city, ESS first tries the firm's private line circuits to the branch. If they're busy, ESS tries the firm's WATS lines. If they are busy, too, the call is routed to the direct dial network. And it all happens in micro-seconds.

NWB pioneered another new service in Omaha in 1967. But amidst all the technological rush, there was still time to celebrate the human side of the business. The Company's first woman to retire with 50 years service hung up her headset and *NWB* magazine paused to pay tribute.

The woman was Irene Johnson and she had spent her entire 50 years working St. Paul's long distance boards. Retiring as night chief operator, Mrs. Johnson had a special appreciation for the role she had played for the telephone company: "You can't imagine the effect an emergency call can have on an operator. Nothing so impresses on a girl the importance of her job as having a

Irene Johnson began working for the telephone company when she was 13 years old.

frightened woman call in the middle of the night, whisper to the operator that 'someone has broken into my house and is coming up the stairs.' The emergency calls, the all-night truck dispatchers at two and three in the morning, the sometimes tipsy salesmen who 'just want to talk with someone,' the sadness of a death and the hurried calls to friends and relatives, it all tends to make the job seem a little more important when you know that most folks are asleep — and those who aren't may be depending on you."

The new service pioneered in Omaha in 1967 was the No. 101 ESS PBX system. St. Joseph's Hospital in Omaha was NWB's first customer. Within a couple of years, the Company had about half of all the No. 101 installations in the country. Company officials decided the No. 101 had significant advantages for both customers and the Company. What the No. 101 did was provide business customers with Centrex service plus all the Custom Calling features of ESS.

While the Company was introducing all these new products and services, it was also confronted with a variety of human relations problems. Some required new techniques for communicating with employees, one involved the first nationwide strike in 21 years, another involved a hard struggle to change ingrained attitudes and others had to be dealt with in courtrooms and hearing rooms.

CWA Vice President D. K. Gordon (left, seated) and NWB Assistant Vice President O. R. Taylor sign the 1968 contract. Union representatives (from left): H. L. Gunderson, R. Schramm, D. P. Fortin, B. McCarthy and E. J. Follis. NWB representatives: R. J. Hargitt, L. C. Blanc, K. W. Ross and O. W. Selindh.

Northwestern Bell's nine-year-old employee discussion program, which had been a model for other companies, was featured in the Autumn 1964 issue of *Bell Telephone Magazine.* Author was Vern L. Bronn, who had sparkplugged NWB's pioneering effort. The purpose was not only to communicate vital information but also to build two-way communication between bosses and employees. Biggest problem, Bronn reported, was convincing busy supervisors the time was indeed well spent.

After an 18-day strike, NWB and the CWA agreed in May 1968 on a new three-year contract with wage increases retroactive to March 28. It was the first nationwide strike against the Bell System since 1950.*

The same month the strike ended, two black leaders, Dr. Earle Person, an Omaha dental surgeon, and Gleason Glover, director of the Minneapolis Urban League, spoke to Company officers and department heads at their annual spring conference.

"The Negro is tired of social audits by white sociologists," Dr. Person said. "He feels that it is time for a social audit of white bigotry . . . In my view, the city was meant to be a creative place . . . It is [there] the problem must be solved . . . "

"Whatever else is done, it is clear that the problems confronting black men cannot be solved unless decent jobs are made available," Glover said. "The problem facing American industry . . . today is to get more qualified minority men and women on payrolls in meaningful jobs and to give them every assistance in progressing to the full extent of their ability."

Throughout the decade, Northwestern Bell shared in

---

*In the years after World War II, NWB started offering tuition reimbursement for approved college courses in 1962 and a Savings Plan for salaried employees in 1969. And as a result of agreements with CWA, NWB introduced free Extraordinary Medical Expense (EME) coverage in 1960; Basic Medical Expense (BME) in 1963 with NWB paying the full cost by 1970; low-cost supplementary life insurance in 1967; and eliminated all Social Security pension adjustments in 1969. CWA and the Bell System bargained nationally for the first time in 1974 and agreed on establishment of an agency where permitted by law and a dental care plan to begin Jan. 1, 1976. Throughout the years, other agreements improved pension, vacation and holiday benefits and incorporated cost-of-living wage adjustments.

An island named "Alcatraz;" a dog named "Duke"

A March 1965 blizzard in Minnesota created drifts 15 to 30 feet high and experiences like these: Repairman Bob Silver spent a night stalled in a truck near Walnut Grove; Luverne operators spent a night in the Rock County Jail, the only place with available beds; Olivia (Minn.) Operator Eloise Vander Plas got to work on a farm tractor; and fellow Operator Pat Wittman hired a plane.

After the blizzard, floods devastated the territory for over a month. Some vignettes: at Winona, Minn., a telephone building was circled by 150 well points hastily sunk to drain away excess ground water and protect a basement that threatened to buckle under the pressure; at Sioux City, Iowa, NWB rented cranes to hold cable above rising waters; and at Davenport, Iowa, installers' trucks towed motorboats, the only way to reach flooded job sites.

But the two most interesting stories were about an island named "Alcatraz," and a dog named "Duke."

"Alcatraz" wasn't on any map. It was just another telephone pole (near Savage, Minn.) with an equipment box attached to it. When the Minnesota River began to rise a quarter of a mile away, Plant men raised the equipment cabinet four feet and relaxed. Six days later, it was obvious four feet wasn't enough to protect the repeater unit that kept 300 circuits in operation between Minneapolis and Shakopee, Minn. For 48 hours, telephone men piled sandbags in a 70-foot circle, 13 feet high, around the pole that had acquired the nickname "Alcatraz." For eight days and nights, telephone men stood guard over the strange island as pumps atop the sandbags struggled to suck water out faster than it seeped in. When the flood crested 20 inches below the top of the sandbags, the repeater unit, well below the water line, stayed dry. Television newmen gave the scene national coverage.

Duke saves the day in Des Moines.

In Des Moines, flood waters weakened the old Sixth Avenue Bridge and tumbled most of it into the water. What was left didn't look safe enough to support a man. Installer-Repairman Jap Brown brought down his English Pointer, Duke, and tied a fish line to the dog's collar. Brown then drove a circuitous route to the other side, whistled and Duke trotted across. Plant men pulled successively larger lines across, finally the heavy cable necessary to restore service to 7,000 telephones.

It was that kind of year. Near Elk River, Minn., the capricious Mississippi cut a new channel and washed out telephone lines. Again the problem was getting a cable across swirling waters. No bridge, no dog and too dangerous for a boat. Enter Engineer Herb Miller, an amateur archer. After tying on a fish line, he took aim and plunked an arrow into a tree 300 feet on the other side. Problem solved, Miller went back to the drawing board.

Jacobson, Johnson, Oberg (from left) after the Plan for Progress ceremony

the nation's struggle to come to terms with minority problems and make quality a reality. In 1962 NWB President A. F. Jacobson and Personnel Vice President M. F. Oberg joined United States Vice President Lyndon B. Johnson in signing a "Plan for Progress" statement which reemphasized the Company's commitment to equal opportunity employment. Full text of the statement was mailed to all NWB supervisors as a reminder of their responsibilities to hire and promote without discrimination.

In 1964 the Omaha Urban League presented a Service Award of Merit to Northwestern Bell for its contribution to equal opportunity employment. Western Electric was also cited.

During the entire decade, in fact, Northwestern Bell found itself taking on significant new responsibilities, both to the community and to employees. President A. F. Jacobson set the tone with a policy statement in 1959: "As citizens of a free and democratic country — and as employees of a privately owned and operated business providing a vital public service — we possess many precious individual rights which carry certain obligations . . . We believe that telephone people should be encouraged to take greater interest in civic, political and governmental affairs." Employees were urged to work for the political candidates of their choice, to become involved in community issues, even when controversial, and to be active in community service groups.

No one guessed at the time how volatile — and how numerous — those issues would be during the '60s.

On some issues, the Company itself could take action. During the decade, Northwestern Bell moved to cooperate with law enforcement agencies to help customers solve the growing problem of obscene, nuisance or harassing calls.* When the growing cluster of microwave antennas on top of Company buildings began to be unsightly, NWB hired designers to come up with more aesthetic solutions. As concern about pollution grew in 1967, the Plant Department ordered 11 vehicles equipped with anti-pollution equipment in order to gain information on their operating cost and performance. As society — and the U.S. Congress — became more concerned about crime, Northwestern Bell, along with the Bell System, prepared to make "911" a universal emergency number. In 1969 Windom, Minn., became NWB's first city to have it.

The same year that modern 911 service was installed in Windom, an old-fashioned manual board was installed in western South Dakota . . . for the second time. In a Rapid City Pioneer project, retirees Howard Kemble and Gene Lethcoe installed the board as a training aid for retarded youngsters . . . and discovered it was the same board they had installed at Sylvan Lake 30 years earlier.

While the Company could help fight pollution and crime, there were some issues it could do nothing about. During 1965, the U.S. became directly involved in Viet Nam and by September of 1966, Northwestern Bell had 150 employees on military leave of absence. *NWB* magazine ran a feature on the experiences of some of them in Viet Nam. Earlier, the magazine had analyzed the anti-war protest movement and campus unrest. The war would profoundly affect Northwestern Bell — not through material shortages, but in the attitudes of the young men and women who walked into the Company's employment offices, of those who left to serve in the military and of those left behind who struggled to understand it.

Some issues threatened to radically alter the way tele-

---

*In 1962 a new Security Department was established to help cut Company losses due to fraudulently placed long distance calls and thefts from coin phones.

phone service was provided in the United States.

In June 1968, the FCC ruled that AT&T's tariff prohibiting interconnection of the Carterfone device was invalid. AT&T had argued strenuously against it.

"The enormous dangers ... must not be underestimated," AT&T stressed. "They would adversely affect the quality and cost of phone service, severely hamper innovation, undermine the basis of regulation and significantly alter the extent of common carrier responsibility to the public.*

AT&T contended the Carterfone could transmit static, radio squeals, etc. that would interfere with others' conversations; that introduction of one such device would lead inevitably to others and divide responsibility for quality of telephone service.

The FCC's 1968 decision did allow telephone companies to prevent use of devices which "actually cause harm." In October, AT&T filed revised tariffs establishing procedures for interconnecting a wide variety of customer-provided equipment, but requiring telephone company interface devices to protect the network. The new tariff was more liberal than demanded, reflecting management thinking of the time — to react as positively as possible. (Subsequently, after considerable experience with interconnection indicated network integrity was in jeopardy, AT&T asked for a "thorough thinking-through" of the whole issue.)

In August 1969, another FCC decision jolted the telephone industry. By a four-to-three vote, it granted the application of Microwave Communications Inc., (MCI) to build a microwave system between St. Louis and Chicago and offer common carrier private line service. Next, Data Transmission Co. (Datran) asked the FCC for permission to construct a nationwide common carrier system exclusively for digital data transmission.

AT&T and the associated companies vigorously op-

---

*The issue had begun in 1959 when a Dallas businessman named Thomas Carter invented a simple device to interconnect two-way mobile radio systems with the telephone network. The device fitted a Carter microphone against the telephone earpiece and a Carter receiver against the mouthpiece. Conversations could then be transferred between the radio and telephone systems acoustically.

Repair work amidst the debris of the Charles City tornado

posed MCI's application, stating it would duplicate existing facilities, result in wasteful use of scarce common
carrier microwave frequencies and undermine nationwide
interstate rate averaging. (These subjects will be treated
more fully in the final chapter.)

Bad news of another sort came roaring out of Midwestern skies in the spring of 1968.

Tornadoes caused extensive damage at Charles City,
Oelwein and Arnolds Park in Iowa, and at Tracy, Minn.

The first blow came mid-May when one of history's
worst series of tornadoes ripped through 12 Midwestern
and South Central states, leaving more than 71 dead and
1,000 injured. Within minutes, a six-block path of destruction swept through the heart of Charles City. In Oelwein,
90 per cent of the business buildings in town were heavily
damaged or destroyed. NWB operators in Charles City
ducked under the switchboard as the tornado ripped off
the roof. No one was seriously hurt. Damage to NWB's
building in Oelwein was slight.

The animal war

This is the story of all God's creatures — even elephants — and their unrelenting assault on a flinching enemy known as the telephone company.

Elephants? "They had 'em tethered near a telephone line in Washburn (near Riverdale, N.D.)," said Don Zimmerman, Riverdale manager in 1963. "They were pretty tall — and their backs got to itching. They scratched them on the telephone lines, twisting and tangling them."

The same year, Ken Durr, Davenport, Iowa, plant supervisor, told of a short that showed up consistently on a line near Burlington . . . but only around sunrise. "Every time our man went out there at 8 a.m.," Durr recalled, "the short was gone. He finally checked at 4 a.m. and saw hundreds of swallows weighting the line down until it touched one below; the birds would take off right after sunrise."

Another Durr classic: "Bats used to get inside an old-type terminal cover and hang upside down from the terminal. When the operator rang through, the current would hit the bats' feet. Jolted, the little fellows responded to nature's call and shorted the line."

Field mice often make nests under the caps that cover pedestals along underground cable lines. "I think they have the idea we installed the pedestals just for them," Elgin, N.D., Manager Jim Gillen said in 1963. "I took a cap off one day and found 15 or 20 of 'em. Last year, one jumped into my shirt. I think I originated the 'Twist' that day."

Up in northern Minnesota, mice aren't a problem, but moose are. Sometimes they butt over poles. And once, according to a 1963 story told by Milt Fish, Warroad manager, a moose got tangled in a line, panicked and ran. "That big old bull moose got all tangled up in the wire and starved to death."

In the same 1963 NWB magazine story, Walt Graham, information supervisor in South Dakota, told this one:

"The Rapid City-Mystic long distance line followed the railroad tracks, but in the canyon below. This wild horse stumbled on the tracks and fell sideways onto the line."

The gopher war is a story in itself. The pesky rodents have teeth that grow as much as 12 inches per year. If the gopher doesn't wear them down gnawing on something, he's in trouble. Telephone lines and cable seem made to order. Excerpts from *NWB* magazine over the years chronicle the long-running battle: Round 1, 1941—"The Midwestern gopher is about to become victim of a wicked conspiracy by Bell Laboratories ... " Round 2, 1947 — "Bell scientists continue the fight against the gopher ... " Round 3, 1950 — "Bell Labs' latest development is enough to discourage even the most stout-hearted gopher ... " Round 4, 1963 — "Once again Bell Labs is planning a defensive in the war against the gopher."

Round 5, 1966 — "The new cable is clean, tough and easy to handle. Northwestern Bell dares any Midwestern gopher to counterattack." Round 6, April 1970 — "Continuing the study, researchers are nearing the elimination of this problem." Round 7, July 1970 — "Studies are continuing near Lisbon, N.D., to learn more about the gopher in his natural habitat." Round 8, *NWB News*, May 26, 1971 — "Kindred, N.D. — A field trial of buried cable just might put the bite on one of NWB's peskiest problems — the pocket gopher." Bell Labs had responded to a plea from Art Johnson, Fargo district plant supervisor, with new types of "gopher-proof" cable.

Asked in the spring of 1975 how the tests turned out, Johnson said, "Fine." "Then we've finally won the gopher battle?" "Well, yes and no. The cable works, but apparently it's too expensive for general use. But we have licked the gopher in one fight. We used to have trouble all the time with buried wire (as opposed to cable). But now, with bronze wrapping on one and two pair wire, we don't anymore."

Call it a split decision.

And then there was Joe, who answered the motel phone in Mobridge, S.D., when Elsie Wohl wasn't on duty. On outside calls, he'd say, "Mo-rest Motel;" on inside calls, he's say "office." He could laugh just like Elsie and had a very good wolf whistle, especially for a mynah bird.

Information operators became directory assistance operators in the 1960s.

In the eerie calm that followed, operators immediately started handling the flood of emergency calls lighting up the boards. At Charles City, they worked in the open air until Plant men rigged plastic covers over them. Emergency batteries supplied power.

Almost all telephone families in the two towns suffered some loss.

Despite their personal concerns, NWB people pitched in to restore service. Some worked 30 hours straight. Telephone crews from Sioux City and Minneapolis arrived the next day. Western Electric crews in Omaha worked all night loading equipment for the stricken areas. Within eight days, service had been restored to nearly every habitable location. The size of the job: 4,700 phones out in Charles City, 2,100 in Oelwein, nearly 150,000 feet of cable destroyed or damaged. Total restoral cost: about $500,000.

On June 13, tornadoes hit Tracy, Minn., and Arnolds Park, Iowa. At Tracy, the tornado left a path of destruction three blocks wide and 15 blocks long. Nine people were killed and 204 homes damaged. At NWB's building, holes were ripped in the roof and windows blown out. More than 400 phones were dead. Tarps were put over the holes in the roof and the crossbar switches continued to function. About 400 phones were out in Arnolds Parks and Wahpeton, directly across Lake Okoboji. Service was restored in three days in all three towns.

Other notable events of 1968: Information operators became "directory assistance" operators at mid-year as a part of the Company's battle against rapidly increasing volumes of calls for "information." Studies showed 50 per cent of calls came from 10 per cent of the customers. Construction of the Bell System's new L-4 transcontinental coaxial cable across 790 miles of NWB territory was completed in the fall. And Company framemen got a new helper called Automatic Number Announcer (ANA). A frameman testing a line could call ANA and get, within seconds, a voice answer telling him that line's number. Previously this sometimes took hours of painstaking wire tracing.

On Jan. 1, 1969, new rates went into effect in South Dakota, raising the price of local service and altering the price structure for long distance calls within the state: lower rates for customer-dialed calls than for those operator-handled; 20 to 40 per cent discounts during certain hours of the day and on weekends; and new one and two-minute rates that would save money for those with only brief messages to convey. It was the first general rate increase in South Dakota in eight years.

On Nov. 1, 1969, a Commission-approved general rate increase went into effect in North Dakota. Local service rates were increased and a rate structure similar to South Dakota's was established for long distance calls within the state. The increase was the first in North Dakota in almost 16 years.

The year 1969 had its warmer and lighter moments, too. A Minnesota couple wrote NWB a thank you note because Owatonna Plant men Donald Dirksen and Red Gruzebeck had carefully replaced cucumber plants they had disturbed while digging up cable ... After a customer's frantic call, St. Paul Plant men dug through a box of 60 phones to discover the one with the customer's $160 hidden in the receiver ... Bismarck, N.D., police thought they'd discovered a gambling ring when they dialed a certain number and got this message: "Hi, this is Ardis. I'm announcing the end of the first heat: Dasher took last place, Dancer's in fifth, etc. ... " The explanation: NWBers trying to pep up a sales contest; the names were team names.

In September, 1,000 Telephone Pioneers of America descended on Minneapolis for their annual General Assembly. *NWB* magazine published a special edition for those attending.

The Bell System's new color scheme was officially announced the same month. The old familiar green installers' trucks were to be replaced gradually by new ones with white tops and gray-green bottoms separated by horizontal blue and yellow reflective stripes. The same basic colors were to be applied to other display materials.

In the Annual Report for 1969, President A. F. Jacobson said he considered competition and consumerism the two biggest challenges facing Northwestern Bell.

"Consumers' expectations are higher and we simply have to make service better and better," Jacobson said. "We're working at the job very hard, and I think we're doing it successfully."

At year's end, the record showed that Northwestern Bell's construction expenditures topped $200 million for the first time — $216 million opposed to $85 million in 1959. New buildings were part of the total. Included were an addition to the Minneapolis downtown building completed in 1966; a 1965 addition to the Des Moines' Tenth Street building that extended it both north and up; an enlargement of the St. Paul downtown building, completed in 1966; and another 12-story addition to Des Moines Headquarters begun in 1969, completed 1971.

The number of phones in service had grown from 2.4 million to 3.8 million; the percentage of customers with dial was up from 92.2 to 99.8; the percentage who could dial long distance calls had jumped from 29 to 91; the percentage of cable miles buried had grown from 68 to 81. Throughout the 1960s, NWB consistently led the System in the percentage in place of buried cable vs. aerial.

Despite the huge construction investments in cable burying and other improvements, there were no local rate increases in three states during the decade. Various

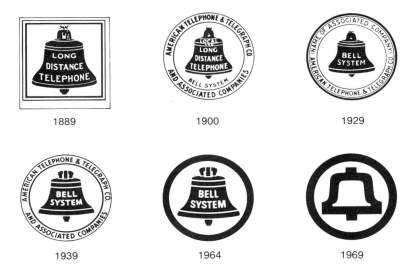

1889 1900 1929

1939 1964 1969

The Bell System changed to the new symbol in 1969. The 1889 version was square so that it could be hung easily from wrought iron brackets.

changes in long distance rates *within* states resulted in a net decrease in rates. And rates for long distance calls across state lines had been reduced six times.

In addition, the increased mechanization of long distance call handling produced a significant share of the overall savings that enabled the Bell companies to hold the line against inflation so long. Working together, state and federal regulators, independent company representatives and Bell System people designed formulas to charge an increasingly large share of local plant investment costs against interstate long distance revenue. Obviously, without local telephones and switching equipment, long distance calling would be impossible. And, with long distance volumes increasing tremendously, local plant was being used more and more for long distance. That's what the new formulas reflected. This transfer of costs was (and still is) an important factor in holding local rates down.

Unfortunately, inflation had continued relentlessly and the rate was accelerating. Inevitably, this pressure would force new rate increases. There were other major problems looming, too.

Going underground

One of the big construction stories of the '60s was Northwestern Bell's progress in burying cable. The work was less costly because of a contribution to cable-plowing technology which Northwestern Bell made years earlier.

No one remembers the exact date now. But for Merv Marsh, Peter Kotschevar, Leon Carpenter, Chuck Hurt and Franc Ryan, a day in May 1954 was special.

For Marsh, Kotschevar and Carpenter, it was the day to do an unusual cable plowing job northwest of St. Cloud, Minn., with a dozen specialists from AT&T and other Bell companies looking on. Marsh, construction foreman at Montivideo, operated a new "miracle" cable plow. Kotschevar was the St. Cloud construction foreman in charge of the crew. Carpenter, as St. Cloud district construction supervisor, had overall responsibility.

Carl Dietl (left) calls signals for Clyde Goedderz in 1961.

For Hurt, a construction supervisor on the Minnesota staff, it was a day of vindication. Bell System experts doubted him a few months earlier in a System-wide construction meeting when Hurt reported how much money and time could be saved by the new plow.

For Ryan, it was the day he was transferred from a "crazy inventor" into a manufacturer with a product in demand. Ryan, a heavy equipment operator at Chariton, Iowa, had been experimenting with the plow for nine years. The past five, he had worked with Northwestern Bell construction men who had faith in him; Hurt; Don White, a Minnesota construction superintendent-outstate; Herbert Bloxam, construction supervisor on White's staff; Kurt Jensen, North Dakota construction superintendent; and "Colonel" Leverson, supervising construction foreman on Jensen's staff.

Previously, cable plowing had been a matter of brute strength, with a half dozen caterpillar tractors required to pull a plow. By the time such a cable train had clawed its way through an area, it was a major job to restore the terrain. Ryan's plow could be pulled by one tractor. It moved as fast as the old, and much less restoral work was required.

At St. Cloud, it took only a few hours for the doubters to become believers. Ryan got orders from throughout the Bell System.

In 1961 Minnesota construction men did it again. They used a homemade plow to bury 45 miles of cable in the rocky soil along the shore of Lake Superior south of Gran Marais. Designed by Carl Dietl, construction supervisor for the Duluth District, and Clyde Goedderz, a Brainerd heavy equipment contractor, the new plow uprooted boulders, slithered around mailboxes and tucked cable into the 18-inch space between the highway and guard railing. Because so much hand digging was eliminated, savings were about $50,000 on the $400,000 project.

Telephone people's determination to put cable underground was well-advised. In the mid-sixties, Northwestern Bell would reach a watershed in storm damage.

Two major storms, among the worst in Company history, hit in March of 1966. Early in the month, high winds, snow and sleet swept Nebraska, Minnesota and the Dakotas, knocking out service to 6,000 customers. A 340-foot microwave tower at Stefan, S.D., toppled under the strain and NWB and Long Lines personnel worked day

Burying cable near Pierre, S.D.

and night to erect an emergency replacement.

The second storm, more severe, struck wide areas of Iowa, Nebraska and Minnesota, leaving telephone damages of more than $2.5 million, and 16,000 customers without service. About 2,000 men from NWB, Mountain States, Wisconsin, Illinois and Southwestern Bell Companies helped with restoral.

In October, 60 to 70 mph winds whipped wet snows across most of Nebraska, causing $1.25 million damage to NWB plant. By nightfall, more than 2,000 poles were down and 94 towns without service. Twenty-nine construction crews from Iowa, Minnesota and South Dakota helped Nebraska Plant men with the week-long restoral job. The total storm damage for the year, $5 million, an NWB record that still stands.

Storms would still cause damage, but by 1967 continued improvement in cable-burying techniques had brought NWB's cost below that for aerial cable, and the Company had 80 per cent of its long distance lines underground.

In fact, a new kind of service interruption was becoming a problem: cable cuts during excavation or ditching work. In the summer of 1966, NWB began using a cable patrol plane to check cable routes and spot construction activity that might result in breaks. One interesting result: near Beresford, S.D., the pilot spotted a farmer cleaning a ditch with a bulldozer. He radioed an NWB control point and a maintenance man was sent to the scene. Had the farmer continued, he probably would have cut the Omaha-Sioux Falls cable, and been terribly embarrassed. The same farmer, using the same bulldozer, had already cut the same cable once in 1966.

Chapter XVII

Hello, World

Telecommunications at a Crossroads

WHILE THE 1960s were years when NWB's biggest problems were internal, the 1970s were to be the years in which "outside" pressures would predominate. Hints of difficulties to come were already in the air as the new decade began. The FCC had earlier opened the door to "competition" which Bell System leaders feared would make it more difficult to provide top-notch service at the lowest possible cost. Accusations by would-be competitors were giving new impetus to those who had always believed the Bell System should be broken up. Inflationary pressures were making it increasingly difficult to put off asking for rate increases. The nation's equal employment opportunity problems were far from solved. And the seeds of a serious recession were sprouting.

Competition was, in fact, threatening dramatic changes in a telephone system that had evolved out of more than 90 years experience. And nobody in Northwestern Bell realized that better than Tom Nurnberger. He had become president of the Company in May 1970 when A. F. Jacobson retired.*

---

*Spring 1975, Jake was still a busy man, serving as a consultant to the Italian Government phone system and continuing a variety of business and civic activities in Omaha.

T. S. Nurnberger

Nurnberger was an adopted son coming home. He had begun his telephone career with Michigan Bell in 1946. By 1958 he was vice president-personnel there. He came to Omaha as Nebraska Area vice president and general manager in 1960, was named vice president-operations in 1966.

That job had been a springboard for many Bell System leaders — Kappel, McNeely, Jacobson, Oberg — and Nurnberger was no exception. He was elected president of Indiana Bell in 1968.*

Now he returned to his adopted Company — and to a whole family of new challenges that had moved in with the Bell System and Northwestern Bell. "Competition" was at the top of the list.

By June 1970, the FCC had received 1,713 applications to provide specialized common carrier service, filed by 35 firms. In May 1971, the FCC announced it would allow open entry of specialized common carriers into direct competition with the established common carriers (telephone companies) for private line services.

The next month, the National Association of Regulatory Utility Commissioners (NARUC) and the Washington State Commission filed suit asking a U.S. District Court to intervene.† Obviously aware that state commissions would be blamed when local rates had to be raised, NARUC stressed that the FCC had violated requirements of the Communications Act of 1934, "by permitting new entrants in the specialized communications field to serve high density routes . . . without giving sufficient weight or consideration . . . [to] whether a diversion of revenue from the existing carriers would result in the remaining cus-

---

*Nurnberger's successor as vice president-operations at NWB was Marvin Oberg who, in turn, became president of American Bell, Inc. in 1974. American Bell, an AT&T subsidiary, was established to advise and assist the government telephone system in Puerto Rico. Jack MacAllister, vice president and chief executive officer for Iowa, replaced Oberg.

†In the spring of 1975 the suit was still awaiting a decision.

tomers — the general public — being forced to bear a heavier burden."

The Bell System was not a party to the NARUC suit. As 1971 ended, it was still trying to give the new FCC policies a fair trial. But pressure was building for some-one in the Bell System to speak out.

In January of 1972, someone did. Speaking before Omaha Rotarians, NWB's Tom Nurnberger issued this early warning: "telecommunications . . . and with it those who provide it, regulate it, use it . . . are at a crossroads." He warned that, as a result of decisions already made, and others still pending, the quality of telephone service was likely to deteriorate and its cost, to most users, increase significantly.

Vital Speeches magazine reprinted the talk and gave it national distribution. Excerpts:

"Until now, telephone companies have had end-to-end control of the call process and regulators at state and fed-eral levels exercised continued surveillance over the entire operation . . . I wonder," he continued, "if fragmenting the over-all responsibility for service won't deteriorate serv-ice? Who will [regulators] hold accountable for service quality?

"It was apparent years ago," Nurnberger said, "that if we had charged every customer exactly what it cost us to provide him service, many people would have done without . . . Telephone service rates have been historically based on statewide and nationwide average costs. Serv-ices that produced a good profit helped carry the load of low profit services . . .

"Suppose we were to price your calls to reflect our direct costs of providing service along a particular route," President Nurnberger suggested. "You could expect that your call to New York or Chicago . . . would be cheaper. But your calls to places on lightly used routes would be . . . substantially higher. It would seem to me such a pricing scheme would have a profound impact on the economic growth of these small towns . . .

"Creating equal competitive opportunities throughout our industry sounds fair enough. But before we loosen restrictions further, let's look carefully at the long-term implications and be sure they are in the public interest."

But the private carriers were already moving in

rapidly. That same year, Nebraska Consolidated Communications Corp. (later called N-Triple-C) received FCC approval to construct a Minneapolis to Houston specialized common carrier microwave route. By August, it was building microwave stations in Omaha, Des Moines and Minneapolis. And a dozen other companies were asking permission to build similar facilities in NWB territory. "Each week," *NWB News* reported, "competitors install an average of two PBX or key systems (multi-button phone facilities) for businesses that a few years ago were served by Northwestern Bell."

In September 1973, speaking to members of the National Association of Regulatory Utility Commissioners (NARUC), AT&T Chairman John deButts called for a "moratorium on further experiments in economics . . . " He asked for a systematic evaluation of the impact of competition on the public at large.

During the year, Edward P. Larkin, a member of the New York State Commission, and Ben T. Wiggins, NARUC president, made forceful statements warning against the FCC's competition policies. Both NARUC and the United States Independent Telephone Association initiated broad inquiries into the effects of those policies on the public. Despite their questions, the tide toward interconnection of privately owned equipment and private line competition rolled on.

In a March 1974 talk to Pioneers, Nurnberger pointed out that, under federally sponsored "competition," the nation's railroads had languished. "But despite the railroad lesson, federal regulators seem determined to handicap us with the same sort of competition, where we have to operate with our hands tied." In April 1974, NWB began a series of seminars with management and customer contact employees to be sure they understood federal antitrust rules. Employees were to compete vigorously, but stay within both the letter and the intent of antitrust laws.

But much that affected NWB was taking place far outside its territory. On April 11, the FCC announced it would conduct a broad inquiry into the economic impact of interconnection. In May, NARUC released a report of its inquiry, stating that it believed that business lost to competitors would leave state regulators "no practical alternative but to grant more increases in home telephone rates." Also in May, the U.S. Court of Appeals in the District of Columbia sent back to the FCC, for reconsideration, an earlier FCC decision allowing RCA to compete with the Hawaiian Telephone Company for private line service between the U.S. and Hawaii. "It is all too embarassingly apparent" the Court said, "that the Federal Communications Commission has been thinking about competition not in terms primarily as to its benefit to the public but specifically with the objective of equalizing competition among competitors."

June 13, AT&T put its Hi-Lo rates for private lines into effect, a move the FCC had delayed for 16 months. In July, N-Triple-C filed a triple damage antitrust suit against AT&T, NWB and Lincoln Telephone and Telegraph, charging combination and conspiracy of trade. The complaint focused on the cancellation of the Nebraska state government microwave system contract held by N-Triple-C for about five years. NWB answered that the charges were without merit.

In September, the accounting firm, Touche, Ross & Co., issued a report that said, among other things, that "because of Western's pricing policies and practices, [its] lower costs have not increased [Bell System] profits, but have been passed on to operating companies in the form of lower prices." The FCC had commissioned the study.

Two months later, the U.S. Justice Department filed an antitrust suit against AT&T, asking that Western Electric be separated from the Bell System and that it be split into two or more competing firms, that at least some of the Long Lines Department be split from at least some of the Bell operating companies. The suit also asked the Court to decide what should be done with the Bell Telephone Laboratories. AT&T, Western and Bell Labs were named defendants and the operating companies, including NWB were named co-conspirators. The charge: monopolization of telecommunications services and equipment in the U.S.

"The users will be the losers if the Bell System is broken up," AT&T Chairman deButts answered. "But we do not for a single moment believe it will be. We are confident that we are and always have been in full compliance with the 1956 consent decree, which remains in full force and effect."

Equipmentman Gordy Bierman (left) and Plant Manager Dave Horky examine the damage after the fire and explosion at Schwan's.

The Justice Department's action got mixed reviews. "Curiously," wrote *TIME* magazine, "the trustbusters have doubts about whether or not a Bell breakup would improve the economics or quality of communications service. They do not seriously quarrel with Bell's argument that the industry as presently structured has produced the world's best telephone service, and at fairly reasonable costs. They also concede that Bell profits have not been inordinate, in fact have remained relatively static in terms of return on invested capital."

The Des Moines Register, on the other hand, thought the suit was a necessary review . . . "It may well be that tighter regulation and supervision of the communications industry is a more practical solution than attempts to break up the conglomerate and induce competition. But first the lawsuit should bring out the facts of the situation."

The Omaha World-Herald suggested "that the huge and intricate system represented by AT&T has given the country an excellent telephone network, overall, at reasonable rates and with continuing innovation. We can't imagine that breaking up this system in favor of competitive forces only vaguely mentioned by the Justice Department would be of any net benefit to the public."

For Schwan's Sales Enterprises of Marshall, Minn., however, the debate was academic. On a Saturday in March 1974, an explosion and fire destroyed Schwan's, an ice cream producer and the town's largest employer. At Schwan's, NWB had a 770 PBX, 150 telephones and several business and WATS lines plus a paging system. By Sunday morning, NWB had temporary lines installed in what was left of the factory. The crews began putting Schwan's back in business in an old bank building. The bank hadn't planned to leave for a week, but moved immediately to aid the stricken firm. Northwestern Bell had to rush the bank's phones at the same time it was putting Schwan's back in business. From Sunday morning until Monday night, crews worked without sleep. By then they had each of Schwan's 15 business and WATS lines back in operation, plus enough telephones and paging facilities to get things moving again . . . It was a timely demonstration of Bell System service. Eight months earlier, Schwan's had been contacted by a competing firm, but stayed with NWB because of its service.

In the midst of competitive pressures and antitrust suits, Northwestern Bell had another dragon to contend with in the '70s.

*　*　*

Inflation had continued to rise throughout the 1960s and, beginning in 1967, increased at a sharply faster rate. Telephone rates in the five states had remained stable for over a decade, but the high cost of everything was beginning to tell by 1970. North Dakota had received a rate increase in 1969, its first in 16 years. By the end of 1971, with rate applications pending in four states, NWB earnings per share had slumped 17 per cent below what they had been at the end of 1969.

Three rate decisions in 1972 offered temporary help. Iowa and Minnesota increased their rates for the first time in 14 years, Nebraska for the first time in 15. But inflationary pressures were relentless. In 1974 Northwestern Bell sold a $150 million debenture issue at a record annual cost to the Company of 10.14 per cent. So despite rate increases in South Dakota, Iowa, Minnesota and

Nebraska, the Company's earnings dropped again in 1974. In his 1974 Annual Report message, President Nurnberger emphasized that improved earnings were essential to the Company's credit (bond) rating " . . . because our ability to borrow money is so vital to everything this business stands for, and everything our customers and the regulatory bodies expect of us . . . putting our financial house in better order will have to be one of Northwestern Bell's top objectives for 1975 . . . the cost of telephone service has too often not kept pace with the rapid rise in the cost of living . . . "*

The earnings slump had come despite Northwestern Bell's constant battle against increasing costs. The introduction of new computer procedures to replace tedious (and costly) manual operations was a big part of the effort.

In 1970 Accounting in Omaha began providing time-sharing computer access to all Company departments. (A time-sharing computer can perform tasks for many users simultaneously.)

On May 1, 1970, a Customer Name and Address (CNA) bureau began serving the entire Company from Omaha. Its purpose: to speed the process of determining a customer's name and address when only the phone number was known. Service representatives often need this information when tracing billing errors or answering customer questions. At the CNA bureau microfiche cards (a form of microfilm) were on file, each containing 10,000 lines of information. The CNA operator could read information simply by placing a card in an enlarger. Average response time was reduced from two minutes to 25 seconds.†

---

*Despite the rate increases, the average cost of basic one-party residence telephone service had increased only 27 per cent since 1964. By comparison, the cost of living jumped 66 per cent during those years.

†In 1974 Minneapolis Accounting converted the customer name and address records to microfiche, reducing 100,000 pages of paper records to a stack of 4- by 6-inch microfiche cards three inches high. The Company saved more than 26 tons of computer print-out paper per month, and cut costs 75 per cent. Minnesota also used microfiche to store long distance records and the customer payment register.

In July 1970, Iowa became the first NWB state using the new Universal Service Order form (USO) at all its locations. And Spencer, Iowa, became the first location in Northwestern Bell territory to be fully converted to CRB (Customer Records and Billing) in March of 1973, giving a glimpse of how the entire business will be operated in the computerized future.

With CRB, a service rep records a customer's order on the Universal Service Order (USO) and an order typist sends it to the computer in Accounting via a communications display terminal (CDT). The CDT, a teletypewriter that displays what is typed on a TV-like screen, sends the order to the computer only when the typist is satisfied it is correct. The computer may store the order until needed or distribute it, via teletypewriter, to Plant, Traffic, Directory or Accounting. Once the order has been worked, the typist recalls the order image to the screen and records any changes made by the installer. The corrected information then goes back to the computer. From that point on, the customer's entire service record is in the computer and can be displayed on business office CDT screens, or printed out for other departments as needed.

The conversion at Spencer represented the end result of six years of careful planning which began in the mid-1960s. But it was only a milestone on the long road to converting all Iowa locations* and, eventually, all Company locations, to CRB.†

By the end of September 1971, Sioux Falls personnel had moved into their new area headquarters building, and in November, Northwestern Bell's first Traffic Service Position System (TSPS) went into service in the building, enabling Sioux Falls' residents to dial their own person-to-person and collect calls, and freeing operators

---

*Iowa CRB conversion was to be completed throughout the state by the end of 1975.

†Directory people were developing ways to use CRB to streamline their operations. One result was DIR/ECT (for DIRectory projECT), a computerized system which can take directory information from the CRB system and produce Directory Assistance listings or, via a photocomposer, set the type for directory pages. The Company's first trial of DIR/ECT began at Mason City, Iowa, early in 1975.

The Company's first Traffic Service Position System, Sioux Falls, cut operator call-handling time at least one-third.

from using cords or making billing records.* TSPS performs basically the same functions as the older TSP unit installed at Sioux City, Iowa, in 1965. Sioux City was the first NWB city to have TSP and one of the first in the nation. But that system used mechanical switches while TSPS is a computerized system and can be tied in with any type of long distance switching equipment.

Customers in Minneapolis, St. Paul, Coon Rapids and White Bear Lake, Minn., vicinities got TSPS in 1972 and by May 1975, Omaha customers also were able to dial their own credit card and collect calls via TSPS.

Starting in October 1971, Minneapolis customers who dialed numbers that had been changed or disconnected began getting the information they needed directly from a

---

*By reading the TSPS console's number displays and pushing the proper buttons, the operator directs the switching and billing equipment to do the work that requires use of cords, dials, timers and mark sense tickets at a traditional board. On a person-to-person call, for instance, the operator finds out who the customer wants, pushes a button to send the call on its way, stays on line to make sure the called person is available, then pushes a second button to start the billing tape and a third to release the connection. Fifteen to 30 separate motions are required to handle the same call on a traditional board. By pushing the right buttons, the TSP operator can have the calling number displayed, the called number or even the charges for a coin call.

computer voice answer called Automatic Intercept System (AIS). Triggered by the number dialed, the computer repeated the number, told its status and gave the new number if available. The system, second in the Bell System, was expanded to include St. Paul in 1972.

With Iowa's conversion in the spring of 1971, all areas were using optical scanners to read mark sense cards. Previously, one machine "sensed" the soft graphite pencil marks on a mark sense card and translated the information into holes punched in the cards. Then other machines processed the newly punched cards. The new optical scanner could read the marked information directly off the cards and into the computers. This system was 10 times faster. In the process, operators got a new kind of pencil that didn't smudge their hands.

Northwestern Bell became 100 per cent dial Nov. 7, 1971, with the conversion of Gordon, Nebr. Part of a $4 million project in the Gordon area, the program took four times longer than usual, engineers said, because of the dif-

The time-share computer in Omaha processed programs for more than 100 NWB groups in the five states during 1971.

ficult terrain. Some "roads" couldn't be found, others were
so rough that tires on heavily loaded trucks blew out. One
repeater station was 18 miles from the nearest hard-sur-
face road. There was no water until a well was dug, no
power until the building was built.

The conversion to dial — begun in Omaha in 1921 —
had taken 50 years. Ironically, in 1971 Northwestern Bell
also installed its eighth electronic central office and had
provided direct distance dialing to 94 per cent of its customers.

Northwestern Bell's policy is to put in new equipment
whenever a community outgrows the old, or when the old
will no longer give good service or if the efficiency of the
new system is so great that both Company and customer
would save money by getting rid of the old. And, like
Casper Yost a half-century before, telephone people are
still seeking ways to provide economical dial service in
small communities.

Another Bell System first was chalked up by Northwestern Bell in 1972 when Western Electric delivered its
new No. 5A crossbar module to Hanover, Minn. Previously, Western shipped central office components to the
field, assembled and tested them there. With the new 5A,
much assembly and testing was done at the factory, while
the central office building was being built. Then the 21-ton
unit was shipped to Hanover on a large flat-bed semi-
trailer. Field installation was completed in weeks, instead
of months, and Hanover's old dial switches were replaced
by new. Willow Lake, S.D., received a similar unit in
December 1972.

And then the whole pre-assembly process was carried
a step further. When residents of Hudson, S.D., awoke one
July morning in 1973, there was a brand new 12- by 50-
foot telephone building sitting next to the old one. Brought
in by truck, the prefabricated building contained pre-
assembled dial equipment which, when hooked up,
replaced the old.

In the fall of 1973, Omaha's Directory Assistance Unit
II was the first to have the Bell System's new No. 5
Automatic Call Distributor — Phase II, which enabled
operators to forward calls to other locations as necessary
and which would eventually enable them to get the name
sought directly from a display unit rather than by

Living with investigations

If the U.S. Justice Department's antitrust suit against the Bell System in 1974 seemed something like a re-run to veteran Bell employees, there was reason:

In January of 1956, the U.S. District Court in Newark, N.J., entered a final judgment in an antitrust suit which the U.S. Justice Department had filed against AT&T in 1949. The Justice Department had sought to separate Western Electric from the rest of the Bell System. The judgment (consent decree) left Western as part of the Bell System but required that it limit its production generally to communications equipment for Bell System operating companies and that it make all its patents available to others on reasonable terms.

In 1966 the FCC abandoned its long-standing policy of "continuing surveillance" and began a full-scale investigation of Bell System rates and earnings. (It's still underway.) AT&T protested, emphasizing that under continuing surveillance, interstate rates had been lowered 22 per cent since 1940, while other prices doubled.

TV Commentator David Brinkley had some pungent comments of his own at that time: "The FCC has begun a long investigation of the telephone company to see how much money it makes. However it turns out, it is true this country's phones are the world's best by far . . . the telephone company says it needs to make 8 per cent on its invested money. Well, it seems modest enough, since that is about the average for American industry . . . " (That was in 1966. Higher money costs require higher earnings today.)

Brinkley went on to note how an Austrian Government official had spoken wistfully of his college days in America, when he got a phone easily and quickly. Now, though entitled to a phone because of his official post, he had been waiting two years and had no idea when he'd get one.

"I don't know whether the phone company makes enough money or too much, or what," Brinkley concluded, "but I do know there's nothing in the world to compare to it."

shuffling through sheets of paper.

The Bell System's first No. 3 crossbar system went into service at Howells, Nebr., in June 1974. Designed to serve 200 to 800 lines, No. 3 was billed as No. 5 crossbar's "country cousin." It was factory-assembled and ready to "plug in."

The same year, Waterloo, Iowa, Repairman John Leary experienced what surely was another Bell System first. After Leary explained to a customer that squirrels had chewed through the telephone cable, but now it was repaired, the customer replied: "This has happened so many times. Could you leave some extra wire in the squirrel feeder so they'll eat it there?"

Early in 1975, the Bell System's first Dimension* PBX was installed in Minneapolis. Small and sophisticated, it is actually a mini ESS office on the customer's premises. Ray Shannon, marketing supervisor, said he thought NWB got the first one "because we have a reputation for offering new services and being able to get things in and working for the customer." (By June 1, NWB had installed six more. Of the Bell System's nine Dimension PBXs in operation, Northwestern had sold seven.)

But all the while the Company was struggling to cut costs and provide customers with the latest equipment, it was also struggling to do its share in the nation's continuing effort to make equal opportunity a reality for all citizens. And now America was placing increasing emphasis on women's rights.

* * *

Almost from the beginning, the telephone company had been considered "a good place for women to work." But the country was changing, and old ideas were being measured with a new yardstick.

Despite the progress that had been made toward equal opportunity, the U.S. Equal Employment Opportunity Commission (EEOC) in December of 1970 filed a petition with the FCC asking that AT&T's request for higher rates be denied because of what EEOC called "pervasive, system-wide and blatantly unlawful" discrimination in the

---

*Trademark of AT&T

employment of women, blacks and Spanish surnamed Americans. The FCC denied the petition; it could see no logical connection between rates and employment policies. But it did establish a separate docket to consider EEOC's charges.

In April 1971, Nurnberger signed a new Affirmative Action Program, reaffirming the Company's earlier commitment to providing equal opportunities. He explained that the Company needed a new program (1) to emphasize that it intended to take positive action, rather than wait for indications of discrimination; (2) because federal and state agencies had issued new guidelines which required positive action to assure compliance; and (3) because a program with clearly stated objectives — target dates, percentages, numbers — was more apt to be effective in an organization the size of NWB.

After the EEOC filed detailed charges against the Bell System in November that year, Bruce G. Schwartz, NWB personnel vice president, emphasized that the Company had come a long way. In 1962 slightly less than one per cent of its employees were of minority races; in the fall of 1971 the percentage was 2.5, compared to 2.3 per cent minority population in NWB territory.

"The opportunity for women to receive promotions has increased," Schwartz said. "At the end of 1969, Northwestern Bell had 57 women above the first level of management, and at the end of October 1971, 77. If you take a reasonable viewpoint and admit that society's basic structure and deep-rooted traditions cannot be changed overnight in a democracy, we have done very well. But at the same time we admit that more can and will be done."

A sampling of NWB women interviewed by *NWB News* in June of 1971 seemed to agree with Schwartz on both counts: that progress had been made and that more could be done. Following are some of their responses:

Jan Stoney, employment relations supervisor in Omaha: "It's obvious . . . that few opportunities . . . at the third level and above have been available to women . . . There is no question that the Company is trying to change this . . ."

Leone Corkery, assistant manager in Cedar Rapids: "Women are beginning to be offered jobs that a few years ago they never would have dreamed of getting." *Leslie*

The Rapid City Flood

The rain began about 7 p.m. on June 9, 1972, but it was not the soothing spring shower that usually brings life to the fields and flowers of the Black Hills. Almost seven inches of rain fell in less than two hours, turning streams into churning torrents. Canyon Lake Dam on the west side of Rapid City broke, spilling a seven-foot wall of water down through the darkness and causing one of the worst floods in Midwestern history.

Daylight revealed the destruction: bare foundations where homes had been, shattered buildings and automobiles clogging usually peaceful streets. Over 200 people lost their lives, some 2,000 homes were destroyed and 9,300 phones were out in this city of 44,000. Many Northwestern Bell men and women in Rapid City suffered great personal losses. Motor Equipment Supervisor Robert Vanderbeek, 42, was among the fatalities. Vanderbeek, his wife and 14-year-old son all drowned when a boat capsized. A 12-year-old son survived.

Telephone people tackled restoration tasks resolutely, though many worked in the shadow of anguish, not knowing if family and friends had survived. Plant managers assessed telephone damage and planned emergency measures. Vehicles with mobile telephones were dispatched to stricken areas. Crews ran temporary lines to install phones where needed. Emergency telephone service was established at the Civil Defense Office. Radiotelephones were rushed in to serve the temporary police headquarters at Central High School.

During the morning, maintenance and construction crews arrived from throughout South Dakota and telephone people from Iowa, Nebraska, North Dakota and Minnesota were dispatched to the Black Hills. Western Electric rushed equipment by air freight from North Carolina, New Jersey and Missouri. Seventeen truckloads of cable came from Omaha; another from Denver.

More than 300 Northwestern Bell people worked 18-hour shifts to restore long distance service to all 13 com-

Pat Coyle (left) and Russel Evans work to salvage flood-damaged cable south of Rapid City.

munities isolated by the flood and to reconnect phone service to habitable homes. A flood of incoming calls continued for days, as people tried to learn the fate of friends and relatives. The long distance control center in Omaha reported 750,000 attempts to call South Dakota Saturday and Sunday. Work schedules were forgotten as operators stayed at their boards.

Though the flood caused damage that would take weeks or even months to repair permanently, within 48 hours NWBers had installed enough temporary communications facilities to put Rapid City and nearby communities back in business. In less than five days, 4,000 phones were back in service.

NWB President Tom Nurnberger expressed his feelings with these words: "The men and women of Northwestern Bell reacted to the emergency quickly, efficiently and unselfishly. I am proud of them, and of the Company's ability to respond in such circumstances. The situation was not typical, but I'm convinced that the performance of Northwestern Bell and its people was. This, I think, illustrates a basic principle of our business, and that is the strong sense of responsibility we have toward our customers."

Weimer, frameman in Bismarck, N.D.: "I took a man's aptitude test and when there was an opening, I was considered and hired." *Georgia Engelkes,* engineer at Sioux Falls: "After my first projects proved successful, there wasn't any concern about me wearing skirts."

Catherine Chambers, district traffic supervisor in Minneapolis: "I might be a living example of opportunity for women at NWB . . . I'll agree there have been some injustices to women. I've known many who have trained their male bosses." *Teresa Hickman,* assistant accounting supervisor in Omaha: "As I see it, there has to be a good future for women in business. After all, it's not just a man's world . . . "

In January of 1973, the U.S. Department of Labor, the EEOC and the Bell System companies (including NWB) signed an agreement which was subsequently approved by a U.S. District Court. The EEOC agreed to move for dismissal of its case against the companies and to work with the Bell System to resolve pending law suits and charges of discrimination. The Bell System, in turn, made commitments to facilitate the hiring and movement of qualified minority and women employees into better jobs and to encourage them to fill formerly non-traditional roles.*

The agreement also called for establishment of a Transfer and Promotion (T&P) Application Plan. Northwestern Bell was a step ahead. It had put its own plan, the first of its kind in the Bell System, into effect in October 1971. Under it, non-management employees with six months' service (later changed to one year) could file requests for transfer and promotion.

In May 1974, a new management promotion pay policy agreement, similar to the 1973 non-management agreement, was signed by AT&T and federal authorities.

---

*At NWB, as a result of various provisions of the agreement: 221 non-management employees got pay raises under a new Promotion Pay Plan; 105 women non-management employees who may have been paid less than men when promoted got lump sum back pay equal to the difference. And 84 women or minority employees who may have been delayed in obtaining craft jobs received lump sum payments ranging from $100 to $400. At the time, NWB had more than 15,000 women employees.

Installer-talker Pankowski is one of NWB's many employees who visit schools to discuss telephone careers.

Statistics for the end of 1974 indicate the effectiveness of Northwestern Bell's efforts: there were 885 men in jobs historically held by women, 491 women in what had been "men's" jobs; there were 150 minority persons in management, compared to 12 in 1968; 2,197 women compared to 1,453. At the end of 1974, after just over three years' operation, more than 5,100 employees had been transferred or promoted via T&P.

In May of 1975, AT&T and the federal government entered into a supplemental agreement calling for additional efforts. It noted that while the Bell System's combined 1973 and 1974 performance represented "a substantial accomplishment," many companies had not met 1973 intermediate targets for various job classifications and were therefore found to be "not in compliance."

However, Northwestern Bell was the first of five Bell System companies whose 1973 and 1974 records were considered "good faith efforts to meet EEO targets." As a result, NWB was not affected by most of the provisions of the supplemental agreement.

But perhaps the best summation of the changes taking place took place in an elementary school classroom at Millard, Nebr., in April of 1973. When Installer Dave Pankowski walked in, the youngsters shouted, "It's the telephone man." He did the standard routine, showed his tools, admonished the youngsters to stay away from poles, manholes and fallen wires, and then surprised the girls by telling them that they, too, could grow up and be installers at Northwestern Bell if they wished.

* * *

All the while that Northwestern Bell was adjusting to new challenges — equal opportunity employment, competition, the antitrust suit and new technologies — an old enemy called bad weather continued its harassment.

In January 1971, a blizzard dumped 6 to 20 inches of snow across the Midwest, forcing travel to a standstill and closing many businesses. Omaha Lineman Dick Gaskin, driving a 10-ton boom truck, came upon a stalled car containing a woman about to give birth. With Gaskin's truck breaking trail, they made it to the hospital two hours later, but in time. AT&T Network Chief Randy Homier spent 49 hours on emergency duty, finally made it almost home and found he had to dig his way *in*.

As far as Omaha was concerned, an even worse blizzard hit eastern Nebraska in January 1975. Thousands were stranded overnight in stores, taverns and office buildings, including 200 or so NWBers, mostly Traffic people, snowed-in at the Headquarters building and at the 78th and Girard location. Food for the Girard people was brought in by snowmobile.

Ron Henry, plant assignment clerk, attracted considerable news coverage with his timely "take charge" action during the storm. When the car he was in stalled, Henry got out and started helping everyone else. Three hours later he had: (1) pushed at least 70 cars and 2 pickup trucks; (2) directed a car full of elderly women to a police cruiser after their car was in an accident, and (3) borrowed a woolen cap to protect his own bare head.

Nor were blizzards the only weather problems. June 18, 1974, a tornado blasted the Des Moines suburbs of Ankeny, Pleasant Hill and Runnels, killing two, shredding homes and causing $330,000 worth of telephone plant damage. Several NWBers lost their homes and others lost garages, cars and roofs. The Company's new work center was badly damaged in Ankeny.

May 6, 1975, a vicious tornado blitzed an extensive

section of western Omaha, killing three, destroying 1,000 dwellings and piling cars in heaps. Total damage was estimated at $185 million. Some 35 NWB employees lost their homes or had heavy damage; 2,900 phones were out and the Company maintenance garage at 75th and Pacific was 50 per cent destroyed. Ten NWB trucks were demolished and nine others badly damaged.

But considering the tremendous damage to other facilities, telephone damage was relatively light, due to the amount of buried plant. Damage from the Iowa tornado and two earlier blizzards also was light compared to similar storms 25 years earlier.

* * *

Other milestones of the '70s: In 1970 *NWB* magazine celebrated its 50th anniversary. Present were the first two editors, Guy Leavitt, 80, and Sig Bergh, 84. Together they had edited the first 300 issues, a period ending when Sig retired in 1950. (Leavitt died in 1971, Bergh was still making his home in Omaha spring 1975.)

Sept. 2, 1970, the first issue of *NWB News* was delivered to all employees at their work locations. The newspaper format allowed frequent and economical coverage of Company news.

In 1971 Rex Reed, who started his career as a lineman at Ames in 1947, was named AT&T vice president-labor relations. The same year, Council Bluffs became the first location in NWB territory to have Dial Tone First. Customers could call operator or 911 from a coin phone without depositing a coin. By the end of 1974, 9.4 per cent of NWB's coin phones had Dial Tone First. In the fall of 1972, NWB offered decorator telephone housings in five cities; customers bought the housings, NWB supplied and serviced the working parts. Soon, decorator phones were offered at all Company locations.

In October 1972, the FCC approved an exchange of properties in which United Telephone Company of the West took over Kimball and Potter, Nebr., and Audubon and Exira, Iowa. NWB took over Buxton, Hatton, Hillsboro, Mayville, Northwood, Portland, Reynold and Thompson, N.D., and Hudson, Iowa. The result: more efficient service areas for both companies. Employees could stay with their exchanges, or transfer within their old

Lineman near Atlantic, Iowa

companies . . . And in April of 1974, more than 2,000 attended AT&T's 89th annual shareholder meeting in Minneapolis.

*   *   *

Meanwhile, Northwestern Bell continued to fight the painfully expensive battle of doing away with eight-party lines in rural areas. Year after year the old pole lines along dirt and gravel roads came down, replaced by buried cable that would give the farmer better service, but by the end of 1974, Northwestern Bell still had 120,000 eight-party customers left. The estimated cost to eliminate eight-party lines: $207 million.

Northwestern wasn't the only Company with problems in providing rural service. In July 1971, Nebraska's (and maybe the nation's) smallest telephone company went out of business. The Eli Telephone Co. had five northwest Nebraska rancher customers and a switchboard not much bigger than a bread box. Located in Eli's post office-general store, the board was operated 7 a.m. to 8 p.m. only. When the Eli Company went out of business, the ranchers exchanged their old magneto phones for new dial sets and got round-the-clock service from the Cornhusker Telephone Co. in Merriman, Nebr. NWB helped two ways. For $1, it sold part of an abandoned long distance line from Eli to Merriman, and it loaned Equipmentman Maurice Green of Alliance for two weeks to help the ranchers rebuild their lines.

At the other extreme, in 1972, NWB did the most massive pre-wiring job in its history, to serve the new 57-story IDS building in Minneapolis. NWB brought in nine 2,700-pair feeder cables, some terminating as high as the 49th floor. Fully occupied, the building was to have 16,000 phones plus every type business equipment available.

Massive construction expenditures, both urban and rural, were a primary reason why President Nurnberger was expressing concern about inflation and NWB's earnings picture in the 1974 Annual Report.

In a five-year period, Northwestern Bell's construction expenditures had more than doubled, jumping from $213 million to $441 million. And the $441 million was more than 40 times the 1945 total at World War II's end.

In 1974 alone, 2.3 million customers in Iowa, Minnesota, Nebraska, North Dakota and South Dakota dialed an average of 20 million local calls each day — up one million from 1973. The long distance network handled 409 million calls during 1974, up 34 million from the year before. Installer-repairmen drove 36.5 million miles to businesses and residences, put in 1.3 million telephones, removed 1.1 million others. The net gain was 217,000, bringing the total number of telephones served to 4.8 million.

There was plenty left to do: old dial offices would have to be replaced. Electronic Switching Systems — already serving 16 per cent of Northwestern's customers — would eventually offer new speed and efficiency to all customers. TSPS would permit them to dial all their calls.

The services Northwestern Bell's communications network provides, like the equipment that provides it, are also in the process of constant change. It took Northwestern Bell a half century to convert all its exchanges from manual to dial. Less than 18 years ago, Northwestern Bell began the conversion to direct dialing. Today, that second step is more than 99 per cent complete.

Now at the end of a century of service, the men and

Fargo's exchange building uses recycled heat from the building to cut energy costs.

Good Business — Good Citizenship

On Nov. 18, 1974, the boilers in Fargo, N.D.'s exchange were fired up, then turned off. They weren't turned on again all winter, thanks to an ingenious energy saving plan devised by Curt Smith, building maintenance supervisor. He'd seen to it that a 1973 addition to the exchange incorporated every possible energy saving feature. Then he designed a way to make unorthodox use of the chilled water system previously used to dissipate heat generated by telephone equipment. "We used to run at least 90 tons of air conditioning equipment all winter and, at the same, time, run the boilers," Smith explained. His new system transferred heat from the equipment rooms to other, colder parts of the buildings. Savings: $8,500 on fuel oil plus all the power not used for air conditioning.

This was perhaps the most dramatic example of the ways in which NWB cut its energy consumption by five per cent during 1974. Fuel oil consumption was cut six per cent despite a winter colder than 1973 and an increase of 6½ per cent in total Company floor space. The space increase and an increase of eight per cent in total telephones created new demands for electrical power, yet power consumption decreased one per cent, thanks to Company-wide efforts to eliminate unnecessary usage.

Extra attention was focused on vehicle maintenance and it paid off. Bell System statistics had South Dakota first in the System for lowest vehicle repair costs per 10,000 miles for half-ton trucks, and Nebraska first for vehicles other than cars and half-tons, NWB News reported in August 1974. All five areas ranked in the top ten. South Dakota also led the System in running costs of cars, averaging $378 per 10,000 miles vs. the System average of $636. The article featured George Vosicky, Valentine, Nebr., combinationman, and his 1969 four-wheel drive pick-up which had 121,000 miles on it and was still going strong. All told, Company vehicles drove a million more miles in 1974 than 1973 yet used 214,000 fewer gallons of gasoline.

Collection efforts in five NWB communities yielded 1,000 tons of old directories for recycling in 1974. In some cities, employees separated recyclable waste paper from other trash. Omaha's efforts alone resulted in 400 tons. As early as 1972, NWB News had started printing on recycled paper.

That same year, Yost Pioneers celebrated Earth Week by helping build two parks, cleaning unsightly vacant lots and by testing vehicles for harmful exhaust emissions. And in 1974, Yost Pioneers began collecting discarded mercury batteries (from hearing aids, watches, Bellboys, etc.) and made their plan available to other Pioneer chapters. The project, which had been conceived by Don Riggenbach, public relations supervisor, Omaha, won third place in the Pioneer's nationwide "People Who Care" competition.

NWB employees, like Bismarck Manager Gloria Olson (left) and Service Representative Joani Duemeland, continue the goal of providing excellent service to our 2.3 million customers.

women of Northwestern Bell have embarked on a new step. Northwestern Bell's Annual Report for 1974 described it this way:

No one mentioned destiny when Northwestern Bell introduced International Direct Distance Dialing (IDDD) last September in Duluth. But it was destiny of a sort.

People in Duluth take international telephone service seriously. For many, it's part of their livelihood. IDDD enables our customers in Duluth to dial 20 foreign countries without the aid of an operator. Duluth callers can now dial the other great ports and trade centers of the world.

Even in the absence of fanfare, the introduction of international dialing to Duluth (and earlier in the year to Minneapolis, St. Paul and Rochester) signaled another

Appendix B

REGULATION

When Nebraska's Populist-dominated legislature passed a law subjecting telephone rates to state regulation in 1897, it may have been the first state to do so. And when Iowa put telephone rates under the jurisdiction of the Iowa Commerce Commission in 1963, it was next to the last.*

The concept of state regulation of railroads and warehouses began to get a foothold in the 1870s. That's when the United States Supreme Court upheld an Illinois law regulating storage rates grain elevators could charge. With that, the public interest concept for regulating private enterprise was firmly established in the United States. Soon, various states acted to bring railroad rates under state control, too.

Nebraska established a Board of Railway Commissioners in 1885. In 1887 it was reorganized as the State Board of Transportation and given jurisdiction over public warehouses as well as railroads. It was this board that was given control over telephone, telegraph and express companies by the Nebraska law passed on April 8, 1897.

Casper Yost and Nebraska Telephone fought that law strenuously. But within 10 days after its passage, Yost had made up his mind to "see if they use us fairly" before challenging the constitutionality of the law. By May 1 he was writing to the American Company: "You do not believe it, but . . . the telephone business must very soon become a business in which only a good return on the investment will be allowed."

Ten years later, the American Company publicly accepted that idea in the 1907 Annual Report, Theodore Vail's first after returning as president. Vail wrote that there was no "serious objection to [regulatory] control, provided it is independent, intelligent, considerate, thorough and just, recognizing . . . that capital is entitled to its fair return, and good management or enterprise to its reward."

Various states were by then actively investigating the idea of regulating telephone rates. In many localities, the public was disenchanted with the results of having competing telephone companies. Government regulation was seen as an alternative to competition.

---

*Texas is the only state that still leaves regulation of telephone rates to municipal jurisdiction.

Nebraska was into its second round of regulation. Nebraska Telephone had challenged the constitutionality of the State Board of Transportation later in 1897 and lost. But in 1900, the board was declared unconstitutional when the Burlington & Missouri Railroad challenged its authority. Late in 1906, Nebraska voters approved an amendment to the constitution that paved the way for establishment of the State Railway Commission March 27, 1907. This commission has had jurisdiction over telephone rates ever since. The name was changed to Public Service Commission in 1972.

On July 1, 1907, South Dakota established a Board of Telephone Commissioners and gave it power to regulate telephone rates. In 1909 responsibility for telephone regulation was transferred to the Board of Railroad Commissioners. This board has been in existence since 1885. On July 1, 1930, the name was changed to the Public Utilities Commission.

North Dakota was next, with telephone regulation going into effect March 1, 1915. The legislature granted that authority to the Board of Railroad Commissioners which had been established by the Dakota Territorial Legislature in 1885. When North Dakota became a state in 1889, its constitution provided for continuation of the board. In 1940 a constitutional amendment changed the name to the Public Service Commission.

In Minnesota, a Railroad Commission was established in 1871 and later became the Railroad and Warehouse Commission. With the passage of an act known as the Minnette Bill, authority to regulate telephone matters was delegated to the Railroad and Warehouse Commission on July 1, 1915. The name was changed to the Public Service Commission in 1967.

In Iowa, regulation of telephone companies was left to municipalities until July 4, 1963. At that time, the authority was vested in the new Iowa State Commerce Commission. Northwestern Bell officers supplied information to the legislature and otherwise worked to help make the transition to the new system a smooth one.

Appendix C

A HISTORY OF COMPETITION
IN MAJOR TOWNS

In the five states Northwestern Bell serves, only two major cities — Fargo and Jamestown, N.D. — have never had any telephone service but Bell. Scottsbluff, Nebr., Minot, N.D., and Brookings, S.D., are the only ones that have never had Bell exchange service.

A brief history of each state's largest exchanges is presented here alphabetically.

IOWA —

AMES — Bell established 1884; competition from Boone County Company 1904 until sold to Bell 1909; consolidated 1910. Dial since 1955.

BURLINGTON — Bell established 1879; competition from Mississippi Valley (J. C. Hubinger's company) 1896 until court-ordered sale in 1910; Bell purchased in 1913. Dial since 1954.

CEDAR FALLS — Independent established in 1895; various independents operated until sold to Corn Belt Company in 1905; Bell bought control of Corn Belt in 1909 and operated the exchange under the Corn Belt name until merger in 1917. Dial since 1954.

CEDAR RAPIDS — Bell established in 1880; competition from Cedar Rapids and Marion Telephone Company 1895 to 1909 when Bell bought control and consolidated the two plants under the independent name; merged into Bell in 1915. Dial since 1931.

CLINTON — Bell established 1880; Tri-City Company started competition in 1895 and converted to dial in 1910; NWB bought Tri-City in 1928 and consolidated the two exchanges, furnishing manual service to all. Reconverted to dial 1956.

COUNCIL BLUFFS — Bell established 1879; competition from the Independent Telephone Company of Council Bluffs in 1905; Bell bought control in 1911 and consolidated under the independent name with Gen. Grenville M. Dodge as president; merged into NWB in 1924. Dial since 1940. First Electronic Switching System office July 1971.

DAVENPORT — Established by Western Union in 1879; sold to Bell soon after; competition from Union Electric Company 1902-1911 when Union Electric discontinued operations. Dial since 1935.

DES MOINES — Established 1879 by Western Union; sold to Bell shortly after; competition from Mutual Company 1896 until Bell bought control 1909; consolidated 1910. This was the first large consolidation in the five states. It cost $32,000 to rearrange switchboards and other equipment so that 7,700 Bell and 7,300 independent customers could be served by one unified system. About 1,600 instances of dual service were eliminated. Dial since 1929. First ESS office November 1971.

DUBUQUE — Bell established 1879; Western Union started a competing exchange later the same year and sold to Bell soon after. Competition came again, from Dubuque Company, in 1900; Bell bought control 1908; consolidated 1915. Dial since 1951.

FORT DODGE — Bell established 1882-83; competing Fort Dodge Company established 1898 and bought out Bell in 1910; converted to dial 1955; operated by Central Telephone & Utilities Corp. since 1956.

IOWA CITY — Bell established 1881; competition from Johnson County Company 1900-1909 when Bell bought and consolidated. Dial since 1932.

MARSHALLTOWN — Bell established 1881; competition from Marshall Company 1895-1908 when Bell bought control and consolidated under the independent name; merged into NWB 1930. Dial since 1938.

MASON CITY — Bell established 1885 and sold out to the competing Green & Western Company in 1895; the latter sold to the Western Electric Telephone System in 1901 (no relation to W.E. Mfg.). Bell bought control of the Western System in 1905 but did not merge it into NWB until 1929. Dial since 1957.

MUSCATINE — Bell established in 1881; competition from Mississippi Valley Company 1898 until the independent exchange was dismantled in 1910. Dial since 1955.

OTTUMWA — Established by Western Union 1879; soon sold to Bell; competition from the Ottumwa Company 1897-1915 when Bell bought and consolidated. Dial since 1954.

SIOUX CITY — Bell established 1880; competition from the Home Company 1894-95 to 1898 when Bell bought it; competition again from the Sioux City Company which installed a dial system in 1905. Bell bought control of the automatic in 1912 but franchise laws prevented consolidation for years. Bell continued operation of its small manual board until consolidation in 1927.

WATERLOO — Bell established 1881; competition started in 1895 by Waterloo and Cedar Falls Company which sold to Corn Belt in 1905. Bell bought control 1909, consolidated the exchanges and operated them under the Corn Belt name until merged in 1917. Dial since 1941.

MINNESOTA —

AUSTIN — Established in 1894 as an independent and sold to Bell in 1898. Competition from 1903-1918 with the Interstate Company which was sold to and became Tri-State in 1910. Tri-State took over Austin in the 1918 division; converted to dial in 1921; Bell reacquired in the 1933 purchase of Tri-State. Merger completed in 1942.

DULUTH — Bell established 1879-80; competition from the Zenith Company 1907-1918, when Bell bought and consolidated. Dial since 1950. First ESS office June 1974.

MANKATO — Bell established 1889 or before; competition from Mankato City Company started in 1898; Bell discontinued exchange service in 1915 but did handle long distance until 1965 when it was turned over to the Mankato Company.

MINNEAPOLIS — Bell established 1879; competition from Mississippi Valley Company (Tri-State predecessor) in 1898; Tri-State converted to dial in 1916. Bell acquired the independent plant and customers in the 1918 division of territory with Tri-State; consolidation completed in 1920. Conversion of Bell manual offices to dial began in 1927. First ESS office March 1970.

ROCHESTER — Bell apparently established exchange service early in 1881 and discontinued it within a few months. An independent exchange was established in 1896 by the Rochester Company and dial service was offered for a brief period. This company then operated manually until reconverted to dial in 1921. It sold to Tri-State in 1922. NWB bought control of Tri-State in 1933.

ST. CLOUD — Bell established 1882; Tri-State started competition with 12 long distance phones in 1912; Bell acquired the Tri-State properties in 1918. Dial since 1955.

ST. PAUL — Bell established 1879; competition from Mississippi Valley (Tri-State predecessor) in 1898; Tri-State converted to dial in 1916. Bell plant sold to Tri-State in 1918 division of territory. St. Paul was Tri-State headquarters. NWB bought control of Tri-State in 1933 and completed merger in 1942. First ESS office September 1967.

WINONA — Bell established 1880; competition from Winona Company 1894-1910 when Bell took it over; Tri-State established toll lines in 1912, took control of the exchange in the 1918 division of territory with Bell and converted it to dial in 1930. Ownership reverted to Bell in Tri-State purchase, 1933; merger completed in 1942.

NEBRASKA —

COLUMBUS — Bell established 1881; competition from Platte County Independent started, as early as 1898. In 1916, prodded by the City Council, Bell sold to the independent company. The Council had ordered both companies to put downtown plant underground. Dial since 1928. Bell handled long distance operations until 1956 when General Telephone took over both local and long distance operations.

FREMONT — Bell established 1882; competition from Fremont Independent from 1902 until Bell bought and consolidated in 1915. Dial since 1955.

GRAND ISLAND — Bell established 1880; competition from the Home Company in 1903. The Woods brothers of Lincoln acquired a substantial interest in the independent property a few years later and it was sold to Bell in the 1912 deal with Lincoln Telephone. Dial since 1956.

HASTINGS — Bell established 1881; a competing automatic exchange was established by local interests in 1905. When the Bell manual exchange was sold to Lincoln Telephone in 1912, the Lincoln company found itself competing with a former ally. It bought the local independent in 1914 and consolidated the exchanges with manual service. Reconverted to dial 1950.

KEARNEY — Bell established 1881; competing Kearney Company was established around the turn of the century. Bell sold to the independent company in 1916 after dissatisfied customers had petitioned the State Railway Commission to force consolidation. Converted to dial 1928. Bell kept the long distance board until 1956 when General Telephone took over both local and long distance operations.

LINCOLN — Bell established 1880; the Lincoln Company started a competing automatic exchange in 1904, bought Bell manual in 1912.

NORFOLK — Bell established 1888; competition from the Norfolk Independent from 1909 until Bell bought the bankrupt company in 1912. Dial since 1959.

NORTH PLATTE — Established by local interests in 1895; name later changed to North Platte Company. Bell established a competing toll station in 1902 and bought the independent property in 1912. Dial since 1959.

OMAHA — Bell established 1879; the Independent Company of Omaha started a competing automatic exchange in 1907 which Bell bought at a receiver's sale in 1912. Dial since 1921. First ESS office September 1970.

SCOTTSBLUFF — Established by local interests in the early 1900s; later reorganized as the Platte Valley Company and became a part of United Telephone in 1959. Dial since 1959. Never any competition.

NORTH DAKOTA —

BISMARCK — Bell established 1882 and discontinued operations in 1889. Shortly afterwards, exchange service was provided by the Hughes Electric Company, apparently without a Bell license. Hughes sold the exchange to the North Dakota Independent Company, probably in 1906. Bell bought control of N.D. Independent in 1911 and merged it into NWB in 1924. Dial since 1955.

FARGO — Bell established 1881. Never any competition. Dial since 1939.

GRAND FORKS — Bell established 1882, discontinued for lack of patronage in 1887 and reopened in 1890. Tri-State built a competing exchange in 1904 which it sold to N.D. Independent in 1906. Bell bought control of N.D. Independent in 1911 and merged it into NWB in 1924. Dial since 1950.

JAMESTOWN — Bell established 1883. Never any competition. Dial since 1958.

MINOT — Established by local interests in 1903 and now owned by Northern States Power. Dial since 1948. NWB operates the long distance board.

SOUTH DAKOTA —

ABERDEEN — Established 1886, without a Bell license, by J. L. W. Zietlow who later organized the Dakota Central Company with Aberdeen as headquarters. Converted to dial 1905. NWB took control of Dakota Central in the Tri-State purchase of 1933.

BROOKINGS — A franchise was granted to J. L. W. Zietlow in 1897 and apparently he built the exchange in the next year or so. Acting on an option in the franchise, the City of Brookings bought the telephone company in 1903 and has operated it ever since. Dial since 1958. NWB operated the long distance board until 1961.

HURON — Established 1882 by the Southeastern Company (Bell) but abandoned a few years later. Zietlow established a second exchange in 1898, converted to dial in 1910. Huron became a part of the Bell System when NWB bought control of Dakota Central in 1933. Merger was completed in 1942.

RAPID CITY — Bell established 1881; competition from the Harrison Company 1897-1906 when Bell bought the independent. Meanwhile, 1902-05 the Rapid Valley Company was organized, primarily to serve rural customers, but it also had a few town subscribers. Rapid Valley closed its board in 1930 and its customers were served by NWB on a service station basis. Rapid Valley reopened its switchboard, with a trunk connection to the Bell board. Competition ended about 1937 but some rural customers served by a succession of independent companies since. Dial since 1954. First ESS office Rapid City November 1973.

SIOUX FALLS — Bell established 1882. Competition started in 1900 by local interests who sold to the New State Company in 1908. Bell bought control of New State in 1917 and completed merger in 1919. Dial since 1950. First ESS office March 1973.

INDEX

INDEX

INDEX

INDEX

INDEX

INDEX

INDEX

INDEX

INDEX

INDEX